GCSE MATHS
INTERMEDIATE LEVEL

Jean Holderness

Causeway Books

Cover and diagrams by Allen Associates

Published by Causeway Press Ltd.,
P.O. Box 13, Ormskirk, Lancs L39 5HP
First published 1987. Reprinted 1987 (three times)
Reprinted 1988, 1989, 1990, 1991, 1992

British Library Cataloguing in Publication Data

Holderness, Jean
    GCSE maths – intermediate level.
    1. Mathematics-1961-
    I. Title
    510   QA39.2

ISBN 0-946183-33-3

Other titles in this series:
GCSE Maths: Higher Level
GCSE Maths: Foundation Level

Typesetting and printing by
The Alden Press, Oxford

Preface

This book is planned for use on a 2 year or 1 year course leading to the Intermediate level papers of the GCSE. It is based on the syllabuses of the four English boards plus the Welsh and Northern Ireland boards, as published for use in 1988.

The findings of the Cockcroft Report, and the aims and assessment objectives of the examinations have been guidelines followed in the writing of this book.

Students will have been learning Mathematics from an early age, so they will have already met many of the topics in this book. The earlier chapters will help to review and consolidate the learning of former years. A good understanding of the basic topics, leading to a sense of achievement, will form a firm foundation to build on when progressing through the syllabus. The order of the book has been carefully planned, although, of course, it need not be followed rigidly. As well as the main chapters there are miscellaneous sections which include aural practice exercises, multi-choice exercises, revision exercises which could be used as practice papers, suggestions for practical work and investigational work, and suggestions to students for study, revision and preparation for the examination. In addition there are puzzle questions throughout the book, some traditional and some original.

Many people have encouraged and helped me during the preparation of this book. I am grateful to them all, especially to my publishers.

Jean Holderness

To Tessa and Sam

Contents

		page
	To the student: 1 Learning Mathematics	**1**
Chapter 1	**Arithmetic**	**3**
	Numbers, tables	3
	Prime numbers and factors	6
	Tests of divisibility	7
	Square numbers, cube numbers	7
	Fractions	9
	Money, time, the calendar	13
	Units of measurement	15
	Unitary method	15
	Use of calculator	16
Chapter 2	**Algebra**	**22**
	Expressions	22
	Equations	23
	Directed numbers	26
	Indices	29
Chapter 3	**Geometry**	**33**
	Symmetry	33
	Transformations: reflection, rotation	34
	Angles	36
	Parallel lines, angles and parallel lines	37
	Triangles	40
	Constructions: to draw parallel lines with a set-square, construction of triangles	44
	Congruent figures, congruent triangles	47
	Transformations: translation	48
Chapter 4	**Statistics**	**56**
	Introduction	56
	Tally tables	56
	Presenting the data in a table	57
	Diagrams: pictograms, bar chart, pie chart, straight line graph	57
	Misleading diagrams	61
	Which diagram to draw	62
	Collecting data	66
	Sampling	67
	Questionnaires	68

Chapter 5   **Decimals**   **70**
                    Decimals, significant figures, standard index form   70
                    Kinds of numbers: integers, rational numbers, irrational
                    numbers   73
                    Use of calculator   74
                    Weights and measures in the Metric System   79
                    Approximations and estimations   80
                    Reading numbers on clocks, dials and scales   80

                    Miscellaneous Section A   **87**
                    Aural practice   87
                    Multi-choice exercise   87
                    Revision exercises   91
                    To the student: 2   Independent work   99
                    Practical work and Investigations   100
                    About chapters 6 to 10   105

Chapter 6   **Probability**   **106**
                    Experimental probability   106
                    Theoretical probability   111
                    Use of sample spaces   112
                    The OR rule, the AND rule   113
                    Tree diagrams   114

Chapter 7   **Quadrilaterals**   **122**
                    Quadrilaterals, trapezium, kite, parallelogram, rectangle,
                    rhombus, square   122
                    Diagonals   123

Chapter 8   **Polygons. Solid Figures**   **129**
                    Polygons: regular, non-regular   129
                    Solid figures: cuboid, cube, prism, tetrahedron, pyramid,
                    cylinder, cone, sphere   134
                    Nets of solid figures   134

Chapter 9   **Averages**   **140**
                    The mean, the median, the mode   140
                    Frequency distributions for discrete data, histogram, vertical
                    line graph, averages   142
                    Combining means   144
                    Dispersion: the range   145

Chapter 10   **Graphs**   **151**
                    Coordinates, straight line graphs   151
                    Simultaneous equations   154
                    To find the gradient of a line drawn on a graph   154

CONTENTS

Miscellaneous Section B   **160**
Aural practice   160
Multi-choice exercise   160
Revision exercises   164
Practical work and Investigations   169
To the student: 3 Improving your work   175

Chapter 11   **Circles**   **176**
Angle, chord and tangent properties   176
Constructions   179
Locus   183

Chapter 12   **Areas and Volumes**   **189**
Perimeters   189
Areas of rectangle, square, triangle, parallelogram, trapezium   189
Circles: Circumference, area   190
Length of arc and area of sector of a circle   191
Pythagoras' theorem   195
Solid figures. Volumes of cuboid, cube, cylinder, prism   197
Surface areas of cuboid, cylinder   198

Chapter 13   **Further Algebra**   **204**
Removing brackets   204
Fractions   204
Transformation of formulae   207
Common factors   208
Curves   209

Chapter 14   **Grouped Statistical Data**   **214**
Histogram, modal class and mean   214

Chapter 15   **Percentages**   **221**
Percentages   221
Profit and loss   222
Simple Interest, Compound Interest, loans, appreciation,
depreciation   223
VAT, Income tax   224

Miscellaneous Section C   **231**
Aural practice   231
Multi-choice exercise   231
Revision exercises   236
Practical work and Investigations   240
To the student: 4 Making plans for revision   248

Chapter 16   **Ratio and Rate**   **249**
Ratio and proportion   249
Direct and inverse proportion (arithmetical methods)   251
Variation (algebraic methods)   252
Rate   253
Rateable Value   254
Rate of exchange   255
Speed   256

Chapter 17   **Similarity**   **260**
Similar figures   260
Transformations: enlargement   260
Similar triangles   262
Centre of enlargement   264

Chapter 18   **Scale Drawing**   **268**
Horizontal and vertical lines   268
Compass directions   268
Bearings: 3-figure bearings   268
Angles of elevation and depression   269
Scale drawing   269
Bearings: alternative notation   273

Chapter 19   **Transformations. Vectors**   **278**
Translation   278
Enlargement   278
Reflections in the axes, and in the lines $y = x$ and $y = -x$ 279
Rotations about the origin   280
Vectors   283
Addition, subtraction, multiplication by a number   284

Chapter 20   **Trigonometry**   **291**
The ratios sine, cosine, tangent   291
To find a side, in a right-angled triangle   291
To find an angle   293

                 Miscellaneous Section D   **303**
Aural practice   303
Multi-choice exercise   303
Revision exercises   307
Practical work and Investigations   312
To the student: 5   Learning formulae. Practice Exams   318

Chapter 21   **Functions and Graphs**   **320**
Functions   320
Graphs of linear, quadratic and other functions   321
Gradients   325
Sketch graphs   326
Expanding brackets   330

Chapter 22   **Sets**   **334**
                   Introduction   334
                   Venn diagrams   334
                   Probability and Venn diagrams   336

Chapter 23   **Patterns**   **342**
                   Number patterns   342
                   Sequences of numbers   342
                   Inequalities   346
                   Geometric patterns   348
                   Tessellations   348

Chapter 24   **Graphs of Numerical Data**   **355**
                   Conversion graphs   355
                   Time-distance graph   355
                   Time-speed graph, acceleration   356
                   Sketch graphs   359
                   Scatter diagrams, line of best fit   362

Chapter 25   **Calculating**   **369**
                   Introduction   369
                   Mental arithmetic   369
                   Use of a calculator   372
                   Accuracy of measurements   374
                   Accuracy of answers   375

                   Miscellaneous Section E   **380**
                   Aural practice   380
                   Multi-choice exercise   380
                   Revision exercises   385
                   Practical work and Investigations   396
                   Revision checklist   404
                   Formula checklist   406
                   To the student: 6   The examination   408

                   Index   **410**

                   Answers   **413**

x

Topics for Practical Work and Investigations

A budget for a year, 396
A holiday abroad, 100
A scale model, 396
A snowflake curve, 317
An ABC book, 400
Areas, 173

Banking, 100

Cardioids and other designs from circles, 245
'Casting out nines', 102
Centres of a triangle, 401
Collecting data for Statistics, 66, 150, 220, 364
Cubes, 104
Curve stitching and string art, 245
Curves of pursuit, 316

Estimation, 313
Experimental probability, 106

For the Computer programmer, 105, 174, 247, 317, 403

Geometrical models, 170

History of measurement, 171
History of numbers and calculation, 171

Introduction to trigonometry, 246

Make your own maths magazine, 316
Models of the main solid figures, 240

Moebius bands, 101
Motoring, 169
My house, 312

Palindromes, 400
Pascal's triangle, 314
Pentominoes and hexominoes, 173
π, 243
Planning a day's sightseeing trip, 313
Planning a party for children, 397
Planning for a wedding, 240
Probability of winning in competitions, 170
Pythagoras' theorem, 241

Regular polygons, 172
'Russian multiplication' or 'Peasants' multiplication', 103

Savings, 312
Sevenths, 104
Shapes in everyday life, 171

Tests of divisibility, 101
The cost of keeping a pet, 315
The Fibonacci series, 397
The parabola, 244
The sieve of Eratosthenes, 103
3-d tessellation designs, 402
To find the day of the week for any date (1800–2099), 401

Ways of paying for goods and services, 240

To the teacher:

This book has been planned for a 2 year course or a 1 year course leading up to the GCSE examination at the Intermediate level.

The book begins with elementary work in Arithmetic, Algebra and Geometry. This gives a good start to the course. Students will gain a greater understanding of these topics which they may not have learnt fully at an earlier age, and thus they gain confidence. It is essential for them to have a good basic foundation of elementary work to build on later. Since these topics are used in later chapters there is constant recall.

In any class there will be a range of ability. Some students will benefit from doing all the straightforward questions in a chapter to master the techniques, others could more profitably just do a selection from these and then go on to the last exercise of the chapter where the questions are more varied.

To encourage more practice in mental arithmetic and in using fractions, decimals are not introduced in Chapter 1, but are left until Chapter 5. Once decimals are used, the calculator is relied on more and mental arithmetic and fractions tend to be neglected. It is assumed that students have calculators. They eliminate much of the routine work, giving more time for mathematics. However, there is a danger of relying on them too much, and mental arithmetic suffers, so try to keep a balance. Many of the questions in this book can be done without a calculator. The final chapter in the book should give useful revision practice both in mental arithmetic and in using a calculator.

Statistics has been separated into small sections. Although it is an easy subject, if too many ideas are introduced too quickly they tend to get all muddled up. It is desirable to allow time for practical work to be carried out as this aids understanding so the suggestions for practical work in Statistics and Probability have been incuded in the relevant chapters.

The rest of the book has been planned on the same basis, with further work in Arithmetic, Algebra and Geometry being covered in stages. In much of the work, especially in the earlier chapters, the same order has been followed as in the Higher Level book. This means that if it becomes apparent that some students have been placed on the wrong course, they could be transferred after a few weeks without too much difficulty in adjustment. However, the content of Chapter 5, which was rather long, has been reduced by leaving some topics for later chapters.

After every 5 chapters, that is roughly one term's work if using the book over two years, there is a Miscellaneous section. This includes the following:
Aural practice. For some Boards this is already a compulsory part of the examination. Many of the questions in the main parts of the book can be used for further aural practice, and topics not included here, such as estimating angles, can be practised using any suitable diagrams in the book.
Multi-choice exercise. As this is mainly for the use of those taking the London and East Anglian Group paper 3A, the questions have been restricted to those on the

syllabus for that paper. However, multi-choice questions are useful for others for revision practice. Occasionally it is better for students to work quickly without having to put down every detail of the answer.

Revision exercises, based on the work of the previous chapters. These could be used as practice papers. In this case, select the most suitable questions, depending on your syllabus, using about 12 of the 15 in each case.

Suggestions for practical work and investigational work. Although at present this is an optional part of the course, time spent on this is invaluable for adding interest and understanding to the subject. A variety of suggestions have been included so that students can choose to work on a topic they enjoy. Some of the ideas are more suitable for group work than individual work. For students to achieve their best with independent work it helps if there is a good supply of lined, squared, graph and plain paper, thick and thin cardboard, safe glue, scissors and a collection of reference books. Note:- The suggestions **may** be suitable to count as a component of the examination but the requirements of the Boards differ and you must check with your own syllabus to see if this is so.

There are puzzle questions fitted in at the ends of chapters. Some of these are traditional and some original. They are there to give interest, and perhaps to develop into further investigations. They are arranged in a miscellaneous order with the more difficult ones towards the end. They are not necessarily matched to the work of preceding chapters. The main value of the puzzles would be lost if the answers were too readily available so they have not been included.

Notes on Syllabuses

This book has been written using the following syllabuses as published in 1986 for use in 1988.

London and East Anglian Group	Mathematics A and B	Level Y	(L)
Midland Examining Group	Mathematics	Intermediate level	(M)
Northern Examining Association	Mathematics Syllabus A	Level Q	(N)
Southern Examining Group	Mathematics	Level 2	(S)
Welsh Joint Education Committee	GCSE Mathematics	Level 2	(W)
Northern Ireland Schools Examinations Council	Mathematics Syllabus A and B	Intermediate level	(NI)

These syllabuses have a great deal in common but there are also several differences, so there are some sections of this book which you will not need for your particular syllabus. In a few cases it is difficult to decide from the wording of a syllabus whether a particular topic is included. The specimen papers, and later on the actual papers, will help to clarify these points. Also, syllabuses may be changed from time to time. So this list is given as a guide to the topics in this book which **you** do not need, (those marked ×), but you are advised to check your own syllabus for the year of the examination and amend this list where necessary.

Chapter		L	M	N	S	W	NI
3	Conditions for triangles to be congruent	×	×	×	×	×	
3	Transformations: reflection, rotation, translation (and in Chapter 19)						×
6	Probability of non-independent events	×			×		
	Tree diagrams				×		
8	Angles of non-regular polygons	×	×	×		×	×
9	Vertical line graph for discrete data	×	×		×	×	×
	Range as a measure of dispersion	×	×	×		×	×
11	Constructions using ruler and compasses only	×	×			×	
12	Area of trapezium				×	×	
	Length of arc and area of sector	×	×		×		
	Volume of prism			×	×		×
	Surface area of cylinder	×	×	×	×		
15	Compound Interest		×				
16	Variation (algebraic methods)	×	×		×	×	×
17	Conditions for triangles to be similar	×	×	×	×	×	
	Centre of enlargement (and in Chapter 19)					×	×
18	Bearings, alternative notation	×	×	×	×		×
19	Vectors	×	×		×	×	×
21	Graphs of the type $y = x^2 + bx + c$	×			×	×	×
	Graph of $y = \sqrt{x}$	×	×		×	×	×
	Gradient of a curve	×		×	×	×	
	Expansion of $(x + a)(x + b)$	×	×		×	×	×
22	Sets	×			×	×	×
23	Inequalities	×		×			×
24	Acceleration	×				×	
	Scatter diagrams	×	×		×	×	×

1 Learning Mathematics

Maths is not a new subject since you have been learning it all your life, but in this book are all the topics you need to learn for the Intermediate level of the GCSE in Maths.

We hope that you will enjoy studying Maths. Just think of some of the ways in which Maths is linked with our lives, for example:
Shapes in the natural world involving symmetry, curves, spirals, etc.
Shapes in architecture and design.
Management of our money.
Understanding of diagrams, graphs and maps.
Ability to think logically, so as to plan ahead.
You can think of many more examples of how Maths is essential in today's world.

Learn to think for yourself. Do not rely on being told how to do everything. The more things you can work out for yourself the better you will do.

Try to discover things for yourself. Look for patterns in numbers and shapes. From a particular result, could you deduce a general formula? As an example, suppose you have a spare moment waiting for a lesson to begin and you put your ruler down on your exercise book and draw lines on either side of it, then you move the ruler and cross the lines with two others, getting a shape in the middle. Now you can discover many things about that shape:- What is it? Are there any equal lines or angles, or any point or lines of symmetry? What is the sum of the angles? What is its area? By altering the angle at which the lines cross can you get a different area? What is the smallest possible area? Can you draw a sketch graph of the relationship between angle and area? If you add more lines to the drawing you can make more discoveries.

As you work through this book, try to learn the important facts and methods of each chapter. If you do not understand the main ideas, ask someone to help you, either your teacher, someone else in your class or anyone else who can explain them to you. But when you have to answer an unusual question, before you ask for help, try to use your own commonsense and reason it out.

If you work steadily, you can gain a grade C, D or E in GCSE, and if you miss these targets there is the chance of a grade F. (If you find some of the work too difficult, it may be better for you to be entered for the Foundation level of the exam. Your teachers will advise you about this.)

About the first 5 chapters

You will probably be able to do most of this work already. This is an opportunity to make sure that you know all about the basic ideas in Arithmetic, Algebra and

Geometry, as you will then use these in future work. The important facts are followed by some worked examples and then there are straightforward exercises to give you practice. The last exercise in each chapter has more challenging questions for you. You may do them at this stage or you may leave them to return to later, to give you more revision practice. Learn the important facts, methods and formulae as you go along. There is a chapter introducing Statistics, including suggestions for practical work. Try to find time to do some practical work even if it is not part of your examination.

After the 5 chapters there is Miscellaneous Section A. This can be used at any time, and mainly includes the material of the previous chapters.

There are puzzle questions fitted in at the ends of some chapters. Try some of these if you are interested. Some of them have a catch in them, so don't be caught out. These questions are clearly headed 'Puzzles' so that you know that they are not part of your examination course.

There are some topics in the book which you do not need to learn. The reason for this is that in different parts of the country people take slightly different examinations, so that whilst everyone needs to understand most of this work there are certain topics which may not apply to your particular examination board. Your teacher can advise you about which these are, and there are some details on pages xii and xiii.

Now, get started and **enjoy your Maths**.

1 Arithmetic

Numbers

A calculator is an invaluable tool for saving time and doing accurate calculations, but there are basic arithmetical operations which you should be able to do mentally, quickly and accurately, and for which you should not waste time pressing calculator keys.

There will be many situations in your life when you need to work something out quickly and you will not have your calculator available. So make sure you are mentally alert.

To check your tables

On squared paper, or with columns drawn on lined paper, copy this chart. You are going to fill in the results of multiplication, so the numbers in the first few squares down the first empty column are 12, 22, 10, 16, etc. You will work down each column in turn. Before you begin, note the time. You should complete the chart within 5 minutes. If you take longer, then repeat the exercise, using numbers in a different random order, until you improve. Then check the accuracy of your work, which should be completely correct.

You could also make a similar chart to improve your speed of addition, if you think this is necessary.

	2	8	6	9	4	11	3	7	5	12
6	12	48	36	58	24	66	18	42	30	72
11	22	88	66	99	44	121	33	77	55	132
5	10	40	30	45	20	55	15	35	25	60
8	16	64	50	92	32	88	24	55	40	96
12	24	96	72	108	48	132	36	84	60	144
3	6	24	18	27	12	33	9	21	15	36
10	20	80	60	90	40	110	30	70	50	120
4	8	32	24	36	16	44	12	28	20	48
9	18	73	54	81	36	99	27	63	45	111
7	14	57	43	63	28	77	21	49	35	84

10 mins

Now try these questions. They are intended to improve your speed and accuracy so concentrate and do them quickly.

Exercise 1.1

1.
8×7	$30 + 90$	$21 - 6$	6×12	$100 \div 5$
6×4	$8 + 7$	$30 \div 5$	6×0	$99 + 7$
20×1	11^2	30×20	$\sqrt{64}$	99×0
20×3	$56 \div 7$	$20 - 8$	13×1	12^2

2.

$32 \div 4$	$27 \div 9$	$55 \div 5$	$72 \div 12$	$15 \div 5$
$42 \div 7$	$132 \div 11$	$72 \div 9$	$30 \div 6$	$49 \div 7$
$96 \div 12$	$60 \div 6$	$36 \div 3$	$77 \div 11$	$45 \div 5$
$56 \div 8$	$144 \div 12$	$35 \div 7$	$60 \div 5$	$81 \div 9$

3. What is the remainder when   What must be added to

1   18 is divided by 5   **6** 8×7 to make 60

2   39 is divided by 7   **7** 4×3 to make 20

3   68 is divided by 11   **8** 5×9 to make 50

4   52 is divided by 4   **9** 7×11 to make 80

5   100 is divided by 8   **10** 9×9 to make 100

4. Write in figures the numbers

1   Two hundred and sixty-five thousand, three hundred and eighty-four.

2   Twelve thousand and forty.

3   One and a half thousand.

4   Thirty and three-quarters.

5   Four million, four hundred and forty thousand, four hundred and four.

6   In 100 567, what do the 1, the 5 and the 6 stand for?

7   In 2 908 134, what do the 2 and the 8 stand for?

5. Find the value of

1	$5 \times 3 \times 1$	**4**	$10 \times 20 \times 40$	**7**	$180 \div 5$
2	$4 \times 2 \times 0$	**5**	$5000 \div 20$	**8**	$(8 \times 12) - (7 \times 12)$
3	$10^2 - 9^2$	**6**	$89 + 99$	**9**	$(6 \times 19) + (4 \times 19)$
				10	$\frac{2}{3}$ of $36 + \frac{1}{3}$ of 36

6.

1   Find two numbers whose sum is 13 and whose product is 36.

2   Find two numbers whose sum is 11 and whose product is 30.

3   Find two numbers whose sum is 52 and whose product is 100.

4   Find two numbers whose sum is 16 and whose product is 15.

5   Find two numbers whose sum is 16 and whose product is 48.

6   Find three numbers whose product is 36 and whose sum is 11.

7   Find three numbers whose product is 60 and whose sum is 12.

8   Find two numbers whose product is 72 and which differ by 1.

9   Find two numbers whose product is 24 and which differ by 5.

10   Find two numbers whose product is 77 and which differ by 4.

7. **1** How many more 4's than 5's are there in 40?
    2 How many more 8's than 12's are there in 96?
    3 Find two consecutive numbers whose squares differ by 11.
    4 Find two consecutive numbers whose squares add up to 181.
    5 Find three consecutive numbers whose squares add up to 50.

8. **1** Find one-half of each of these numbers
    88   18   8   14   60   24   42   52   90   96

    2 Find one-third of each of these numbers
    18   99   60   24   45   27   3   21   39   75

    3 Find one-quarter of each of these numbers
    8   28   80   100   52   44   4   24   160   36

    4 Find one-fifth of each of these numbers
    60   20   45   10   100   15   35   75   55   200

    5 Find two-thirds of each of these numbers
    6   15   24   9   30   60   33   90   75   18

9. **1** Start from 100 and count down in 6's until you reach a number less than 10. What number is this?

    2 Start from 1, then 2, then 4, and double the number every time until you reach a number greater than 1000. What number is this?

    3 Start from 25 000 and keep dividing by 5 until you reach a number less than 10. What number is this?

    4 Start with 1 and keep adding 7's until you reach a number greater than 100. What number is this?

    5 Start from 0 and add 1, then 2, then 3, and so on until you reach a number greater than 100. What number is this?

10. **1** Write down any number between 1 and 10, multiply this by 3, then to the result add 8. Double this answer. Now subtract 3, multiply by 5, add 7. Subtract 2 and divide by 10. Add 17, divide by 3 and take away the number you started with. What is your answer?

    2 Write down any number between 1 and 10, add 3 and multiply the result by 6. Then subtract 12, divide by 3, multiply by 10. Add 5, divide by 5 and add 7. Subtract 12 then divide by the number you started with. What is your answer?

    3 Write down any number less than 5, double it and add 3. Square the result, add 3 and divide by 4. Subtract 1 and multiply by 2. Subtract 4, divide by the number your started with, add 14 and halve the result. Take away the number you started with. What is your answer?

Operations in brackets should be carried out first. If there are no brackets, multiplication and division should be carried out before addition and subtraction.

Example 1

$4 \times 6 - 5 \times 3 = 24 - 15 = 9$

$4 \times (6 - 5) \times 3 = 4 \times 1 \times 3 = 12$

$4 + 6 \times 5 - 3 = 4 + 30 - 3 = 31$

$(4 + 6) \times 5 - 3 = 10 \times 5 - 3 = 50 - 3 = 47$

$(4 + 6) \times (5 - 3) = 10 \times 2 = 20$

A fraction line can take the place of a bracket.

$\dfrac{3 + 5}{6 - 2}$ means $(3 + 5) \div (6 - 2)$ which equals $\dfrac{8}{4} = 2$

Exercise 1.1, continued

11.   Find the value of

1	$4 \times 7 + 5$	**5**	$\dfrac{5 + 4}{7 - 4}$	**8**	$7^2 - 4^2$
2	$4 \times (7 + 5)$			**9**	$(7 - 4)^2$
3	$4 + 7 \times 5$	**6**	$4^2 + 7^2$	**10**	$(7 + 4) \times (7 - 4)$
4	$(4 + 7) \times 5$	**7**	$(4 + 7)^2$		

Prime Numbers and Factors

A prime number has no factors (except itself and 1). The first few prime numbers are 2, 3, 5, 7, 11, 13, 17, ...
Other numbers can be expressed in prime factors.

Example 2

$240 = 2 \times 120$

$\quad\ \ = 2 \times 2 \times 60$

$\quad\ \ = 2 \times 2 \times 2 \times 30$

$\quad\ \ = 2 \times 2 \times 2 \times 2 \times 15$

$\quad\ \ = 2 \times 2 \times 2 \times 2 \times 3 \times 5$

$\quad\ \ = 2^4 \times 3 \times 5$

(A quicker way to split it up would be

$240 = 10 \times 24$

$\quad\ \ = 2 \times 5 \times 4 \times 6$

$\quad\ \ = 2 \times 5 \times 2 \times 2 \times 2 \times 3$

$\quad\ \ = 2^4 \times 3 \times 5)$

Tests of divisibility, used when finding prime factors of a number.

Divisibility by 2

If the units figure is even, i.e. 2, 4, 6, 8, 0, the number has a factor 2.

Divisibility by 3

Add up the digits in the number, and if the answer is more than 9 you can add up the digits of that answer, and repeat until you get a 1-figure number. If this number divides by 3 then 3 is a factor of the original number. For example, for 2841, $2 + 8 + 4 + 1 = 15$ (and $15 \rightarrow 1 + 5 = 6$). This divides by 3 so 3 is a factor of 2841.

Divisibility by 5

If the units figure is 5 or 0 the number divides by 5.

Square numbers

If a number is multiplied by itself, the resulting number is a square number, sometimes called a perfect square.
e.g. $5 \times 5 = 25$ so 25 is a square number and its square root is 5,
$12 \times 12 = 144$ so 144 is a square number and its square root is 12.
You can find square roots on your calculator.
To find the square root of 169 press 169 $\boxed{\sqrt{}}$ and the answer is 13.
If you find the square root of a number on your calculator and the result is not an exact whole number then the original number is not a square number.

Cube numbers

e.g. $5 \times 5 \times 5 = 125$ so 125 is a cube number and its cube root is 5.

Exercise 1.2

1. Which of these numbers are prime numbers?   21,   23,   25,   27,   29.

2. What are the next two prime numbers after   **1** 30   **2** 80?

3. Express these numbers in prime factors.

1	48	**4**	60	**7**	70	**10**	100	**13**	121
2	99	**5**	180	**8**	96	**11**	39	**14**	81
3	52	**6**	24	**9**	64	**12**	80	**15**	150

4. Which of these numbers are divisible by   **1** 2   **2** 5   **3** 3?
   132,   135,   156,   225,   400.

The largest number which divides exactly into 60 and 96 is 12. This is called the **highest common factor** of 60 and 96.

5. Find the highest common factor of the following pairs of numbers.

1	88, 99	**6**	24, 8	**11**	42, 63
2	60, 80	**7**	27, 6	**12**	32, 44
3	45, 35	**8**	52, 39	**13**	72, 12
4	18, 21	**9**	14, 20	**14**	56, 72
5	28, 16	**10**	77, 49	**15**	10, 45

The smallest number into which 4 and 6 divide is 12. This is called the **lowest common multiple** of 4 and 6.

6. Find the lowest common multiple of the following sets of numbers.

1	3, 5	**5**	10, 20, 30	**9**	2, 5, 7
2	8, 12	**6**	11, 22, 44	**10**	21, 42
3	4, 5, 6	**7**	4, 6, 9		
4	6, 8, 9	**8**	2, 3, 9		

7. Find the values of

    1 2^4 **2** $2^3 \times 3^2$ **3** $2^2 \times 5 \times 7$ **4** $2 \times 3^2 \times 5$ **5** $2^3 \times 11$

8. Write the number 30 **1** as the product of three prime numbers **2** as the sum of three prime numbers.

9. From the numbers 8, 12, 16, 19, 20

    1 Which number is a prime number?
    2 Which number is a square number?
    3 Which number is a multiple of 5?
    4 Which number is a factor of 84?
    5 Which two numbers have a sum which is a square number?
    6 Which two numbers have a sum which is a cube number?

10. From the numbers 18, 19, 20, 23, 25, 27 write down

    1 the prime numbers
    2 a square number
    3 the numbers which are multiples of 3
    4 a cube number
    5 two numbers whose sum is 44.

11. From the numbers 8, 37, 50, 73, 81, 91, 360

    1 Which number is a square number?
    2 Which number is a cube number?
    3 Which two numbers are prime numbers?
    4 Which number is a multiple of 13?
    5 Which number is a factor of 72?
    6 Which number can be written in index form as $2^3 \times 3^2 \times 5$?
    7 Which number is equal to the sum of two other numbers in the list?
    8 Which number when divided by 9 leaves a remainder of 5?

12. What number is this?

    It is less than 100, it is a prime number, it is one less than a multiple of 7 and its digits add up to 5.

13. What number is this?

    It is less than 100, it is two more than a square number and it is a multiple of 11. When divided by 9 there is a remainder of 3.

14. What number is this?

    It is a factor of 180, it is a 4 less than a square number, and when it is divided by 7 there is a remainder of 3.

15. What are the missing figures if **1** 62*3 divides exactly by 9, **2** 51*7 divides exactly by 11,   **3** 19*2 divides exactly by 7?

16. Express **1** 111 and **2** 1001 in prime factors.

17. These numbers follow a pattern. Write down the next two numbers in the sequence.

    1   1, 9, 25, 49,   **6**   1, 8, 27, 64, 125,
    2   1, 3, 6, 10, 15,   **7**   80, 70, 61, 53, 46,
    3   2, 4, 8, 16,   **8** $\frac{1}{2}, \frac{2}{3}, \frac{3}{4}, \frac{4}{5},$
    4   100, 93, 86, 79, 72,   **9**   2, 5, 8, 11,
    5   1, $\frac{1}{2}, \frac{1}{3}, \frac{1}{4}, \frac{1}{5},$ **10**   0, 3, 8, 15, 24,

18. Extend this number pattern to 65^2.

    $$5^2 = 0 \times 10 + 25 = 25$$
    $$15^2 = 10 \times 20 + 25 = 225$$
    $$25^2 = 20 \times 30 + 25 = 625$$

    Use the pattern to find the value of 85^2.

19. Find the values of **1** $\sqrt{25 \times 144}$ **2** $\sqrt{25 + 144}$ **3** $\sqrt{25} + \sqrt{144}$

20. Use your calculator to find the square roots of

    1   225   **3**   1089   **5**   5625   **7**   441   **9**   4225
    2   1764   **4**   256   **6**   196   **8**   1936   **10**   10201

Fractions

Example 3

Reduce $\frac{60}{75}$ to its lowest terms.

$$\frac{\overset{\overset{4}{\cancel{12}}}{\cancel{60}}}{\underset{\underset{5}{\cancel{15}}}{\cancel{75}}} = \frac{4}{5}$$

Example 4

Change $\frac{5}{6}$ into a fraction with denominator 24.

6 becomes 24 when multiplied by 4, so multiply the numerator and the denominator by 4.

$$\frac{5}{6} = \frac{5 \times 4}{6 \times 4} = \frac{20}{24}$$

Example 5

Change $3\frac{7}{8}$ to an improper fraction.

$$3\frac{7}{8} \left(= \frac{24}{8} + \frac{7}{8} \right) = \frac{31}{8}$$

Example 6

Change $\frac{45}{7}$ to a mixed number.

$$\frac{45}{7} \left(= \frac{42 + 3}{7} \right) = 6\frac{3}{7}$$

In **addition and subtraction** questions, do the whole number part and the fraction part separately.

Example 7

$$4\frac{5}{6} + 2\frac{5}{8} = 6\frac{20 + 15}{24} = 6\frac{35}{24} = 7\frac{11}{24}$$

(We change $\frac{5}{6}$ and $\frac{5}{8}$ into fractions with denominator 24 because 24 is the smallest number into which 6 and 8 both divide.)

Example 8

$$3\frac{3}{8} - 1\frac{4}{5} = 2\frac{15 - 32}{40} = 2 - \frac{17}{40} = 1\frac{23}{40}$$

In **multiplication and division** questions, mixed numbers must be changed to improper fractions.

Example 9

$$5\frac{5}{6} \times 2\frac{7}{10} = \frac{\overset{7}{\cancel{35}}}{\underset{2}{\cancel{6}}} \times \frac{\overset{9}{\cancel{27}}}{\underset{2}{\cancel{10}}} = \frac{63}{4} = 15\frac{3}{4}$$

Example 10

$$2\tfrac{5}{6} \div 1\tfrac{1}{4} = \frac{17}{6} \div \frac{5}{4}$$

(Instead of dividing by $\tfrac{5}{4}$, multiply by $\tfrac{4}{5}$)

$$= \frac{17}{\underset{3}{\cancel{6}}} \times \frac{\overset{2}{\cancel{4}}}{5} = \frac{34}{15} = 2\tfrac{4}{15}$$

Example 11

Express 24 pence as a fraction of £3.

$$\frac{24\,\text{p}}{£3} = \frac{24\,\text{p}}{300\,\text{p}} = \frac{\overset{2}{\cancel{24}}}{\underset{25}{\cancel{300}}} = \frac{2}{25}$$

Example 12

Find $\tfrac{3}{20}$ of 1 hour 10 minutes.

$$\frac{3}{\cancel{20}} \times \cancel{70}\,\text{min} = \frac{21}{2}\,\text{min} = 10\tfrac{1}{2}\,\text{minutes}$$

Example 13

Which is greater, $\tfrac{5}{6}$ or $\tfrac{7}{8}$?

$$\frac{5}{6} = \frac{20}{24}, \quad \frac{7}{8} = \frac{21}{24}, \quad \text{so } \frac{7}{8} \text{ is greater.}$$

Exercise 1.3

1. Reduce these fractions to their lowest terms.

   1 $\dfrac{24}{88}$ **3** $\dfrac{18}{45}$ **5** $\dfrac{33}{132}$ **7** $\dfrac{75}{200}$ **9** $\dfrac{24}{54}$

   2 $\dfrac{60}{84}$ **4** $\dfrac{35}{56}$ **6** $\dfrac{21}{36}$ **8** $\dfrac{11}{110}$ **10** $\dfrac{26}{39}$

2. Change these mixed numbers to improper fractions.

   1 $1\tfrac{3}{4}$ **3** $2\tfrac{1}{3}$ **5** $4\tfrac{5}{6}$ **7** $9\tfrac{1}{11}$ **9** $3\tfrac{1}{7}$

   2 $6\tfrac{5}{12}$ **4** $3\tfrac{7}{20}$ **6** $7\tfrac{7}{10}$ **8** $5\tfrac{7}{8}$ **10** $8\tfrac{2}{5}$

3. Change these improper fractions to mixed numbers.

    1 $\dfrac{23}{5}$ **3** $\dfrac{37}{10}$ **5** $\dfrac{11}{4}$ **7** $\dfrac{13}{5}$ **9** $\dfrac{100}{3}$

    2 $\dfrac{17}{6}$ **4** $\dfrac{25}{8}$ **6** $\dfrac{55}{9}$ **8** $\dfrac{40}{11}$ **10** $\dfrac{105}{12}$

4. **1** $\frac{1}{2} + \frac{1}{3} + \frac{1}{4}$ **6** $4\frac{3}{8} + 3\frac{1}{3}$

    2 $\frac{5}{8} + \frac{1}{6}$ **7** $5\frac{5}{9} + \frac{1}{6}$

    3 $2\frac{7}{10} + 1\frac{3}{5}$ **8** $\frac{1}{2} + 2\frac{5}{6}$

    4 $3\frac{3}{8} + 1\frac{4}{5}$ **9** $2\frac{3}{4} + 1\frac{4}{5}$

    5 $2\frac{5}{12} + 2\frac{1}{3}$ **10** $4\frac{1}{8} + 1\frac{7}{12}$

5. **1** $\frac{5}{8} - \frac{1}{6}$ **6** $5\frac{5}{14} - 3\frac{6}{7}$

    2 $2\frac{11}{12} - \frac{7}{8}$ **7** $2\frac{2}{3} - 2\frac{5}{9}$

    3 $2\frac{5}{6} - 1\frac{1}{4}$ **8** $\frac{1}{2} + \frac{1}{3} - \frac{1}{6}$

    4 $7\frac{5}{12} - 5\frac{8}{9}$ **9** $2\frac{1}{2} + \frac{7}{10} - \frac{2}{5}$

    5 $1\frac{7}{20} - \frac{4}{5}$ **10** $1\frac{3}{4} - \frac{4}{5} + 2\frac{7}{8}$

6. **1** $\frac{3}{8} \times \frac{2}{3}$ **6** $\frac{5}{6} \times \frac{9}{10}$

    2 $\frac{5}{6} \times \frac{7}{8}$ **7** $1\frac{1}{7} \times 10$

    3 $\frac{2}{3} \times 1\frac{1}{8}$ **8** $3\frac{3}{8} \times 1\frac{1}{9}$

    4 $1\frac{3}{4} \times 2\frac{2}{5}$ **9** $4\frac{1}{2} \times 1\frac{5}{6}$

    5 $2\frac{1}{6} \times \frac{9}{13}$ **10** $5\frac{5}{9} \times 6\frac{3}{4} \times 1\frac{1}{15}$

7. **1** $\frac{5}{6} \div \frac{7}{8}$ **6** $2\frac{4}{5} \div 7$

    2 $\frac{3}{10} \div 1\frac{1}{6}$ **7** $3\frac{3}{4} \div 2\frac{2}{5}$

    3 $4\frac{1}{8} \div 2\frac{3}{4}$ **8** $4\frac{4}{9} \div 5\frac{5}{6}$

    4 $7 \div 1\frac{3}{4}$ **9** $2\frac{1}{12} \div 5\frac{5}{8}$

    5 $\frac{7}{12} \div \frac{14}{15}$ **10** $11\frac{1}{4} \div 2\frac{3}{16}$

8. 1 $6\frac{3}{4} - 1\frac{2}{3}$ 6 $4\frac{2}{3} - 4\frac{1}{6}$

2 $5\frac{1}{12} \div 7\frac{5}{8}$ 7 $2\frac{3}{5} \div 1\frac{3}{10}$

3 $2\frac{2}{3} \times 2\frac{3}{4}$ 8 $3\frac{1}{3} \times \frac{3}{10}$

4 $1\frac{3}{4} + 2\frac{5}{12} + 3\frac{5}{6}$ 9 $3\frac{1}{6} + 1\frac{3}{4}$

5 $1\frac{5}{8} \times 1\frac{3}{5}$ 10 $3\frac{1}{7} \times \frac{4}{11}$

9. 1 $(\frac{15}{28} \times \frac{7}{30}) + \frac{7}{8}$ 6 $(\frac{2}{3} - \frac{1}{6})^2$

2 $(2\frac{2}{3} - 1\frac{3}{4}) \times 4$ 7 $1\frac{5}{12} \div (3\frac{1}{5} + 1\frac{1}{3})$

3 $(2\frac{1}{2} \div \frac{1}{4}) - 6\frac{1}{2}$ 8 $12\frac{1}{5} - (2\frac{2}{9} \times 4\frac{1}{2})$

4 $8\frac{3}{4} \times 1\frac{3}{5} \div 4\frac{2}{3}$ 9 $2\frac{1}{4} - (1\frac{1}{2} \times \frac{2}{5})$

5 $(3\frac{1}{7} \times 8\frac{3}{4}) - 2\frac{1}{3}$ 10 $2\frac{1}{10} - 1\frac{3}{5} + 6\frac{1}{2}$

10. Which is greater?

1 $\frac{5}{6}$ or $\frac{7}{9}$ 2 $\frac{8}{9}$ or $\frac{9}{10}$ 3 $\frac{2}{3}$ or $\frac{3}{5}$

Money

100 pence = £1
65 p can be written as £0.65
£2 and 65 p should be written as £2.65

In U.S.A., 100 cents = 1 dollar
In France, 100 centimes = 1 franc.

Time

60 seconds = 1 minute
60 minutes = 1 hour
24 hours = 1 day
7 days = 1 week
52 weeks = 1 year
365 days = 1 year
366 days = 1 leap year
12 months = 1 year

The calendar

April, June, September and November have 30 days.
February has 28 days, and 29 days in leap years.
All the other months have 31 days.

Thirty days hath September,
April, June and dull November,
All the rest have 31,
Excepting February alone,
Which has 28 days clear,
And 29 in each leap year.

Leap years are years whose dates are divisible by 4, e.g. 1988 and 2000.
(1700, 1800, 1900 were not leap years, though.)

Recording the time of day can either be by the 12-hour clock, when morning times are
denoted by a.m. and afternoon times by p.m., or by the 24-hour clock. To avoid
confusion, timetables are often printed with times using the 24-hour clock.

Examples:

	12-hour clock	24-hour clock
1 o'clock early morning	1.00 a.m.	1.00 or 01.00
5 past 1 early morning	1.05 a.m.	1.05 or 01.05
Noon	12.00 p.m.	12.00
Quarter-to-1 early afternoon	12.45 p.m.	12.45
1 o'clock early afternoon	1.00 p.m.	13.00
Half-past 8 in the evening	8.30 p.m.	20.30
One minute to midnight	11.59 p.m.	23.59
Midnight	12.00 a.m.	0.00 or 00.00
One minute past midnight	12.01 a.m.	0.01 or 00.01

(The day changes at the instant of midnight so when the time is shown as 12.00 a.m.
or 0.00 the date has changed.)

On a timetable the 24-hour times could be printed as 4-figure numbers. The full stop
separating the hours and minutes could be left out.
e.g. 1.23 a.m. would be printed as 0123,
     1.23 p.m. would be printed as 1323.

1323 would be pronounced as thirteen twenty-three or thirteen twenty-three hours.
But 1300 would be pronounced as thirteen hundred hours.

Units of measurement

The units of measurement in the Metric System are
metre for length, with associated units kilometre, centimetre, millimetre,
gram for weight (or mass), with associated units tonne and kilogram,
litre for capacity, with associated unit centilitre.
These are explained in more detail in Chapter 5.

As Britain is slow to adapt completely to the metric system, you will find the following units in use in some situations.
Length   inch,   foot,   yard,   mile.
There are 12 inches in 1 foot, 3 feet in 1 yard and 1760 yards in 1 mile. (The symbol
″ is used for inches and ′ is used for feet so 3′6″ means 3 feet 6 inches.)
Weight   ounce,   pound,   stone.
There are 16 ounces in 1 pound and 14 pounds in 1 stone.
The abbreviation for ounce is oz and for pound is lb.
Capacity   pint,   gallon.
There are 8 pints in 1 gallon.

Temperature

In the Celsius scale (formerly the Centigrade scale) written °C, water freezes at 0°C and boils at 100°C.
In the Fahrenheit scale, written °F, salt water freezes at 0°F, water freezes at 32°F and boils at 212°F.

Unitary Method

Example 14

If 21 notebooks cost £7.56, what do 28 similar notebooks cost?

(7 is a factor of both 21 and 28 so we find the cost of 7 notebooks first.)
21 notebooks cost £7.56
7 notebooks cost £2.52   (dividing by 3)
28 notebooks cost £10.08   (multiplying by 4).

Example 15

If there is enough food in an emergency pack to last 12 men for 10 days, how long would the food last if there were 15 men?

(3 is a factor of both 12 and 15, so we first find how long the food would last if there were 3 men.)
The food lasts 12 men for 10 days
The food lasts 3 men for 40 days   (multiplying by 4 because it would last four times as long)
The food lasts 15 men for 8 days   (dividing by 5).

Use of calculator

If the numbers are large, and you have a calculator available, it is sensible to use it to save time.

Be careful that you do not use your calculator for mixed units not based on ten, such as hours and minutes. For example, to add 14 hours 37 minutes and 15 hours 56 minutes it is no use entering $14.37 + 15.56$. You will have to add the minutes first. $37 + 56 = 93$. 93 minutes is 1 hour 33 minutes so carry forward 1 hour. $1 + 14 + 15 = 30$. The answer is 30 hours 33 minutes.

Exercise 1.4

1. 1 How many 5p coins are worth £5?
    2 What is the change from £1 after buying 3 small loaves at 28p each?
    3 If 4 apples cost as much as 5 pears, which is the dearer fruit?
    4 Find the cost of 200 articles at 15p each?
    5 What is the cost of 4 articles at 99p each?

2. Mr Seed bought toys at 5 for 45p and sold them at 4 for 50p. How much profit did he make on each one?

3. What is the total cost of 24 notebooks at 28p each and 24 pens at 22p each?

4. Mr Clark spends £5 on petrol for his car and this takes him 125 miles. What is the cost per mile?

5. Equal numbers of 13p and 15p stamps were bought for £5.60. How many of each kind were there?

6. A bankrupt can only pay his creditors 30 pence in the £. (This means that for each £1 he owes he can only pay 30 p.) How much does a creditor to whom he owes £180 receive?

7. Mrs Davies makes 200 soft toys. The material for each toy costs 48p. Other expenses amount to £5. She sells the toys for £1.25 each. What profit does she make?

8. Find the total cost of 3 bottles of milk at 21p per bottle, 2 packets of tea at 29p per packet, and $\frac{1}{2}$ dozen eggs at 78p per dozen.

9. From a mail-order catalogue Rachel orders 2 items at £6.99 each and 3 items at £11.99 each. What is the total cost?

10. How many articles costing 75 cents each can be bought for 30 dollars?

11. 1 Express £1.60 as a fraction of £2.40.
    2 Express 10 oz as a fraction of $2\frac{1}{2}$ lb.
    3 Express 50 cents as a fraction of 4 dollars 50 cents.
    4 Express 12 minutes as a fraction of $1\frac{1}{2}$ hours.
    5 Express 660 yards as a fraction of 1 mile.

12. 1 Find $\frac{3}{4}$ of £3.60.   3 Find $\frac{3}{10}$ of 2 dollars.   5 Find $\frac{5}{8}$ of 1 lb.

    2 Find $\frac{2}{3}$ of 1 foot.   4 Find $\frac{3}{5}$ of 1 hour.

13.   In a club, two-fifths of the members are Junior members. The remaining 90 members are Senior members. How many members are there altogether?

14.   A cinema is $\frac{1}{3}$ full. After another 60 people come in it is $\frac{1}{2}$ full. How many people does the cinema hold?

15.   Mrs Carr wins some money in a competition. She gives $\frac{1}{3}$ of it to her husband and $\frac{2}{5}$ of the remainder to her daughter. She keeps the remaining money, £300, for herself. How much did she win?

16.   If today is April 24th, what will be the date this day next week?

17.   If a train is travelling at 90 miles/hour, how far does it go in 1 minute?

18.   Alan started school on his 5th birthday in 1984. In which year will he have his 16th birthday?

19.   Change these times to the 24-hour clock.

      4.05 a.m.   2.00 p.m.   3.15 p.m.   6.05 p.m.   11.55 p.m.

      Change these times to the 12-hour clock.

      01.10   5.18   10.30   17.05   21.50

20.   A train left a station at 9.30 a.m. and arrived at its destination at 2.13 p.m. How long did the journey take?

21.   Mike set off on a training ride at 11.50 a.m. and cycled for $4\frac{1}{4}$ hours. At what time did he stop?

22.   On a timetable, a plane was due to leave an airport at 20.55 and arrive at its destination at 02.05 the next day. How long should the journey take? It actually arrived 45 minutes early. At what time did it arrive?

23.   A school's lessons begin at 9.20 a.m. and end at 3.20 p.m. with an hour's break at lunchtime and 20 minutes break mid-morning. If there are 7 lessons of equal length, how long is a lesson?

24.   This flow chart will convert °F into °C.

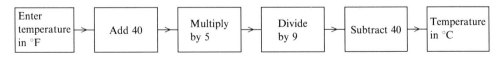

      Use this flow chart to change 41°F into °C.
      By using the flow chart in reverse, change 40°C into °F.

25.   28 bars of chocolate cost £3.64. What would be the cost of 35 similar bars?

26.   If 20 boxes weigh 36 lb, what is the weight of 45 similar boxes?

27.   If a car travels for 100 miles on fuel costing £4.80, what would the fuel cost be, at the same rate, for a journey of 250 miles?

28.   If a store of emergency food would last 20 men for 36 days, how long would the same food last if there were 45 men?

29.   10 men can build a wall in 9 days. How long would 6 men take, working at the same rate?

30.   A carpet to cover a floor of area 20 square yards costs £150. How much would it cost for a similar carpet to cover a floor of area 24 square yards?

Exercise 1.5

1.   Write down a 3-figure number whose digits are all different and do not include 0. Reverse it, i.e. write it down backwards. Take the smaller number of the two from the larger. Reverse this answer and add this number to the answer. What is your total?

2.   What is this number?
     It is a 3-figure number, less than 300. It is divisible by 11. It is 1 less than a perfect square.

3.   1 In a knock-out competition there are 32 teams. How many matches must be played altogether to decide the winning team?
     2 In a football competition there are 6 teams. Each team plays each other team twice, once at home and once away. How many matches are played altogether?

4.   Find 1 $\sqrt{\frac{9}{25}}$ 2 $\sqrt{1\frac{11}{25}}$

5.   Copy and complete this table.
     (It would be useful to memorise these results.)

     Is there any pattern in the unit figures 1 in the squares column, 2 in the cubes column?

number	square	cube
1	1	1
2	4	8
3	9	
.		
.		
.		
10		

6.   An **odd number** has a units figure of 1, 3, 5, 7 or 9.
     An **even number** has a units figure of 2, 4, 6, 8 or 0.

     Are the answers to the following questions even or odd numbers?
     1 odd number + odd number
     2 odd number × even number
     3 even number − smaller even number
     4 even number × (even number + even number)
     5 odd number × (odd number + even number)

7.   Use your calculator to find the answers to these questions.

     1 Which is larger, $\sqrt{225} + \sqrt{64}$ or $\sqrt{225 + 64}$, and by how much?
     2 Which is larger, 2^{11} or 3^7, and by how much?
     3 Which of these numbers are perfect squares?   196, 456, 676.

8. At a school election, 320 children voted for Alan, Bob or David. Alan got 60 more votes than Bob, and David got twice as many votes as Bob. Who won the election?

9. If £2.80 is made up of equal numbers of 5p, 10p and 20p coins, how many coins are there?

10. A car journey takes 42 minutes when the average speed is 56 miles/hour. How long would it take if the average speed was 48 miles/hour?

11. The weekly wages paid by a firm to 5 workmen total £525. What will the weekly wages be if they employ two extra men, and pay them all at the same rate?

12. $1\frac{1}{4}$ pints of milk are poured into an urn containing 10 pints of coffee. What fraction of the mixture is milk?

13. Two books together cost £6.50, one being £1.20 more than the other. What did the cheaper one cost?

14. A wheel makes 2500 revolutions per minute. How long will it take to make 50 000 revolutions?

15. $3\frac{1}{4}$ metres of material is needed for a loose cover for an armchair and $\frac{3}{4}$ metre for a small chair. Find the cost of the material for covering a suite of 2 armchairs and 6 small chairs with material costing £5.50 per metre.

16. Mrs Khan earns £3.40 per hour for a basic week of 40 hours. Overtime is paid at time-and-a-half. If she works 42 hours one week, what will she earn? If one week she earns £176.80, how many hours altogether did she work?

17. Mr Taylor's weekly wage is £120. He reckons that $\frac{1}{4}$ of his wages go in tax and insurance. Of the remainder, $\frac{1}{5}$ pays the rent and $\frac{1}{10}$ is put aside to pay the household fuel bills. How much has he left to spend?

18. Here is part of a bus timetable:

Ashmead School	1554	1602	1608	1616	1622	1629
Brook Lane	1604	1612	1618	1626	1632	1639
Carlton Village	1619	1627	— —	1641	— —	1654
Denham Station	— —	— —	1640	— —	1654	— —

1   Helen finishes school at 4.00 p.m. but it takes her at least 3 minutes to reach the bus stop. What is the time of the next bus she can catch to get to her home in Carlton Village? How long does the journey take?

2   Ismail usually catches a train from Denham station at 4.45 p.m. On which bus must he travel from school? One day he stays late at school and catches the 1622 bus. The next train leaves at 5.30 p.m. How long will Ismail have to wait at the station, for that train?

19. An insurance company quotes these rates for travel insurance.
    (Prices per person.)

	United Kingdom only	Europe	Worldwide
up to 8 days	£3.65	£11.10	£28.60
up to 12 days	£4.00	£11.90	£29.95
up to 17 days	£4.95	£13.25	£31.55
up to 24 days	£5.75	£14.40	£37.10
Winter sports in Europe insured at $2\frac{1}{2}$ times the Europe premium. Double premium for persons aged over 65, Worldwide.			

Find the cost of insurance for these people.

1 Next week Mr Stewart is going on a business trip to Scotland for 5 days.
2 For their honeymoon next January Alan and Jayne are going skiing in Switzerland, for 10 days.
3 Mrs Charnley is going to stay with her married daughter in America for 3 weeks. She is looking forward to the trip although at age 70 it will be the first time she has travelled by air.

20. This table gives the repayments due when goods are bought from a certain firm by hire-purchase. (Amounts are in £.)

Cash price	Hire purchase price		
	Repay over 1 year 12 monthly instalments	Repay over 2 years 24 monthly instalments	Repay over $2\frac{1}{2}$ years 30 monthly instalments
10	0.94	0.53	0.44
20	1.88	1.06	0.88
30	2.82	1.59	1.32
40	3.76	2.12	1.76
50	4.70	2.65	2.20
60	5.64	3.18	2.64
70	6.58	3.71	3.08
80	7.52	4.24	3.52
90	8.46	4.77	3.96
100	9.40	5.30	4.40
200	18.80	10.60	8.80

Mr Jones wants to buy a lawn mower with cash price £60, and decides to pay on hire purchase over 1 year. What is the monthly instalment?
How much will the mower cost him altogether?
Instead of this he then decides to take longer to repay so that he will be able to get a better mower. He finally settles for repayments of £3.96 per month for 30 months. What is the cash price of the mower he chooses, and what will it cost him altogether?

21. Ashton, Barton, Corton, Dayton and Elton are five villages. The distances between each are shown on the mileage chart, (for example, from Barton to Dayton is 15 miles).
A cyclist travels from Elton directly to Ashton. On his return journey he takes the route via Corton. How much further does he travel on the return journey?

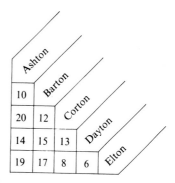

PUZZLES

1. A man has a wad of £5 notes numbered consecutively from 232426 to 232440. What is their total value?

2. What is the next letter in this sequence?
   N   N   N   E   N   E   E   N   E   E   E   –   –   –

3. What is the next prime number after 113?

4. How many squares can be formed by joining 4 of these points.

5. Five children were playing a game of cards.
   A set of cards numbered 1 to 10 are dealt so that they get two each. Paul has two cards which total 11, Mike has two cards which total 7, Laura has two cards which total 17, Kate has two cards which total 4 and Jane has two cards which total 16.
   In this game the winner is the person who has the card numbered 10. Who wins the game?

6. If $1\,m^3$ of earth weighs $1600\,kg$, how much would there be in a hole $50\,cm$ by $50\,cm$ by $50\,cm$?

7. Lorraine said 'Two days ago I was 13, next year I shall be 16'. What is the date today and when is her birthday?

2 Algebra

Expressions

Examples

If apples cost a pence per lb, the cost of 10 lb of apples is $10a$ pence.
If a girl is g years old and her younger brother is b years old, then the girl is $(g - b)$ years older than her brother.
The total weight of 8 parcels of b kg each and 6 parcels of c kg each is $(8b + 6c)$ kg.

If x people share £300 equally then they each get $£\dfrac{300}{x}$.

Simplifying expressions

Addition and subtraction

$a + a = 2a$
$5b - 4b = b$
$3c - 3c = 0$
$3d + 4e + d - e = 4d + 3e$

Multiplication and division

$a \times a = a^2$
$2 \times b \times c = 2bc$
$d \times d \times d = d^3$

$e \div f = \dfrac{e}{f}$

$g \div g = 1$

Rules of indices

$a^3 \times a^4 = a \times a \times a \times a \times a \times a \times a = a^7$

(so the answer can be found by adding the indices)

$b^5 \div b^2 = \dfrac{b \times b \times b \times b \times b}{b \times b} = b^3$

(so the answer can be found by subtracting the indices)

$$(c^3)^2 = c^3 \times c^3 = c^6$$

(so the answer can be found by multiplying the indices)

These methods satisfy the general rules

$$a^m \times a^n = a^{m+n} \qquad a^m \div a^n = a^{m-n} \qquad (a^m)^n = a^{mn}$$

Further expressions

$$a^2 + a^2 = 2a^2$$

$$3b^2 \times 2b^3 = 6b^5 \qquad \text{(this is } 3 \times b^2 \times 2 \times b^3)$$

$$4c^3 \div 3c = \frac{4c^3}{3c} = \frac{4}{3}c^2 \qquad \left(\text{this is } \frac{4 \times c \times c \times c}{3 \times c}\right)$$

$$\sqrt{9d^2} = 3d \qquad \text{(since } 3d \times 3d = 9d^2)$$

Removing brackets

$$3(a + 4b) = 3a + 12b$$
$$c(2c - 3d) = 2c^2 - 3cd$$
$$2e(3e + 5f - 1) = 6e^2 + 10ef - 2e$$
$$3(g + 4h) + 2(3g - h) = 3g + 12h + 6g - 2h = 9g + 10h$$

Substitution

If $a = 2$, $b = 5$ and $c = 0$ then

$$3a + b^2 = (3 \times 2) + 5^2 = 6 + 25 = 31$$
$$4abc = 4 \times 2 \times 5 \times 0 = 0$$
$$a^3 + 2b^2 = 2^3 + (2 \times 5^2) = 8 + 50 = 58$$

Note that $2b^2$ means $2 \times b^2 = 2 \times 5^2 = 2 \times 25 = 50$. It does **not** mean $(2b)^2$ which is 10^2 and equals 100.

Equations

Examples

1    $x + 10 = 17$
     Subtract 10 from both sides
          $x = 7$

2    $x - 8 = 5$
     Add 8 to both sides
          $x = 13$

3    $5x = 16$
     Divide both sides by 5
          $x = 3\frac{1}{5}$

4 $\dfrac{x}{4} = 5$

Multiply both sides by 4

$x = 20$

5   Solve the equation $13x - 20 = 6x + 8$

Subtract $6x$ from both sides

$$7x - 20 = 8$$

Add 20 to both sides

$$7x = 28$$

Divide both sides by 7

$$x = 4$$

To check the equation, substitute $x = 4$ into both sides of the equation separately. The two sides should be equal.

Left-hand side (LHS) $= 13x - 20 = (13 \times 4) - 20 = 52 - 20 = 32$
RHS $= 6x + 8 = (6 \times 4) + 8 = 24 + 8 = 32$
The two sides are both 32, so the equation checks.
If you are not required to do a check as part of the answer, do it at the side of your work, as rough working, or even mentally.

Exercise 2.1

1.   **1** What is the cost, in pence, of 5 kg of butter at a pence per kg?

2 How many minutes are there in $2b$ hours?

3 If a man goes abroad with c francs, and spends d francs, how many francs has he left?

4 What is the total cost, in pence, of 3 lb of apples at e pence per lb and 2 lb of pears at f pence per lb?

5 What is the change, in pence, from £1, after buying g packets of sweets at h pence each?

6 If a pencil costs k pence, what is the cost in £'s of k pencils?

7 What is the cost in pence of 4 eggs, if they cost m pence per dozen?

8 How many minutes are there in $3n$ seconds?

9 If £p is shared equally among q children, how much, in pence, do they each receive?

10 If a clock gains s seconds per hour, and it is set to the right time, how many minutes fast will it be t days later?

2.   Simplify these expressions

1	$3c + 2c - 4c$	**11**	$e^3 \times e^2$	**21**	$ab + ba$
2	$6d - 4d - 2d$	**12**	$f^8 \div f^4$	**22**	$c^3 + c^3$
3	$5e + f + 3e - f$	**13**	$9a \times 5a$	**23**	$4d^2 + 4d^2$
4	$2g - 3h + g - h$	**14**	$8b \times 2c$	**24**	$ef + 3ef - 2ef$
5	$4j + k + 2j - 3k$	**15**	$4e \times 5e^2$	**25**	$2(a + b) + 3(2a + b)$
6	$6m - 7m + 2m$	**16**	$15f^3 \div 5f^2$	**26**	$3(c^2 + 2)$
7	$a \times a$	**17**	$(3g)^2$	**27**	$4(8d - 3) + 5(2d + 3)$
8	$b \times b \times b$	**18**	$\sqrt{(25h^2)}$	**28**	$6ab \div 6bc$
9	$c \div c$	**19**	$8m \div 2n$	**29**	$(3g^2)^2$
10	$d^3 \div d$	**20**	$3n^2 \div 2n^2$	**30**	$\sqrt{(16j^2)}$

3.   If $x = 4$ and $y = 3$, find the value of

1	$2x^2$	**6**	$2y^2$
2	$x^2 + y^2$	**7**	y^3
3	$2x - y$	**8**	$4y - 3x$
4	$2xy$	**9**	$\dfrac{y^2 + 1}{x}$
5	$\dfrac{x + 2}{y}$	**10**	$\sqrt{x + 4y}$

4.   If $a = 5$, $b = 3$, $c = 1$ and $d = 0$, find the value of

1	$4a + b$	**5**	$abcd$	**8**	$(3a - 5c)^2$
2	$a^2 + b^2$	**6**	$\dfrac{a}{c}$	**9**	$\dfrac{a^2 - b^2 + d^2}{(b + c)^2}$
3	$2a^2$	**7**	$\dfrac{a + c}{b - c}$	**10**	$\sqrt{15ab}$
4	$2a - 3b - c$				

5.   Solve these equations

1	$a - 7 = 14$	**6**	$2f + 3 = 17$
2	$b + 17 = 36$	**7**	$g + 3g = 24$
3	$7c = 56$	**8**	$3h = 90 - h$
4	$\dfrac{d}{7} = 20$	**9**	$j - 5 = 0$
5	$11e - 6 = 71$	**10**	$15 - k = 12$

6. Solve these equations

1	$3a + 1 = 13 - a$	**11**	$12 - 2m = 0$
2	$16 - 4b = 0$	**12**	$12n + 5 = 15 - 8n$
3	$12c - 5 = 15 + 8c$	**13**	$3(2p - 1) + 2(p + 1) = 39$
4	$2d + 7 = 31 - 4d$	**14**	$\frac{1}{3}(q + 10) = 6$
5	$3(e + 2) - e = 26$	**15**	$20 - r = 12$
6	$4(2f - 6) + 3(f + 5) = 35$	**16**	$12 - s = 19 - 2s$
7	$\frac{1}{4}(g - 2) = 6$	**17**	$t^3 + 1 = 9$
8	$\dfrac{h}{4} + 7 = 15$	**18**	$\sqrt{u} + 1 = 5$
9	$\frac{1}{5}j - 6 = 8$	**19**	$3(v + 5) = 7v + 15$
10	$8k - 5 = 2k + 43$	**20**	$8w + 3 = 12 - 4w$

Directed numbers

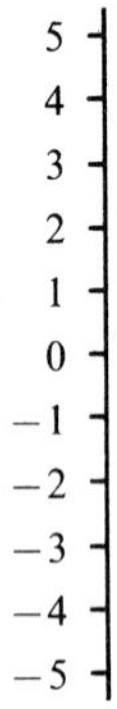

$2 + 4 = 6$

$(-5) + 4 = -1$ (Start at -5 on the number scale. Go up 4 steps, getting to -1.)

$(-5) + 7 = 2$ (Start at -5 on the number scale. Go up 7 steps, getting to 2.)

$5 - 2 = 3$

$5 - 8 = -3$ (Start at 5 on the number scale. Go down 8 steps, getting to -3.)

$(-5) - 1 = -6$ (Start at -5 on the number scale. Go down 1 step, getting to -6.)

Also

$(-5a) + 4a = -a$

$(-5a) + 7a = 2a$

$5a - 8a = -3a$

$(-5a) - a = -6a$

Replace two signs by one, and then work as shown above.

Rules

$x + (+y) = x + y$

$x - (+y) = x - y$

$x + (-y) = x - y$

$x - (-y) = x + y$

Examples

$$(-5) + (+1) = (-5) + 1 = -4$$
$$(-5) - (+3) = (-5) - 3 = -8$$
$$(-5) + (-2) = (-5) - 2 = -7$$
$$(-5) - (-8) = (-5) + 8 = 3$$

$$(-5a) + (+a) = (-5a) + a = -4a$$
$$(-5a) - (+3a) = (-5a) - 3a = -8a$$
$$(-5a) + (-2a) = (-5a) - 2a = -7a$$
$$(-5a) - (-8a) = (-5a) + 8a = 3a$$

Multiplication and division

Rules

$$(+x) \times (+y) = xy \qquad\qquad (+x) \div (+y) = \frac{x}{y}$$

$$(+x) \times (-y) = -xy \qquad\qquad (+x) \div (-y) = -\frac{x}{y}$$

$$(-x) \times (-y) = xy \qquad\qquad (-x) \div (+y) = -\frac{x}{y}$$

$$(-x) \div (-y) = \frac{x}{y}$$

Examples

$$4 \times 6 = 24 \qquad\qquad 12 \div 3 = 4$$
$$4 \times (-6) = -24 \qquad\qquad 12 \div (-3) = -4$$
$$(-4) \times 6 = -24 \qquad\qquad (-12) \div 3 = -4$$
$$(-4) \times (-6) = 24 \qquad\qquad (-12) \div (-3) = 4$$
$$4a \times (-6) = -24a \qquad\qquad 12a \div (-3) = -4a$$
$$(-4b) \times 6b = -24b^2 \qquad\qquad (-12b) \div 3b = -4$$
$$(-4c) \times (-6d) = 24cd \qquad\qquad (-12c^2) \div (-3c) = 4c$$

Exercise 2.2

1. Find the value of

   1 $4 - 6$ **5** $(-2) + 2$ **8** $0 - 8$

   2 $(-5) - 3$ **6** $(-10) - 10$ **9** $2 - 2\frac{1}{2}$

   3 $(-5) + 7$ **7** $7 - 12$ **10** $(-3\frac{1}{4}) + 1\frac{3}{4}$

   4 $6 - 4$

2. Find the value of

   1 $(+4) - (+3)$ **5** $(-4) - (-2)$ **8** $2 + (-5)$

   2 $(-5) + (-2)$ **6** $0 + (-5)$ **9** $6 - (+7)$

   3 $(+3) - (-6)$ **7** $(-3) - (+4)$ **10** $(-2) - (-8)$

   4 $(-1) + (+1)$

3. Simplify

    1 $5a + (-2a)$ **5** $7e + (+2e)$ **8** $(+2h) - (-5h)$

    2 $b - (+2b)$ **6** $(-3f) - (-f)$ **9** $(-2j) - (-5j)$

    3 $(-4c) - (-9c)$ **7** $g + (-g)$ **10** $(-5k) + (+4k)$

    4 $(-2d) + (-d)$

4. Find the value of   Simplify

    1 $1 - 7 + 6 - 12 - 2$ **6** $5x + (-6x) - (+2x)$

    2 $4 + 2 - 5 + 3 - 1$ **7** $(-7x) + (+9x) - (-3x)$

    3 $(-6) + 10 - 5 - 2 + 3$ **8** $x - (-x) + (-2x)$

    4 $(-2) - 1 + 6 - 7$ **9** $4x + (-4x) - (+3x)$

    5 $0 - 8 + 4 + 5 - 2$ **10** $(-3x) + (-5x) - (-4x)$

5. Find the value of

    1 $(+8) \times (+11)$ **5** $0 \times (-6)$ **8** $(-16) \div (-16)$

    2 $(+6) \times (-3)$ **6** $(+21) \div (-7)$ **9** $(+20) \div (+5)$

    3 $(-4) \times (+2)$ **7** $(-60) \div (+12)$ **10** $(-1)^3$

    4 $(-9) \times (-7)$

6. Simplify

    1 $8x \times 2y$ **5** $(-6x) \div 6x$ **8** $(-5) \div (-5x)$

    2 $(-4x) \times 7y$ **6** $3 \times (-2xy)$ **9** $(-2x)^2$

    3 $(+2x) \div (-3x)$ **7** $(-6) \times 4x^2$ **10** $0 \times (-3xy)$

    4 $(-3x) \times (-9x)$

7. If $x = 3$ and $y = -2$ find the value of

    1 $x + y$ **5** $\dfrac{3x}{y}$ **8** y^x

    2 $x - y$ **9** $x^2 - y^2$

    3 $2x + 3y$ **6** xy^2 **10** $(x - y)^2$

    4 $4xy$ **7** $\dfrac{y}{x - 4}$

8. If $a = 1$, $b = -1$ and $c = 0$ find the value of

  1 $b - a$ **5** $6b - 4a$ **8** $a^3 - b^3$

  2 abc **6** $\dfrac{a}{b} + \dfrac{c}{a}$ **9** $2a^2 + 3b^2 + 4c^2$

  3 $5(a + b)$ **7** $(a - b)^3$ **10** $\sqrt{5a - 4b}$

  4 $a^2 + b^2 - c^2$

9. Solve the equations

  1 $3x - 7 = 2$ **6** $3 - x = 6 + 2x$

  2 $2x + 17 = 3$ **7** $6(x + 1) - 10 = -4$

  3 $\dfrac{x}{2} - 6 = -10$ **8** $3 - 3x = 13 - 2x$

  4 $15x - 4 = 3x - 12$ **9** $3(x - 3) = x + 6$

  5 $3(1 - 2x) = 12$ **10** $5x - x = 1$

Indices

The general rules are $a^m \times a^n = a^{m+n}$ $a^m \div a^n = a^{m-n}$ $(a^m)^n = a^{mn}$
These rules are satisfied for all values of m and n and lead to these further rules

$$a^0 = 1 \qquad\qquad a^{-n} = \frac{1}{a^n}$$

Examples

$$3^0 = 1$$
$$5^0 = 1$$
$$3^{-1} = \frac{1}{3^1} = \frac{1}{3}$$
$$5^{-2} = \frac{1}{5^2} = \frac{1}{25}$$
$$10^{-3} = \frac{1}{10^3} = \frac{1}{1000}$$

Exercise 2.3

1. Find the value of

  1 5^3 **3** 2^{-3} **5** 7^{-2} **7** $2^3 \times 4^0$ **9** 3^{-2}

  2 6^2 **4** 6^0 **6** 4^{-1} **8** 10^3 **10** 10^{-1}

2. Simplify, but leave as a power of 10,

    1 $10^2 \times 10^3$ **4** $10^2 \div 10^{-2}$

    2 $(10^4)^2$ **5** $10^3 \times 10^{-1}$

    3 $10^5 \div 10^3$

3. Find the numbers replaced by the letter n in these statements

    1 $4^n = 64$ **4** $7^n = 1$

    2 $3^n = 81$ **5** $2^n = \frac{1}{2}$

    3 $10^n = \frac{1}{100}$

Exercise 2.4

1. Simplify **1** $a + a$ **2** $a - a$ **3** $a \times a$ **4** $a \div a$ **5** $\sqrt{a^2}$

2. Simplify **1** $3a^3 + 4a^3$ **2** $3a^3 \times 4a^3$ **3** $3a^3 \div 4a^3$

3. Simplify $2(x^2 + 5x - 6) + x^2 - 8x + 7 + x^2 - 2x + 5$

4. If $a = \frac{1}{2}$, $b = \frac{1}{3}$ and $c = \frac{1}{5}$, find the values of

    1 $5c - (a + b)$ **2** $2a^2 + 3b^2$ **3** $a(b - c)$

5. Simplify $2(2x + y) + 3(2x - y)$

6. If k lb of apples are bought for x pence per lb and sold for y pence per lb, what is the profit in £'s?

7.   **1** If *distance = speed $\times$ time*, what is *distance* when *speed* $= 70$ and *time* $= 3$?

    2 If *paint* $= \dfrac{area}{18}$, what is *paint* when *area* $= 45$?

    3 If *amount = principal + interest*, what is *amount* when *principal* $= 800$ and *interest* $= 80$?

    4 If *weight* $= 6 \times (length)^2$, what is *weight* when *length* $= 5$?

    5 If *radius* $= \sqrt{\dfrac{7 \times area}{22}}$, what is *radius* when *area* $= 616$?

8.   **1** If the temperature is $+3°$ and it falls by $10°$, what is the new temperature?

    2 If the temperature is $-6°$, by how many degrees must it rise to become $+7°$?

    3 If the temperature is $+10°$ and it falls to $-5°$ overnight, through how many degrees has it fallen?

    4 After rising 9 degrees the temperature is $+1°$. What was it originally?

    5 After falling 4 degrees the temperature is $-9°$. What was it originally?

9. If $p = 1$, $q = 2$, $r = 3$ and $s = 0$, find the value of

    1 $5p + 2q - r + s$

    2 $r - (p + q)$

    3 $\dfrac{2p + 5q + 2s}{4r}$

    4 $2r^2 + q^3 + 2ps$

    5 $\dfrac{p^2 + q^2 + r^2 + s^2}{2pq}$

    6 $(2r - q)(2q - p)$

    7 $\dfrac{q}{r} - \dfrac{p}{q} + \dfrac{s}{p}$

    8 $\frac{1}{2}(2pq + 3qr - 4rs)$

    9 $\sqrt{6pqr}$

    10 $(q + 3r)^2 - p^2$

10. Solve the equations

    1 $3 + 5x = 11 + x$

    2 $7 + 2x = 13 - 3x$

    3 $5x + 10 = 0$

    4 $\dfrac{4x}{5} = 8$

    5 $5(3x + 1) + 3(2x + 1) = 50$

11. I think of a number, multiply it by 5 and add 28. The result is 5 less than eight times the original number. What number did I start with?

12. If $y = 3x + 2$, find the values of y when $x = 0, 6, -3$. For what value of x is $y = 11$? For what value of x is $y = 0$?

13. If $x = 2y$ and $z = 3y$, find z in terms of x.

14. If $x = 3$ and $y = -5$, find the values of

    1 $\dfrac{2y + 2}{4x}$ **2** $2x^2 - y$ **3** $\sqrt{y^2 - x^2}$

15. Start with any number between 1 and 10, double it, from the result subtract 20, then multiply by 3 and add 6.
Next divide by 6, subtract 1 and square the result.
Subtract 100, divide by the number you started with, and then add 20. Subtract the number you started with. What is your answer?

16. If $xy = 24$ and $y = 5\frac{1}{3}$, what is the value of x?

17. The formula for the sum of the squares of the numbers from 1 to n is $\frac{1}{6}n(n + 1)(2n + 1)$. Use this formula to find the value of $1^2 + 2^2 + 3^2 + \cdots + 11^2 + 12^2$.

18. Find the value of $a^2 - c(a + b) + 2b^2$ if $a = 4$, $b = -3$ and $c = -1$.

19. For this video recorder, find a formula for the amount paid after n months, where n is less than or equal to 12? What is the total amount paid for the recorder?

Deposit £60
£25 per month
for 12 months

20. The time taken to cook a chicken is given as 20 minutes per lb plus 20 minutes extra. Find a formula for the time needed for a chicken weighing c lb. Give your answer **1** in minutes, **2** in hours.

21. Find the values of

    1 3^3 **4** $3^2 \times 3^{-1}$

    2 3^{-2} **5** $3 \div 3^{-3}$

    3 3^0

22. If $y = k(x - 5)(x - 6)$, and $y = 2$ when $x = 8$, find the value of k. What is the value of y when $x = 9$?

23. Carol's father was 24 years old when Carol was born. Now he is four times as old as Carol. How old is Carol now?
    (Let Carol be x years old, write down an equation and solve it.)

24. 20 paperbacks are bought, some costing 80 p each and the others costing £1.20 each. The total cost was £21.20. How many of the cheaper kind were there?
    (Let there be x at 80 p and $(20 - x)$ at £1.20, and work in pence.)

25. $(x + 15)$ minutes past 7 o'clock is the same as $(2x - 9)$ minutes to 8 o'clock. Find x.

PUZZLES

8. Copy this long division sum and fill in the missing figures.

```
              2 *
      * 3 ) 1 2 4 *
            * 6
          3 * *
          3 * *
```

9. Down the corridor next to the school hall there are five classrooms, numbered from 1 to 5, and these are occupied by the five 1st forms, 1A, 1B, 1C, 1D and 1E.
   1A is not in room 1, 1B is not in room 5, 1C is not in room 1 or room 5, 1D is in a room with a lower number than 1B. 1C's room is not next to 1B's room. 1E's room is not next to 1C's room. Which class is in room 1?

10. A group of people on a coach outing went into a cafe for a snack. The party leader ordered a cup of tea and a sandwich for everyone, and the total bill came to £18.49. How many people were on the coach?

11. Practical maths. Fold a piece of paper in half, then in half again, and again, . . . , 9 times altogether.

3 *Geometry*

Symmetry

The diagrams show

1. axes of symmetry, marked by dotted lines,
2. points of symmetry, marked

  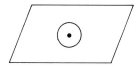 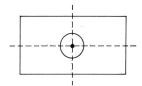

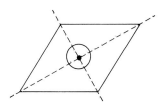 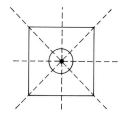 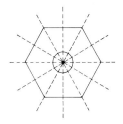

Rotational symmetry

 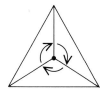 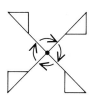 

of order 2   of order 3   of order 4   of order 5

Transformations

Reflection

The dotted lines show the reflections of the triangles in the line AB, which is an axis of symmetry of the completed figure.

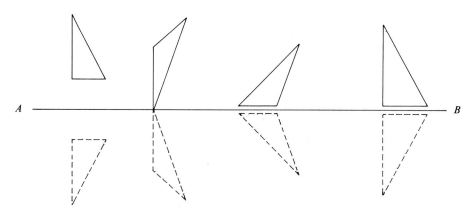

Rotation

The dotted lines show the new positions of the triangles when they have been rotated about the point marked (•)

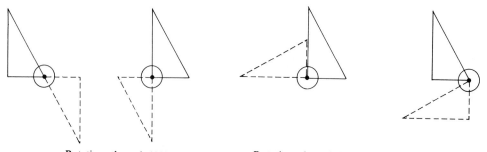

Rotations through 180°   Rotations through 90° anticlockwise

Exercise 3.1

1. Sketch these capital letters and mark in any axes and points of symmetry.
    B   H   M   S

2. Sketch these quadrilaterals and mark in any axes and points of symmetry.

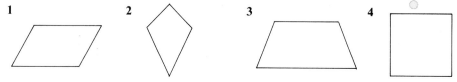

3. Sketch these figures and mark in any axes and points of symmetry.

1 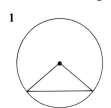   2 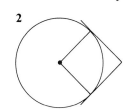   3 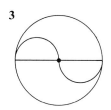   4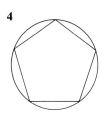

4. Sketch these flags and reflect them in the dotted lines.

1 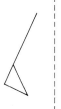   2   3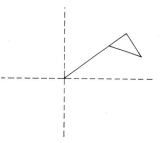

5. Sketch these flags and rotate them about the points marked •

1 through 90° anticlockwise   2 through 180°   3 through 90° clockwise

6. Sketch and complete these drawings so that they have rotational symmetry of order 4, about the point marked •

1   2   3

7. What is the order of rotational symmetry of these figures?

1 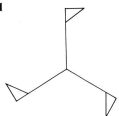   2    3 The outline of a 20 pence coin

8. For each of these diagrams, state how many axes of symmetry there are.

1 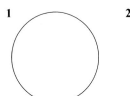 **2** 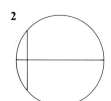 **3** 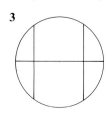 **4**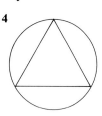

Angles

This is angle *ABC* (or ∠ *ABC*) or angle *CBA*.
If there is no possibility of confusion it can be
called ∠ *B*.

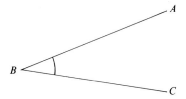

Angles can also be identified by small letters.
This angle is *b*.

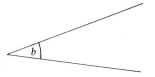

Measurement of angles

1 complete turn or revolution is divided into 360°.

1 half-turn is 180°.

1 quarter-turn is 90°. This is also called a right angle.

The sign for a right angle is

Perpendicular lines are lines which meet each other at right angles.

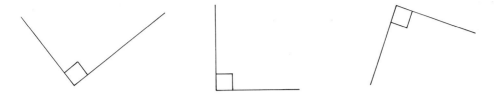

Types of angles

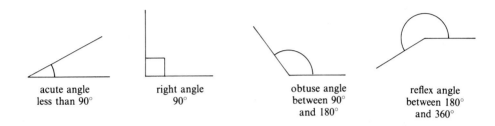

acute angle
less than 90°

right angle
90°

obtuse angle
between 90°
and 180°

reflex angle
between 180°
and 360°

Angles at a point   **Adjacent angles**   **Vertically**
                                        (on a straight line)   **opposite angles**

These add up to 360°   These add up to 180°   These are equal

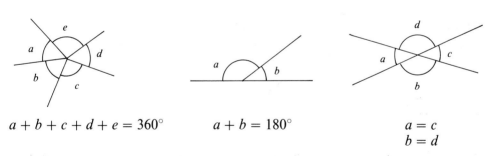

$a + b + c + d + e = 360°$ $a + b = 180°$ $a = c$
                                                                   $b = d$

Parallel lines are lines with the same direction. They remain the same distance apart, so never meet each other.
The sign for parallel lines is similar arrows on the lines.

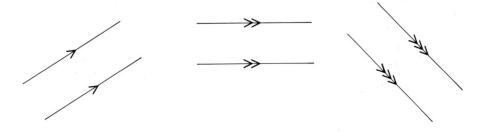

Angles and parallel lines

Corresponding angles These are equal	**Alternate angles** These are equal	**Interior angles** These add up to 180°
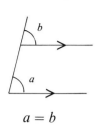	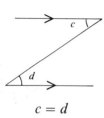	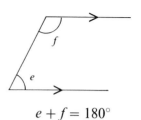
$a = b$	$c = d$	$e + f = 180°$

Exercise 3.2

1. State whether these angles are acute, obtuse or reflex angles.

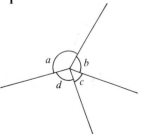

2. Estimate the sizes of these angles, in degrees. Check your estimate by measuring with your protractor.

    1   **2**   **3**

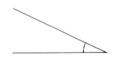 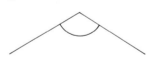 

3. Estimate the sizes of the marked angles, in degrees. Check your estimate by measuring with your protractor. Verify that the angles at a point add up to 360°, adjacent angles on a straight line add up to 180°, and vertically opposite angles are equal.

    1   **3**

  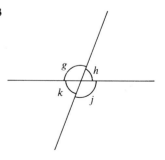

4. Estimate the sizes of the marked angles, in degrees. Check your estimate by measuring with your protractor. Verify that corresponding angles are equal, alternate angles are equal and interior angles add up to 180°.

1

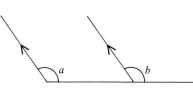

2

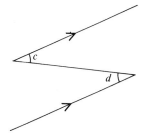

3

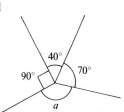

5. Calculate the sizes of angles *a*, *b*, *c*, *d*, *e*, *f*, *g*, *h*.

1

2

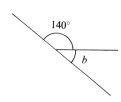

3

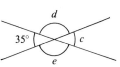

4

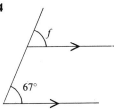

5

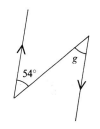

6

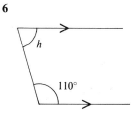

6. Calculate the sizes of angles a, b, c, d, e, f, g, h.

1

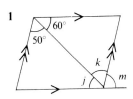

2

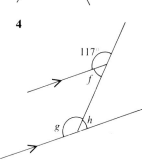

3

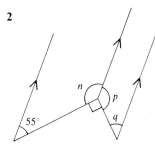

4

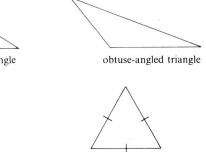

7. Calculate the sizes of angles j, k, m, n, p, q.

1

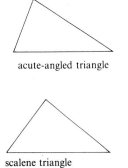

2

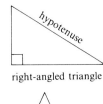

Triangles

Kinds of triangle

acute-angled triangle   right-angled triangle   obtuse-angled triangle

scalene triangle   isosceles triangle   equilateral triangle
(3 sides of different lengths)   (two sides equal)   (all 3 sides equal)

(The sign for lines of equal length is similar small marks crossing the lines.)

Angle sum of a triangle

The sum of the angles of a triangle is 180°

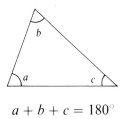

$$a + b + c = 180°$$

Exterior angle of a triangle

If a side is produced, the exterior angle is equal to the sum of the two opposite interior angles

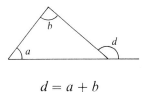

$$d = a + b$$

Isosceles triangle

The angles opposite the equal sides are equal

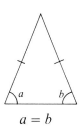

$$a = b$$

Equilateral triangle

All angles are 60°

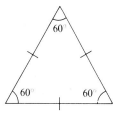

Example 1

Find the size of $\angle ECB$.

$\triangle ABC$ is isosceles, so $b = c$
$b = 69°$ angle sum of $\triangle = 180°$
            $180° - 42° = 138°$
            $138° \div 2 = 69°$
$b = d$ alternate angles,
            $AD \, / / \, CE$
$d = 69°$
i.e. $\angle ECB = 69°$

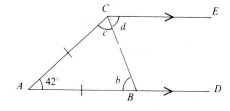

Exercise 3.3

1. Estimate the sizes of the angles in these triangles. Check your estimate by measuring with your protractor. Verify that the sum of the angles is 180°.

1

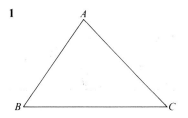

2

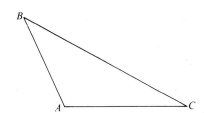

2. Estimate the sizes of the angles in these isosceles triangles. Check your estimate by measuring with your protractor. Verify that the angles opposite the equal sides are equal.

1

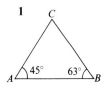

2

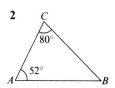

3. Calculate the sizes of the 3rd angles in these triangles.

1

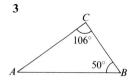

2

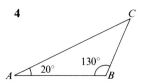

3

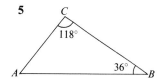

4

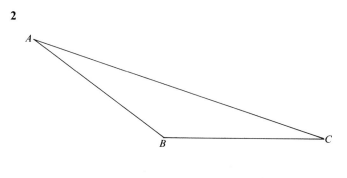

5

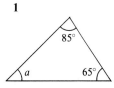

4. Calculate the sizes of angles a, b, c, d.

1

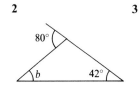

2

3

4

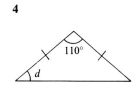

5. If $AB = AC$, which two angles are equal?
    Find the sizes of $\angle ACD$, $\angle CDB$, $\angle DBC$, $\angle BCD$.

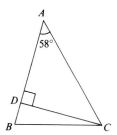

6. Calculate the sizes of $\angle ACD$, $\angle CDB$, $\angle DBC$, $\angle BCD$.

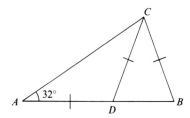

7. Calculate the sizes of the angles marked with small letters.

1

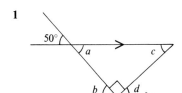

2

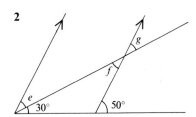

3

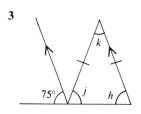

4

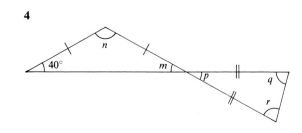

Constructions

Exercise 3.4

1. **To draw parallel lines with a set-square**

   Example

   Draw a line through C, parallel to AB.

   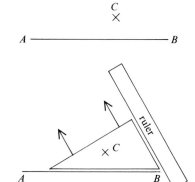

   Place the longest side of the set-square on AB so that, if possible, the set-square is placed over C.
   Place a ruler along one of the other sides of the set-square.

   Keeping the ruler fixed, slide the set-square along the ruler until its longest side passes through C. Draw a line along this edge.

   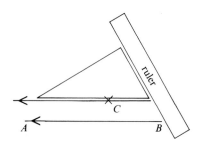

2. **To draw a triangle, given 3 sides**

   Example

   Draw a triangle ABC with $AB = 9$ cm, $BC = 8$ cm and $AC = 7$ cm.

   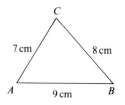

   Draw AB, 9 cm long.
   With compasses, centre A, radius 7 cm, draw an arc.
   With centre B, radius 8 cm, draw an arc to cut the first arc at C.
   Join AC and CB.

   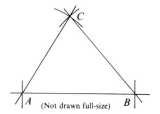

3. **To draw a triangle, given 1 side and 2 angles**

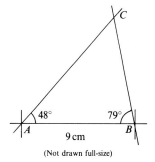

Example

Draw a triangle *ABC* with *AB* = 9 cm, ∠*A* = 48° and ∠*B* = 79°.

Draw *AB*, 9 cm long.
Measure an angle of 48° at *A* and an angle of 79° at *B*. Continue these lines until they meet at *C*.

(Not drawn full-size)

(If instead of being given the size of ∠*B* you had been told that ∠*C* = 53°, you could have calculated the size of ∠*B*, since the 3 angles of a triangle have a sum of 180°, and then you could continue as above.)

4. **To draw a triangle, given 2 sides and the angle included between these sides**

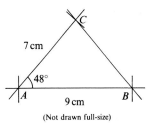

Example

Draw a triangle *ABC* with *AB* = 9 cm, ∠*A* = 48° and *AC* = 7 cm.

Draw *AB*, 9 cm long.
Measure an angle of 48° at *A* and measure off a distance of 7 cm along this angle line, to give the point *C*.
Join *BC*.

(Not drawn full-size)

5. **To draw a triangle, given two sides and a non-included angle**

Example

Draw a triangle *ABC* with *AB* = 5 cm, ∠*A* = 48° and *BC* = 6 cm.

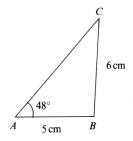

Draw *AB*, 5 cm long.
Measure an angle of 48° at *A* and extend this
angle line onwards.
With compasses, centre *B*, radius 6 cm, draw
an arc to meet this extended line at *C*.
Join *BC*.

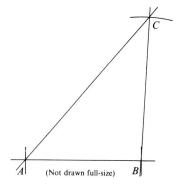

(Not drawn full-size)

(In some cases there could be two points where the arc meets the line, so there
would be two possible triangles of different shapes satisfying the given data.)

Questions 6 to 10. Construct these triangles full-size.

6.

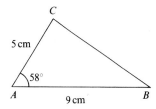

Estimate the length of *BC* and the sizes of ∠ *B* and
∠ *C*. Check your estimates by measurement.

7.

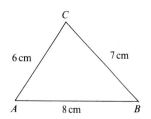

Estimate the sizes of the angles *A*, *B* and *C*, and then
check by measuring them with your protractor.

8.

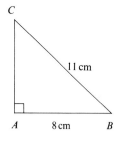

Estimate the length of *AC* and the sizes of angles *B*
and *C*. Check your estimates by measurement.

9.

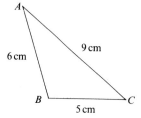

D is the mid-point of *AB*. Mark *D* on your diagram.
Through *D* draw a line parallel to *BC*. Let this line
cut *AC* at *E*.
Measure *AE* and *EC*.

10.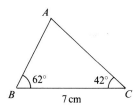

Through *A* draw a line parallel to *BC* and through *C* draw a line perpendicular to *BC*. Let these lines meet at point *D*.
Measure *AD* and *CD*.

Congruent figures are the same shape and the same size.

 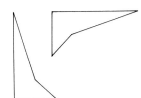 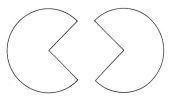

Congruent triangles

If one triangle can be reflected into the position of a second triangle, then the triangles are congruent.

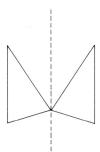 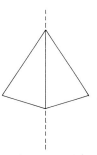

If one triangle can be rotated into the position of a second triangle, then the triangles are congruent.

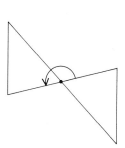 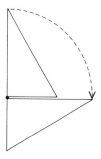

Transformations: Translation

The dotted lines show the translation of the triangles when every point has been moved an equal distance in the same direction.

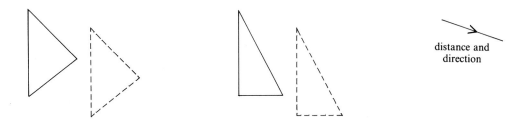

distance and direction

If one triangle can be translated into the position of a second triangle, then the triangles are congruent.

The symbol $\equiv$ means 'is congruent to'.

Example 2

In the diagram it is given that
$\angle BAC = \angle DAC$, and $AB = AD$. Explain
why the triangles are congruent.

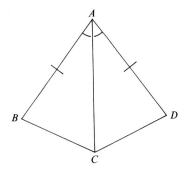

If $\triangle ABC$ is reflected in the line AC then A and C are unchanged. Since $\angle BAC = \angle DAC$ the line AB will be reflected into the line AD, and since the length of AB equals the length of AD the point B will be reflected into the point D.
So $\triangle ABC$ will be reflected into $\triangle ADC$
So $\triangle ABC \equiv \triangle ADC$.

Because the triangles are congruent, we also know that
$$BC = DC$$
$$\angle B = \angle D$$
$$\angle ACB = \angle ACD$$

Conditions for triangles to be congruent.

(1)   (2)   (3)   (4)

We recognise that these triangles are congruent because . . .

In (1) 3 sides of the first triangle are equal in turn to 3 sides of the second triangle. (This reason is written as SSS.)

In (2) 2 sides of the first triangle are equal to 2 sides of the second triangle, also the angles included between the two sides are equal. (SAS)

In (3) 2 angles in the first triangle are equal to 2 angles of the second triangle, and a side of the first triangle is equal to a side of the second triangle, which is in a corresponding position in relation to the angles. (AAS)

In (4) the triangles are right-angled and their hypotenuses and one other pair of sides are equal. (RHS)

Using these conditions in example **2**, notice that 2 sides of $\triangle ABC$ are equal to 2 sides of $\triangle ADC$, and the angles included between the two sides are equal, so the triangles are congruent.

Set this down as follows:

$$AB = AD$$
$$\angle BAC = \angle DAC$$
$\left.\right\}$ these were given
$$AC = AC \qquad \text{(same line)}$$
$$\triangle ABC \equiv \triangle ADC \qquad \text{(SAS)}$$

Exercise 3.5

1. Name the pairs of congruent triangles in the diagram.

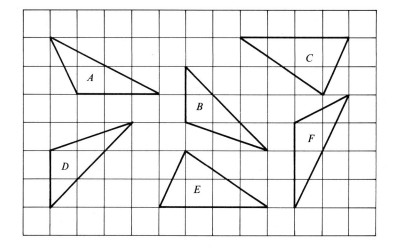

2. In this figure,

    1 Name the point of symmetry.

    2 State which triangles are
       congruent.

    3 Name a length equal to *AB*.

    4 Name an angle equal to
       ∠ *BAC*

    5 What does this prove about the
       lines *AB* and *ED*?

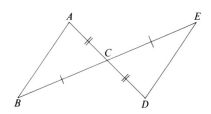

3. In this figure,

    1 Name the axis of symmetry.

    2 Name three pairs of congruent triangles.

    3 Name an angle equal to ∠ *ABC*.

    4 Name a line equal to *BX*.

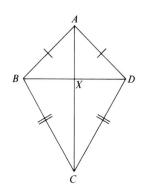

4. An explorer wants to estimate the
    width of a river. He stands directly
    opposite a tree growing on the
    other bank, at *A*, walks 50 m along
    the river bank to *B* where he places
    a stick, walks another 50 m to *C*,
    then walks at right angles to the
    river until he reaches a point *D*
    where the stick and the tree are in
    line. If *CD* = 80 m, how wide is the
    river?

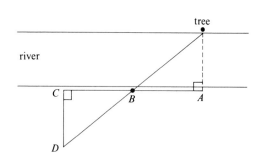

5. In the diagram the lines *AD, BE* and *CF*
    are parallel and equal.
    Name a pair of congruent triangles.
    What angle is equal to ∠ *ACB*?

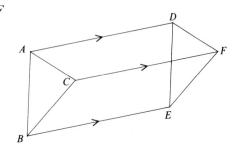

6. In this figure, if $\triangle ABC$ is rotated through
    90° clockwise about point C, its new
    position is $\triangle EDC$, so $\triangle ABC \equiv \triangle EDC$.

    1 Name lines equal to BC and AB.

    2 Name an angle equal to $\angle B$.

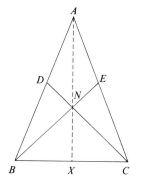

7. In this figure, AX is an axis of symmetry.

    1 Name triangles congruent to $\triangle ADN$,
    $\triangle ABN$, $\triangle ABE$.

    2 Name lengths equal to BE and AD.

    3 Name an angle equal to $\angle ABN$.

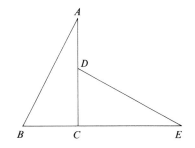

Exercise 3.6

1. From the letters **S H A P E**, which has

    1 only one axis of symmetry, which is horizontal,
    2 2 axes of symmetry,
    3 a point of symmetry but no axes of symmetry?

2. The design shows 8 congruent triangles arranged
    in a rectangle. State the transformation which
    would map

    1 triangle (1) into triangle (2),
    2 triangle (1) into triangle (3),
    3 triangle (1) into triangle (4),
    4 triangle (1) into triangle (5).

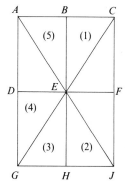

3. An engine turns at 9000 revolutions per minute. Find, as a fraction of a second,
    how long it takes to turn through a right angle.

4. Through how many degrees do you turn when facing South-East and turning
    clockwise to West?

5. **1** Through how many degrees does the hour hand of a clock turn in 1 hour?

    2 Through how many degrees does the hour hand of a clock turn between 1 p.m. and 4.30 p.m.?

    3 What is the size of the obtuse angle between the hands of a clock at half-past two?

6. Use angle properties to write down an equation involving *x* and hence find the value of *x* in the following figures.

1

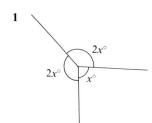

$2x°$

$2x°$

$x°$

2

$(3x - 40)°$ $\times$ $(x + 30)°$

3

$6x°$

$2x°$

$x°$

7. Find the size of $\angle A$ and then find the value of *x*.

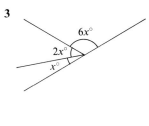

8. In $\triangle ABC$, $AB = AC$, and the bisectors of $\angle B$ and $\angle C$ meet at *I*. (Bisectors are lines which cut the angles in half.)
    Find the sizes of
    1 $\angle ABC$,
    2 $\angle IBC$,
    3 $\angle BIC$.

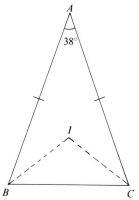

9. (In each part of this question write down an equation involving *x*, and solve it.)

1 The three angles of a triangle are $(x + 25)°$, $(x + 35)°$ and $2x°$. Find *x*. What is the size of the largest angle?

2

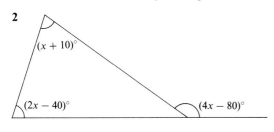

3

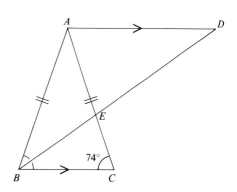

Find *x*. What sort of triangle is it?   Find *x*.

10. In the diagram, $AB = AC$ and $\angle B$ is bisected by *BD*.
Find the sizes of
1 $\angle ABC$,
2 $\angle BAD$,
3 $\angle ADE$.

11. Write down an equation involving *w* and solve it to find the value of *w*.

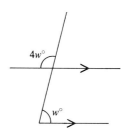

12. **1** Write down an equation involving *x* and solve it to find the value of *x*.
2 Write down an equation involving *y* and solve it to find the value of *y*.
3 Write down an equation involving *z* and solve it to find the value of *z*.

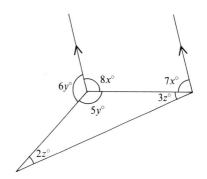

13.   An explorer wants to estimate the width of a river, flowing East–West. She stands due South of a tree growing on the opposite bank, and then walks due West, counting her paces, until the tree is in the North–East direction.
      If by that time she has taken 120 paces, and her usual pace-length is 90 cm, what estimate can she make of the width of the river?

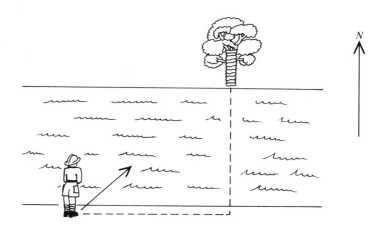

14.   Make a rough copy of this map of 'treasure island' and find the place where the treasure is hidden. 'Halve the distance in a straight line from A to B, and from this halfway point proceed in a straight line at right angles to the line AB until you reach the river. Having crossed the river, march North to the coast. Here you will find a cave where the treasure lies hidden.'

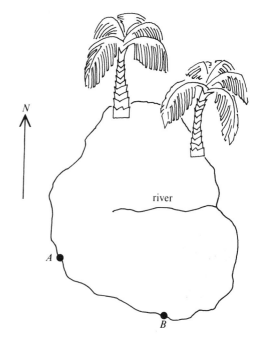

15.   Draw accurately a triangle ABC with AB = 8 cm, ∠A = 56° and ∠B = 64°. From D, the mid-point of BC, draw a line parallel to AB, to meet AC at E. Join AD. Measure the angles ADE and EAD.

16.   Draw accurately a triangle ABC with AB = 7 cm, ∠A = 90° and BC = 10 cm. Measure AC.

17. Name the pairs of congruent figures in the diagram.

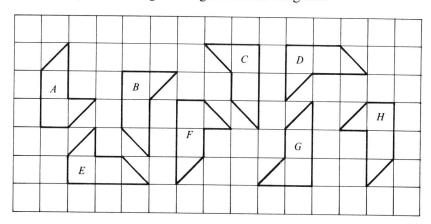

18. Find the sizes of $\angle ACB$ and $\angle DCB$.
     Explain why triangles ABC and DCB are
     congruent. Which length is equal to AB?

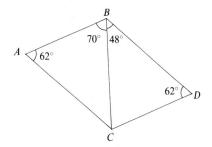

PUZZLE

12. How many triangles are there in this figure?

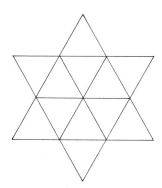

4 Statistics

Statistics involves numerical data.
Firstly, the data must be collected.
Secondly, it is displayed in the form of a list, a table or a graph.
Thirdly, it is studied, in order to make conclusions from it, often involving decisions for the future.

Tally tables

Example 1

The type of vehicle passing along a road gave the following data: Lorry, bus, car, lorry, lorry, lorry, car, lorry, bus, bus, lorry, car, car, van, car, car, bus, car, car, lorry, car, lorry, car, car, lorry, car, van, lorry, lorry, car, van, car, bus, van, lorry, car, bus, car.

The items are entered in a tally chart as they occur.

		Total
Car	JHT JHT JHT I	16
Van	IIII	4
Bus	JHT I	6
Lorry	JHT JHT II	12
		38

Notice that the numbers are grouped in fives, the fifth number going diagonally through the first four. JHT

The groups of 5 are kept in neat columns.
This makes the totals easy to count.

Presenting the data in a table

Example 2

Method of transport to and from school

Copy the table and fill in the figures to satisfy this information.

Of the 50 boys, 10 walk to school, 5 cycle, 3 come on their motorbikes, 8 come by car and 4 come by train. The rest come by bus. All go home by the same method except that 2 who walk to school go home by car and 3 who come by car go home by bus.

	Morning			Afternoon		
	Boys	Girls	Total	Boys	Girls	Total
Walk						
Cycle						
Motorbike						
Car						
Bus						
Train						
Total						

Of the girls, 12 walk to school, 8 cycle, 1 comes on her motorbike, 3 come by car and 16 come by bus. No-one comes by train. 4 of the girls who come by bus walk home and 2 others go home by car instead of by bus.
Fill in the remaining spaces in the table.
What fraction of the pupils come to school by public transport (bus or train)?
What fraction of the pupils go home by public transport?

Diagrams

Pictograms

Example 3

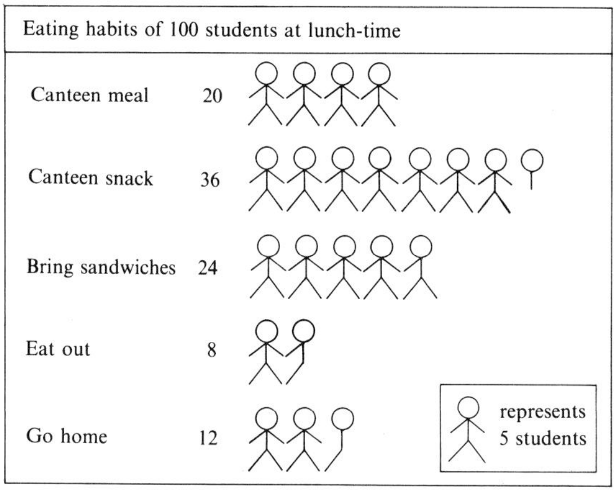

Unless you are spending time on a special project, do not draw elaborate symbols.
Use simple ones, such as used here.

Bar chart

Example 4

Favourite sports of 20 children

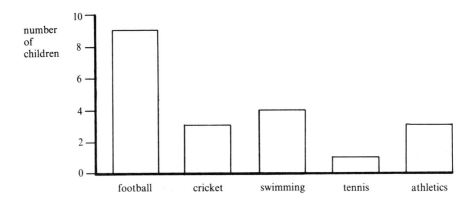

(The rectangles should all have the same width.)

Bar charts could be horizontal instead of vertical.

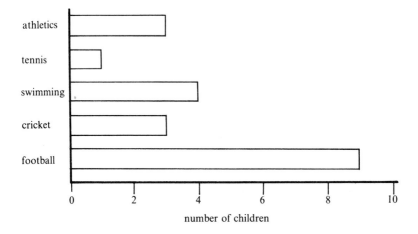

Statistical diagrams and graphs should have headings to describe them. Scales should be clearly marked. Axes should be labelled.

Draw a pictogram and a bar chart to illustrate the data given in the tally chart on page 56.

Pie chart

Example 5

A family with a weekly income of £90 spend it as follows:

	£
Rent	20
Fuel	14
Food	30
Clothing	10
Household goods	6
Other expenses	10
	90

Spending by a family

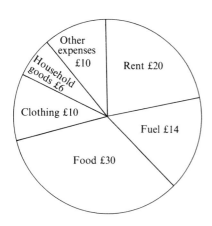

(Working for the pie chart)

Since £90 is represented by 360°,
£1 is represented by 4°.

Rent	$20 \times 4° = 80°$
Fuel	$14 \times 4° = 56°$
Food	$30 \times 4° = 120°$
Clothing	$10 \times 4° = 40°$
Household goods	$6 \times 4° = 24°$
Other expenses	$10 \times 4° = 40°$

(It is not necessary to mark the sizes of angles on the diagram if you show your working clearly as above. The diagram shows the statistical figures and is clearer without the angle markings.)

Straight line graph

Example 6

These figures show the numbers attending a youth-club over the past ten weeks.

20, 35, 28, 25, 33, 41, 37, 46, 48, 42.

We can plot these figures on a graph, putting time on the horizontal axis and attendance on the vertical axis.

Youth club attendance

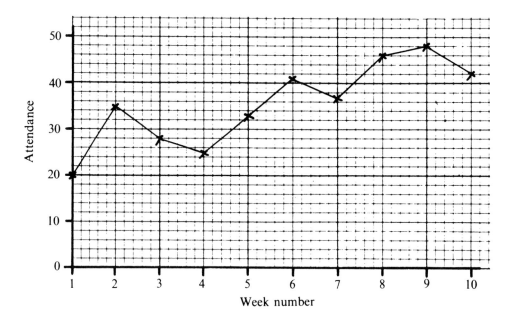

The points are joined from one to the next by straight lines, because this shows increases and decreases more easily, but in this graph the lines have no other meaning. We cannot use the graph to find the attendance at in-between times, because that would be meaningless. The graph does show an upward trend in attendance and we might use this to make a very cautious prediction for future attendances.

From the graph find

1   in which week the attendance was greatest,
2   between which weeks there was the greatest increase in attendance.

Misleading bar charts or line graphs

1. Because the scale does not start at 0, there seems to be a rapid increase. Sometimes the scale is distorted, also.

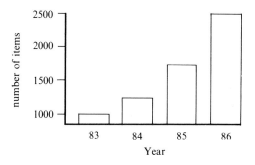 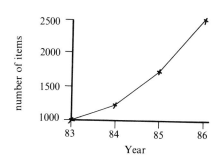

This gives the true picture.

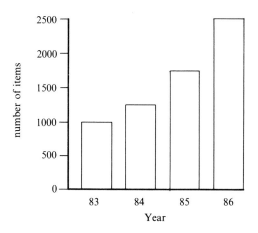 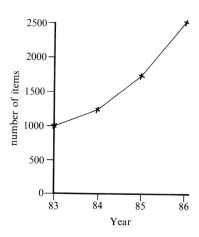

2. Although the profits have increased, the dotted block or line suggests a greater increase to follow in the future.

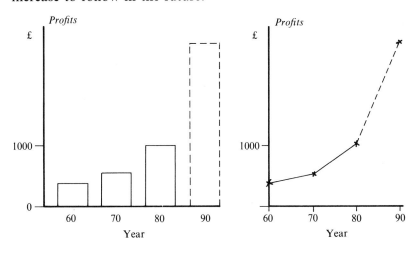

3. These are meaningless as there are no scales or units given. It gives the impression that 'ours is best'.

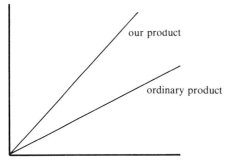

Energy release after eating our product

our product

ordinary product

Misleading pictograms

If  represents a house, use to represent 2 houses.

If you double the measurements of the house instead, the proportion is all wrong. (In fact the new house has eight times the volume of the other one and should represent 8 houses.)

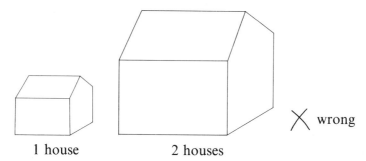

1 house   2 houses   ✕ wrong

People might use this method when they want to give a misleading impression. The method is acceptable if the measurements are calculated properly so that the volumes, or areas in a two-dimensional picture, are in the correct proportion.

Which diagram to draw

A bar chart shows clearly the different frequencies. It is easy to compare them. You can see at a glance which of two similar bars is longer.

A pie chart shows more easily the fraction of the total which each item takes. A sector using more than half of the circle represents more than half of the total, a sector with a small angle represents a small part of the total, and so on. It is not so easy to compare sectors with each other if they are nearly the same size.

A **pictogram** shows information in a similar way to a bar chart, but by making attractive drawings it makes it look more interesting than a bar chart, so people are more likely to look at it.

If you make pictures of different kinds, for example, cars, vans and buses, make them of equal length or you will not be able to compare the frequencies by looking at the diagram.

For example,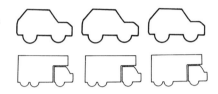

not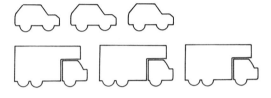

Look for examples of statistical tables or diagrams in newspapers, magazines, books or on television.

Notice the effect of colour or shading. On a diagram the parts with brighter colours seem to be more important than the others.

Look out for examples of misleading statistics.

Statistics is a branch of Mathematics which has a wide variety of uses. The Government collects many kinds of statistics which are often published in journals. Scientists use statistics in their research. Industry uses statistics to plan future action. Insurance companies use statistics to fix the premiums they must charge. Most sports' associations keep statistical records.

(You will notice that the word 'Statistics' can mean the subject (the study of numerical data), or it can simply mean the data.)

You can make an attractive poster or scrapbook using cuttings from newspapers and magazines, showing a variety of statistical data and different types of statistical diagrams.

Exercise 4.1

1. The numbers of livestock in Britain in a certain year included the following:
   Sheep   44 million
   Cattle   14 million
   Pigs   8 million
   (Figures are given to the nearest million.)
   Represent the data on a pictogram or bar chart.

2. A family's income of £120 in a particular week was spent as follows:
    Food   £36
    Rent   £21
    Car expenses   £18
    Clothes   £9
    Fuel   £12
    Miscellaneous   £24
    Represent the data on a pie chart.

3. An arable farm of 90 hectares grows four main crops.
    Barley   56 hectares
    Potatoes   11 hectares
    Carrots   9 hectares
    Green vegetables   14 hectares
    (1 hectare $= 10\,000\,\text{m}^2$)
    Represent the data on a pie chart.

4. In a particular year, the destinations of British holidaymakers travelling to other European countries were as follows:
    Spain 30%, France 14%, Italy 8%, Greece 7%, Eire 5%, Other countries 36%
    Represent the data on a pictogram or a bar chart.

5. Each £1 collected in rates was used by a Council as follows:
    Education   52 p
    Social services   10 p
    Police   9 p
    Highways and transport   9 p
    Fire Service   2 p
    Other expenses   5 p
    The rest was kept in reserve. How much per £1 was this?
    Represent this information on a pictogram.

6. The assets of a building society for 7 consecutive years (to the nearest million £'s) were

Year number	1	2	3	4	5	6	7
Assets (in £1 000 000)	19	21	25	29	34	39	47

    Draw a bar chart or straight line graph to represent the data.

7. The U.K. population figures are given in this list. (Figures to the nearest million.)

Year	1901	1911	1921	1931	1941	1951	1961	1971
Population (in millions)	38	42	44	46	48	51	53	56

    Draw a bar chart to represent the data.

8. The temperature in a classroom was recorded at the same time each day for 3 weeks. (Temperatures in °C to the nearest degree.)

	Mon	Tues	Wed	Thur	Fri
1st week	12	15	16	18	16
2nd week	17	16	16	15	17
3rd week	16	15	14	15	17

Draw a straight line graph to represent the data.

9. The number of passengers carried by a bus company on 14 consecutive days was as follows:
(Figures in 100's to the nearest hundred.)

	Sun	Mon	Tues	Wed	Thur	Fri	Sat
1st week	10	40	30	38	44	52	25
2nd week	15	42	29	37	46	55	20

Draw a straight line graph to represent the data.

10. A camping holiday cost £36. This pie chart shows how the money was used.

Measure the angles with your protractor to the nearest 5° in each case.
Find how much was spent on each of the four items.

11. The bar chart shows how a family spent its weekly income of £110.

The rest of the income was saved for the holiday fund. How much was saved that week?
The following week the income was increased by a bonus to £130, so £12 extra was spent on food, £3 extra on other expenses and the rest of the increase went into the holiday fund. Draw a bar chart showing the spending and saving for this second week.

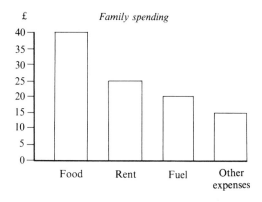

12. A firm made a table showing sales of a product.

	Standard model	De-luxe model	Total
Red			
Green			
Blue			
Total			

Copy the table and fill in the details.
In the standard model there were 60 sold altogether of which $\frac{1}{2}$ were red and $\frac{1}{5}$ were green. For sales in the de-luxe range, 5 more red ones were sold than of the standard model and 4 less blue ones than of the standard model. Altogether 31 green items were sold.
What fraction of the total items sold were blue ones?

13. In a shopping survey, 4 different brands of butter, which we will call brands A, B, C and D, were on sale. The first 50 customers' choices were as follows:

C   C   A   D   D   D   C   C   D   C
C   A   D   D   C   C   A   D   C   A
C   A   B   C   C   A   A   A   A   C
C   C   A   A   A   A   A   C   C   C
B   B   D   C   D   C   C   C   B   D

Tally this information. Draw a bar chart to illustrate the results.

14. Make a tally chart of the number of times the letters a, e, i, o, u occur in this question. Draw a pictogram or a bar chart to illustrate the data.

Collecting data

There are several ways in which you could collect data. Having collected it, present it in a list or a table, or in a statistical diagram. Then study it to see if you can find any interesting conclusions from it.
(The ideas of this section are also relevant to the further Statistics chapters in the book. Keep all collected data as you may be able to use it again later.)

1. Data you can collect from yourself, your friends or your family.
   Examples:
   1 Make a list of how you spend your time on an average weekday, e.g. hours sleeping, eating, at school, on homework, watching TV, etc. Draw a pie chart of the results. Compare this with how you spend your time on Saturday or Sunday, or compare with a friend's results.

2   Make a list of how you spend or save your weekly pocket money. Draw a bar chart of the results. Compare this with the results from a different week.
    If your parents will tell you the amounts, make a list of how the family's weekly income is used, e.g. rent and rates, fuel, food, clothing, fares or car expenses, etc.
    A more detailed project is to find how much money is spent on you each year, e.g. food, clothing, fares to school, school meals, pocket money, presents, etc.

2. Data you can find from books, newspapers and other sources.
    Examples:
    1   Collect the football results of the main leagues from the newspaper. There are many ways in which you can study these.
    2   From the TV timetables in the newspaper or magazines, find how much time in a day is devoted to news, current affairs, sport, nature, comedy, etc. Compare the results for different TV channels.
    3   Find out how the Council spends the money they collect in rates. They will give this information with the rates bill. For every £1 collected, find how much goes on Education, Health, Housing, etc. and show this in a bar chart or pie chart.
    4   Make a temperature chart showing the daily temperature outdoors (in the shade) for several days. It is interesting if you can do this in the summer and then in the winter. If you made a rain gauge you could also collect rainfall figures.
    5   If you do experiments in Science or other subjects you can use the results to do a statistical study.
    6   You can do traffic surveys. Find the number of cars passing your home or school or some other point in a given time. You can repeat this at different times of the day. Estimate the ages of cars by noting the single letter in the registration number. Classify the traffic into categories such as cars, buses, heavy goods vehicles, etc. You could do a survey of the different makes of cars.

Sampling

When we need data about a certain population we often just take a sample. If you wanted to know the favourite meal of pupils in your school you would not be able to ask everyone so you would select certain people and ask them.
If a farmer wanted to know how well his potatoes were growing he would not uproot the whole crop, he would just dig up a sample. (Here the population is the whole crop of potatoes. In statistics the word 'Population' does not need to refer to people.)
It is no use choosing a sample if it is biased, that is, likely to give unfair results. The best kind of sample to take is a **random sample**. In this, every member of the population has the same chance of being chosen. It is not always possible or easy to get a random sample so we have to compromise.
The sample should represent fairly each group in the population, and it should be large enough to give proper results.

If you wanted the views of pupils in your school, for a random sample you would put all their names in a hat and draw out names for the people in your sample. You could use numbers instead of names and use a computer to list some random numbers instead of drawing them out of a hat. There are also lists of random numbers available.

It might be more sensible to decide to choose two members from each class, and these could then be chosen randomly from each class register. If there are equal numbers of boys and girls in your school, it might be better to choose one boy and one girl from each class, so that boys and girls are fairly represented in the sample.

You would have to decide how many people you need in your sample. If there are 1000 pupils in your school a 10% sample would mean a sample of 100, a 5% sample would mean a sample of 50. A smaller sample might not accurately represent the views of the whole school, and too large a sample would make the data collection take too long.

Questionnaires

To conduct a survey amongst a group of people one way is to ask them to answer a questionnaire. You can either give them the questionnaire to fill in themselves or you can ask the questions and write down their answers.

Decide exactly what information you want and how you are planning to use the answers. Keep the questionnaire as short as possible, and keep the questions short, clear and precise. Avoid questions which people may not be willing to answer because they are embarrassing or offensive. The best questions can be answered by Yes/No, or categories such as

strongly agree	agree	don't know/ no opinion	disagree	strongly disagree

where you can put a tick in one of the boxes.

'How long do you spend watching TV?' is a very vague question, and will produce equally vague answers, so you will find it difficult to analyse the data.

'How long did you spend watching TV yesterday? Tick one of the following.'

not at all	up to 1 hour	between 1 and 3 hours	between 3 and 5 hours	over 5 hours

is much more precise, and you have only to count the ticks in each category to have some useful data about viewing habits.

It is a good idea to try out your questionnaire on a few people first to see if it is clear enough and likely to give you the data you need, or whether it needs improving. This is called a **Pilot survey**.

If you are asking members of the public for their views, you have not the resources, time or authority to make a proper sample. You will probably have to question people in the street or shopping area, and your sample will have to consist of people in that area at that time. (But a survey on where people shop could be biased if you select your sample from outside the largest supermarket in the area.) You can try to make your sample representative by including people of different ages, and equal numbers of men and women. Be very polite when you approach people, and thank them afterwards for their help. Remember that some people will be in too much of a hurry to stop to talk to you. Before you do such a survey, discuss your plans with your teacher and with your parents.

PUZZLES

13. Barry was given a box containing 125 small bars of chocolate. On the wrapper of each bar there was a token, and Barry could exchange 5 tokens at the local shop for a similar bar of chocolate. How many extra bars of chocolate did he get?

14. What number is this? If you add 4 to it you get the same answer as when you multiply it by 4.

15. How many squares are there in this figure, and how many contain the dot?

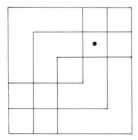

16. Robert has to saw a 10-metre pole into 1-metre lengths. How long will it take him if he cuts one length every 3 minutes?

17. If 1000 + 1 + 50 + 500 spells MILD, what does 100 + 1 + 5 + 1 + 50 spell?

18. A bag contains several discs, some red and some yellow. I have to take some out of the bag without looking. If I want to be sure that I pick at least 4 discs of the same colour, what is the least number of discs that I should take out of the bag?

19. The rail journey from Ashfield to Beechgrove takes exactly 4 hours and trains leave each way on the hour and on the half-hour. If you were on a train going from Ashfield to Beechgrove, how many trains going from Beechgrove to Ashfield would you pass during the journey?

5 Decimals

In the number 234.567 the figure 5 represents five-tenths because it is in the first decimal place, the 6 represents six-hundredths and the 7 represents seven-thousandths. It is usual to write a nought before the decimal point if there is no other number there, e.g. 0.51, not just .51, and 0.02, not just .02.

Addition, subtraction, easy multiplication and division

When adding, subtracting, or when multiplying or dividing by whole numbers, keep the figures in their correct positions relative to the decimal point.

Examples

1    $1.56 + 2.1 + 3.0075 + 14.834$

      1.56
      2.1
      3.0075
   14.834
   ————
   21.5015

2    $12.1 - 3.0025$

   12.1000
    3.0025
   ————
    9.0975

3   12.36×4

   12.36
       4
   ————
   49.44

4    $27.052 \div 8$

   8) 27.0520
     ————
      3.3815

Powers of 10

When multiplying by 10, 100, 1000, . . . the numbers grow larger, so the figures move upwards (to the left), 1, 2, 3, . . . places, assuming that the decimal point is fixed. Add 0's to fill any empty places between the figures and the decimal point.

Example 5

$$2.56 \times 10 = 25.6$$
$$3.5 \times 100 = 350$$
$$0.0041 \times 1000 = 4.1$$

When dividing by 10, 100, 1000, . . . the numbers become smaller, so the figures move downwards (to the right), 1, 2, 3, . . . places, assuming that the decimal point is fixed. Add 0's to fill any empty places between the decimal point and the figures.

Example 6

$$31.8 \div 10 = 3.18$$
$$23 \div 100 = 0.23$$
$$5.56 \div 1000 = 0.00556$$

Example 7

$$2.89 \times 20 = 28.9 \times 2 = 57.8$$
$$0.4261 \times 300 = 42.61 \times 3 = 127.83$$
$$45 \div 40 = 4.5 \div 4 = 1.125$$
$$31.92 \div 3000 = 0.03192 \div 3 = 0.01064$$

Multiplication

To multiply two (or more) decimal numbers, first ignore the decimal points and multiply, then restore the decimals in the answer keeping as many decimal places in the answer as there were altogether in the question.

Example 8

2.31×0.7	(3 decimal places altogether)
$(231 \times 7 = 1617)$	
$2.31 \times 0.7 = 1.617$	(restoring 3 decimal places)

Example 9

0.004×0.3	(4 decimal places)
$(4 \times 3 = 12)$	
$0.004 \times 0.3 = 0.0012$	(including two 0's to restore 4 decimal places)

Division

Instead of dividing by a decimal, multiply both numerator and denominator by 10, 100, 1000, . . . as necessary, to make the denominator into a whole number.

Example 10

$$0.07 \div 0.2 = \frac{0.07}{0.2} = \frac{0.7}{2} \qquad \text{(multiplying both numerator and denominator by 10 to make 0.2 into 2)}$$

$$= 0.35$$

Example 11

$$3.6 \div 0.04 = \frac{3.6}{0.04} = \frac{360}{4}$$

(multiplying both numerator and denominator by 100 to make 0.04 into 4)

$$= 90$$

If the division is not exact, it will be necessary to stop after a suitable number of decimal places.

Example 12

Find the value of $22 \div 7$, correct to 3 decimal places.

$$7 \overline{\smash{\big)}\ 22.0000}$$
$$\quad\ 3.1428$$

Since the figure in the 4th decimal place is 8, the figure in the 3rd decimal place must be corrected up from 2 to 3.

$22 \div 7 = 3.143$, correct to 3 decimal places.

The rule for decimal places is:
Work to one more place than you need. If this extra figure is 5 or more, add 1 to the final figure of your answer.

Example 13

3.2976	= 3.3	to 1 decimal place
	= 3.30	to 2 decimal places
	= 3.298	to 3 decimal places
0.8692	= 0.9	to 1 decimal place
	= 0.87	to 2 decimal places
	= 0.869	to 3 decimal places
0.0827	= 0.1	to 1 decimal place
	= 0.08	to 2 decimal places
	= 0.083	to 3 decimal places
0.00426	= 0.004	to 3 decimal places
	= 0.0043	to 4 decimal places

Significant figures

2.51, 25 100 and 0.0251 all have 3 significant figures, that is figures not counting 0's at the beginning or end of the number.
However, 0's in the middle of a number are counted, so 2.01, 20 100 and 0.0201 also have all got 3 significant figures.
To write a number to less significant figures than it has, use similar rules to those for changing to less decimal places.

Example 14

To 3 significant figures, $3\,657\,000 = 3\,660\,000$
$$9483 = 9480$$
$$587.9 = 588$$
$$4.962 = 4.96$$

To 2 significant figures, $3\,657\,000 = 3\,700\,000$
$$9483 = 9500$$
$$587.9 = 590$$
$$4.962 = 5.0$$

Standard Index Form

A number is written in standard index form when it is written as $a \times 10^n$, where a is a number between 1 and 10 (not including 10) and n is an integer (positive or negative whole number, or 0).

Example 15

Express 6320 and 0.0371 in standard index form.

$6320 = 6.32 \times 1000 = 6.32 \times 10^3$

$0.037 = 3.7 \times \dfrac{1}{100} = 3.7 \times 10^{-2}$

Kinds of numbers

1. **Integers**
   Positive integers   1, 2, 3, . . .   (These are also called the Natural numbers.)
   Zero, nought   0
   Negative integers $-1, -2, -3, \ldots$

   The integers on a number line

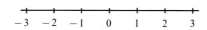

2. **Rational numbers**
    These include integers, fractions and mixed numbers of the type $\frac{p}{q}$, where p and q are integers.
    Fractions can be written as exact decimals, e.g. $\frac{5}{16} = 0.3125$, or as decimals which have a recurring pattern, e.g. $\frac{5}{9} = 0.55555\ldots$ and $\frac{5}{11} = 0.454545\ldots$, so these are also rational numbers.
    Rational numbers all have their places on the number line.

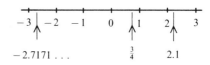

3. **Irrational numbers**
    1 Square roots.
    Some numbers such as 4, 6.25, 0.0009 have exact square roots.
    $$\sqrt{4} = 2, \qquad \sqrt{6.25} = 2.5, \qquad \sqrt{0.0009} = 0.03$$
    Other numbers do not have exact square roots and these are irrational numbers.
    For example, $\sqrt{2}$ is approximately 1.4142.
    If you square 1.41421 on your calculator you will find the result is less than 2.
    If you square 1.41422 on your calculator you will find the result is greater than 2.
    So between 1.41421 and 1.41422 there is a number whose square is 2, but this number cannot be found exactly. We can find it to any suitable accuracy but it is not an exact decimal or one which repeats in a set pattern.
    Here is an enlargement of the number line between 1.414 and 1.415.

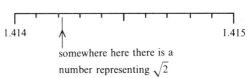

    2 There are other irrational numbers, such as π and many trigonometric functions.
    π is the value $\dfrac{\text{circumference}}{\text{diameter}}$ of a circle. There may be a key for π on your calculator. $\pi = 3.142$ to 3 decimal places.

Use of a calculator

A calculator will save you time in doing routine calculations but do not use it for simple arithmetic which you can do more quickly in your head.
You can use it for the functions addition, subtraction, multiplication and division, and there may be other function keys.
Do not give final answers to 8 figures. Make a sensible approximation, depending on the question and the accuracy of the original data. Usually an answer correct to 3 significant figures is sufficient.

To square a number

For example, to square 12.
You could press $12 \boxed{\times} 12 \boxed{=}$
Or try $12 \boxed{\times} \boxed{=}$ (This will give 144 on some calculators, and is quicker.)
There may be a key labelled x^2
If so, press $12 \boxed{x^2}$
There may be a key labelled y^x. Here, to square, $x = 2$.
Press $12 \boxed{y^x} 2 \boxed{=}$
Use this key to find 12^3. Here, $x = 3$.
Press $12 \boxed{y^x} 3 \boxed{=}$ and you will get 1728.

To find the square root of a number

For example, to find the square root of 49.
You should have a square root key $\boxed{\sqrt{}}$ on your calculator.
Press $49 \boxed{\sqrt{}}$ and you will get 7.
If there is also a cube root key $\boxed{\sqrt[3]{}}$ try $64 \boxed{\sqrt[3]{}}$ and you should get 4.
If there is not a cube root key, on the y^x key there may be the inverse function $\boxed{\sqrt[x]{y}}$.
Using x as 3 will give a cube root.
So for $\sqrt[3]{64}$ press $64 \boxed{\sqrt[x]{y}} 3 \boxed{=}$ and you should get 4.

(There are more details about using a calculator in Chapter 25.)

Checking calculator answers

It is easy to get a wrong answer from a calculator by pressing the wrong keys, so look at the answer and see if it seems right.
You could also do the calculation twice, possibly entering the numbers in reverse order, to see if you get the same result.

Check the size of the answer

$5813 + 1967$
To 1 significant figure the numbers are 6000 and 2000.
The answer should be approximately $6000 + 2000 = 8000$.
5813×1967
The answer should be approximately $6000 \times 2000 = 12\,000\,000$.
$5813 - 1967$
The answer should be approximately $6000 - 2000 = 4000$.
$5813 \div 1967$

The answer should be approximately $\dfrac{6000}{2000} = 3$.

(The exact answers are 7780, 11 434 171, 3846; and 2.955 to 4 significant figures.)

Check the units figure

5813 + 1967
The unit figures are 3 and 7.
3 + 7 = 10 so the units figure in the answer is 0.
5813 × 1967
3 × 7 = 21 so the units figure in the answer is 1.
5813 − 1967
You cannot use 3 − 7 so use 13 − 7 = 6 and the units figure in the answer is 6.
(You cannot do a similar check for division.)

Check by doing the reverse operation

If $a - b = c$, then $c + b$ should equal a.
If $a \div b = d$, then $d \times b$ should equal a.
If $\sqrt{a} = e$, then e^2 should equal a.

Exercise 5.1   (*Do not use your calculator, except for checking, before question 17.*)

1. **1** 1.32 + 2.5 + 3.792   2. **1** 21.03 − 0.017

    2 5.87 + 1.03 + 0.1   **2** 7.92 − 0.97

    3 0.004 + 0.08 + 0.157   **3** 0.0257 − 0.0163

    4 9.99 + 0.03   **4** 10 − 0.918

    5 20.05 + 4.903 + 0.878   **5** 5.828 + 2.192 − 3.134

3. **1** 3.87 × 4   4. **1** 3.88 ÷ 4

    2 0.005 × 12   **2** 0.0056 ÷ 7

    3 0.208 × 7   **3** 0.208 ÷ 5

    4 3.14 × 3   **4** 19.287 ÷ 9

    5 1.928 × 5   **5** 36.0006 ÷ 6

5. Write as decimals.

    1 $\frac{3}{4}$ **2** $\frac{2}{5}$ **3** $\frac{7}{10}$ **4** $\frac{37}{100}$ **5** $\frac{1}{8}$

6. **1** 1.32 × 10   **6**   21.32 ÷ 1000

    2 2.5 × 100   **7**   0.0272 × 100

    3 3.792 ÷ 10   **8**   3.1 × 1000

    4 1.03 × 1000   **9**   3.1 ÷ 1000

    5 0.15 ÷ 100   **10** 0.0004 × 10

7. **1** 29.71×20

    2 3.4×300

    3 0.005×60

    4 0.08×400

    5 0.1234×2000

8. **1** 0.8×0.09

    2 0.05×0.06

    3 0.12×0.011

    4 0.9×0.7

    5 0.004×0.5

9. **1** If $314 \times 28 = 8792$, find 3.14×2.8

    2 If $507 \times 131 = 66\,417$, find 0.507×0.131

    3 If $218 \times 91 = 19\,838$, find 21.8×9.1

    4 If $15 \times 16 = 240$, find 1.5×0.16

    5 If $31 \times 41 = 1271$, find 0.31×0.0041

10. **1** $15.6 \div 0.4$

    2 $2.391 \div 0.03$

    3 $21.89 \div 1.1$

    4 $270 \div 0.9$

    5 $0.0316 \div 0.04$

11. Find the values of the following, correct to 2 decimal places.

    1 $20 \div 7$

    2 $15.5 \div 0.3$

    3 $0.052 \div 0.6$

    4 $8.74 \div 1.2$

    5 $0.91 \div 0.8$

12. Write these fractions as decimals, correct to 3 decimal places.

    1 $\frac{2}{3}$ **2** $\frac{5}{7}$ **3** $\frac{4}{9}$ **4** $\frac{1}{6}$ **5** $\frac{8}{11}$

13. Write these numbers correct to 3 decimal places.

    1 29.7122 **2** 1.62815 **3** 202.9157 **4** 4.6798 **5** 0.003527

14. Write the numbers of question 13 correct to 3 significant figures.

15. Write these numbers correct to 3 significant figures.

   1 56 752   **2** 82.9804   **3** 253.312   **4** 206.789   **5** 1000.5

16. By using approximate values, estimate answers for these questions.

   1 3.99×5.01 **4** $0.0049 \div 0.096$

   2 $17.82 \div 5.82$ **5** 395×0.12

   3 $(0.028)^2$

17. Use your calculator to find answers to question 16, correct to 3 significant figures.

18. Use your calculator to find answers to the following, correct to 3 significant figures.

   1 $2 \times 3.14 \times 17$ **4** $\dfrac{3.14 \times 0.782}{22.4 - 15.5}$

   2 $\dfrac{0.002\,19}{7 \times 11}$

                        5 $73.6^2 - 26.4^2$

   3 $(81.7 + 1.52) \div 62.8$

19. Use your calculator to find the square roots, correct to 3 significant figures, of 6.23, 62.3, 623 and 6230. (Do you notice any pattern in the answers?)

20. Express in standard index form.

   1 15 000   **5** 23.2   **8** 0.006

   2 364   **6** 3124   **9** 200

   3 0.000 952   **7** 0.025   **10** 0.962

   4 0.5276

21. Find the values of

   1 1.86×10^3 **5** 7.6×10^{-5} **8** 9.876×10^3

   2 7.65×10^{-3} **6** 2.3×10^{-1} **9** 1.01×10^{-1}

   3 9.33×10^{-2} **7** 4×10^2 **10** 5×10^{-3}

   4 8.56×10^4

22. Say whether the answers to these questions are natural numbers, integers, rational numbers or irrational numbers.

   1 $(1\frac{1}{2})^2$ **2** $\sqrt{1\frac{1}{2}}$ **3** $(-6)^2$ **4** $(-6) \times 1\frac{1}{2}$ **5** $\sqrt{6 \times 1\frac{1}{2}}$

Weights and measures in the Metric System

In the metric system the main units are metre (length), gram (weight) and litre (capacity). The main prefixes are milli-($\frac{1}{1000}$), centi-($\frac{1}{100}$) and kilo-(1000).

Length

1000 millimetres (mm) = 1 metre (m)
100 centimetres (cm)   = 1 metre   (so 10 mm = 1 cm)
1000 metres   = 1 kilometre (km)

Weight

1000 milligrams (mg) = 1 gram (g)
100 centigrams (cg) = 1 gram
1000 grams   = 1 kilogram (kg)
1000 kilograms   = 1 tonne

Capacity

1000 millilitres (ml) = 1 litre (l)
100 centilitres (cl) = 1 litre
1000 litres   = 1 kilolitre (kl)

The area and volume tables are derived from the length table.

Area

100 mm^2 $= 1 \text{ cm}^2$ since $(10 \text{ mm})^2 = (1 \text{ cm})^2$
$10\,000 \text{ cm}^2$ $= 1 \text{ m}^2$ since $(100 \text{ cm})^2 = (1 \text{ m})^2$
$1\,000\,000 \text{ m}^2$ $= 1 \text{ km}^2$ since $(1000 \text{ m})^2 = (1 \text{ km})^2$
(Also $10\,000 \text{ m}^2 = 1$ hectare)

Volume

1000 mm^3 $= 1 \text{ cm}^3$ since $(10 \text{ mm})^3 = (1 \text{ cm})^3$
$1\,000\,000 \text{ cm}^3$ $= 1 \text{ m}^3$ since $(100 \text{ cm})^3 = (1 \text{ m})^3$

Volume and Capacity are connected because 1 litre = 1000 cm^3
Volume, weight and capacity are connected because
1 cm^3 of water weighs 1 g,
1 litre of water weighs 1 kg.

Some approximate comparisons

1 inch	...	$2\frac{1}{2}$ cm	1 cm	...	0.4 inches
1 foot	...	30 cm	1 m	...	40 inches
1 yard	...	0.9 m	1 km	...	$\frac{5}{8}$ mile
1 mile	...	1.6 km	1 kg	...	2.2 lbs
1 lb	...	450 g	1 tonne	...	1 ton
1 gallon	...	$4\frac{1}{2}$ litres	1 litre	...	$1\frac{3}{4}$ pints

Approximations and estimations

When you go shopping, it is useful to make an approximate calculation of any bill so that you can see if you have enough money, and you can check that you do not get the wrong change.

For example, in a shop suppose you select 3 articles at £1.99 each, 2 at £2.95 each and 1 at £4.90. Before you go to the cash desk you could do an approximate calculation to see if you had enough money to pay for them. It is nearly 3 at £2, 2 at £3 and 1 at £5 so you would need nearly £17. You also expect to get just over £3 in change if you pay with a £20 note.

(When the exact amount is shown on the till you can check your exact change.)

It is also useful to practise estimating distances, weights and time.

Reading numbers on clocks, dials and scales

Example 16

Decide between which two whole numbers the reading lies. This one lies between 4 and 5 so starts 4.

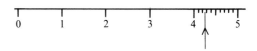

Here is an enlargement of the part of the scale between 4 and 5.
Decide between which two tenths the reading lies. This one lies between 2 and 3 so it is 4.2.

If you have to answer correct to 1 decimal place decide whether it is nearer 2 or 3. This one is nearer 3 so give the answer as 4.3.

If you have to estimate the answer to 2 decimal places, imagine an enlargement of the part of the scale between 4.2 and 4.3. The reading is nearer 4.3 than 4.2 so it is bigger than 4.25. It is approximately 4.27.

Dials on Gas and Electricity Meters

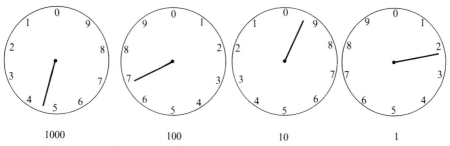

(Notice that the numbers on adjacent dials go in different directions.)

The 1000's figure is between 4 and 5 so the reading is 4000.
The 100's figure is between 6 and 7 so the reading is 600.
The 10's figure is between 9 and 0 so the reading is 90. (The pointer on this dial is turning anticlockwise and the reading has passed 9.)
The units figure is between 2 and 3 so the reading is 2.
The complete reading is 4692.
(There may also be a dial marked $\frac{1}{10}$ which you can ignore.)

Note: In this example you can see that the reading on the 10's dial is 9, and so the pointer will soon go to 0 and start a new revolution. That is why the pointer on the 100's dial is nearly at 7. If you were unable to tell whether its reading was 6 or 7, you could deduce from this that it is still 6, until the 10's pointer reaches 0.

Exercise 5.2

1. How many
    1   mm in 5 cm
    2   g in 3 kg
    3   pence in £10
    4   cm in $\frac{1}{2}$ m
    5   days in a year
    6   m in 4 km
    7   cents in 2 dollars
    8   mg in 6 g
    9   cm³ in 8 litres
    10 days in January

    11 cm² in 1 m²
    12 degrees in $1\frac{1}{2}$ right angles
    13 minutes in $2\frac{1}{2}$ hours
    14 mm in 2 m
    15 centimes in 3 francs
    16 weeks in a year
    17 mm³ in 1 cm³
    18 seconds in $\frac{1}{2}$ minute
    19 m² in 1 km²
    20 ml in 1 litre?

2. 1   How many mm is 80 mm short of 1 metre?
    2   Add together the number of grams in 3 kg, the number of seconds in 4 minutes and the number of mm in 8 cm, then divide the total by the number of pence in £8.30. What is the answer?
    3   A caterer uses 300 g of potatoes per day for each person. Find the cost of providing potatoes for 40 people for 5 days at 25 p per kg.

2.   **4**   If 40 equal packets weigh 100 kg, what does one weigh?

     5   Equal pieces 20 cm long are cut from a ball of string containing 10 metres. How many pieces can be cut?

3.   How many packets of sweets, each containing 110 g, can be made up from $5\frac{1}{2}$ kg of sweets?

4.   How many lengths of wood 0.4 m long can be cut from a piece 2.8 m long?

5.   1 stone is 14 lbs. Marie weighs 8 stones 8 lbs. What is her weight in kg, to the nearest kg, taking 1 lb as equivalent to 454 g?

6.   The speed limit in a town is 30 miles per hour. What is this in km/hour, taking 1 mile as equivalent to 1.6 km?

7.   If a car travels 12 km on a litre of petrol, how much will petrol cost for a journey of 270 km, if the price is 40 p per litre?

8.   500 sheets of paper weigh 3 kg. What is the weight, in g, of 1 sheet? The pile of sheets is 7 cm thick. What is the thickness, in mm, of 1 sheet?

9.   Give the readings shown on these instruments.

    1   Weight in kg.

    10   11

    2   Temperature in °F.

                  95   100   105   110

    3   Weighing scale in kg and g   **4**   Measuring glass

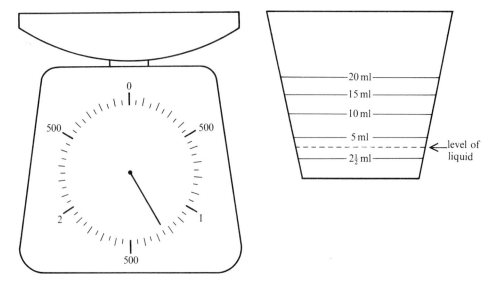

10. Give the readings shown on these meter dials.

11. Copy and complete this electricity bill.

Meter reading		Units used	Pence per unit	Amount
Present 41525	Previous 40342	– – –	5.4	– – –
			Quarterly charge	£6.50
			Total now due	

Exercise 5.3

1. Divide 1720 by 0.8.

2. What is the square root of 0.16?

3. Simplify 0.1 × 0.2 × 0.3.

4. 0.0035×8000

5. Express $\frac{9}{250}$ as an exact decimal.

6. Subtract 0.006 from 0.06.

7. Find the exact value of $4.2752 \div 0.4$.

8. Find the exact value of $\dfrac{1.4 \times 0.05}{0.07}$.

9. What fraction, in its simplest form, is equivalent to 0.075?

10. If $A = 5.14$, $B = 3.709$ and $C = 13.3$, find

    1 $A + B + C$ **2** $A \div 100$ **3** $10(C - A)$

11. Write down any even number between 1 and 11. Add 1.83 and multiply the total by 5. Now subtract 10.9 and then divide by 10. Add 0.675 and double the result. Subtract the number you started with. What is your answer?

12. Express 9876.524 correct to

    1 the nearest whole number,

    2 2 decimal places,

    3 3 significant figures.

13. Find the value of n if

    1 $0.0064 = 6.4 \times 10^{n}$ **2** $3280 = 3.28 \times 10^{n}$

14. An integer n lies between $\sqrt{250}$ and $\sqrt{260}$. What is the value of n?

15. Find the value of $(9 \times 10^{-2}) \times (1.2 \times 10^{3})$, and express your answer in standard index form.

16. **Approximations and estimations for a million.** First make a quick estimate, using the answers as a guide. Then, if necessary, use your calculator to make a more accurate answer.

    1 What is a million as a power of 10?

      A 10^{4} **B** 10^{5} **C** 10^{6} **D** 10^{7} **E** 10^{8}

    2 What distance is a million mm?

      A 1 m   **B** 10 m   **C** 100 m   **D** 1 km   **E** 10 km

    3 If a square has an area of a million square millimetres, how long is one side?

      A 10 cm   **B** 1 m   **C** 10 m   **D** 100 m   **E** 1000 m

    4 If a million small cubes of edge 1 cm are put together to make a large cube, how large is each edge of the large cube?

      A 1 m   **B** 10 m   **C** 100 m   **D** 1000 m   **E** 10 000 m

5 What weight is a million grams?

  A 1 kg   **B** 10 kg   **C** 100 kg   **D** 1000 kg   **E** 10 000 kg

6 If a cubical tank holds a million litres, how long are its edges?

  A 1 m   **B** 10 m   **C** 100 m   **D** 1000 m   **E** 10 000 m

7 How long is a million seconds?

  A 1 day   **B** 12 days   **C** 100 days   **D** 3 years   **E** 30 years

8 When was a million days ago (approximately)?

  A 750 B.C.   **B** 750 A.D.   **C** 1066   **D** 1666   **E** 1815

9 If a million pennies are collected for charity, how much is raised?

  A £100   **B** £1000   **C** £10 000   **D** £100 000   **E** £1 000 000

10 If the million pennies are placed side-by-side along a line, each one touching the next, how long is the line?

  A 100 m   **B** 200 m   **C** 1 km   **D** 10 km   **E** 20 km

17. 1250 cm³ of a liquid weighs 1 kg. What is the weight of 1 litre of the liquid?

18. The earth is approximately 93 million miles from the sun. Taking 1 mile as equivalent to 1.6 km, find this distance in km, to 2 significant figures, expressing your answer in standard form.

19. The weight of a litre of hydrogen is 0.0899 g. Find the weight of 1 cm³ of hydrogen, expressing your answer in standard form.

20. **1** Find the reading on this gas meter.
     2 The previous reading was 8350 units. How many units have been used since then?

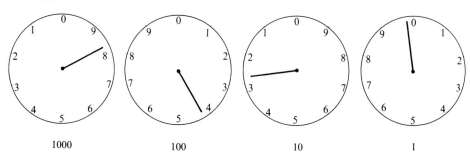

21. Write down the time shown on this clock when it is in the afternoon,

  1 in the 12-hour system,
  2 in the 24-hour system.

22. Copy and complete this gas bill. (Use the notes below.)

Meter reading		Gas used	Therms	Pence per therm	£
Present	Previous				
5798	5548	. . . (a)	. . . (b)	37	. . . (c)
				Standing charge	9.50
				Amount due	. . . (d)

(a) is the difference in the meter readings
(b) is (a) multiplied by 1.032
(c) is (b) multiplied by the price per therm
(d) is (c) plus the standing charge.

(The amount of heat in the gas being supplied is calculated by the Gas Company and that is why they are using the multiplier 1.032 in this case to calculate the number of therms used.)

PUZZLES

20. Copy the diagram and starting in the top left-hand square, draw a continuous line passing through each square once only, so that the sum of the numbers in each group of four squares is 24.

6	6	3	15	5	3
6	9	3	10	6	3
3	3	3	8	8	5
5	10	4	2	3	10
3	6	11	2	3	9
5	8	4	7	10	9

21. If it takes 5 men 5 days to plough 5 fields, how long does it take 1 man to plough 1 field, working at the same rate?

22. Seasonal greetings. On graph paper, label the x-axis from 0 to 12 and the y-axis from 0 to 8, using the same scale on both axes. Mark these points. Join each point to the next one with a straight line, except where there is a cross after the point.
(5, 6)   (4, 6)   (4, 8)   (5, 8) ×   (8, 6)   (8, 8)   (8.8, 8)   (9, 7.8)
(9, 7.2)   (8.8, 7)   (8, 7)   (9, 6) ×   (1, 2)   (3, 4) ×   (1, 6)   (1, 8)
(2, 7)   (3, 8)   (3, 6) ×   (11, 7)   (12, 8) ×   (6, 6)   (6, 8)   (6.8, 8)
(7, 7.8)   (7, 7.2)   (6.8, 7)   (6, 7)   (7, 6) ×   (10, 8)   (11, 7)   (11, 6) ×
(4, 7)   (4.8, 7) ×   (3, 2)   (1, 4) ×
Complete the diagram.

Miscellaneous section A

Exercise A1 Aural Practice

If possible find someone to read these questions to you.
You should do all of them within 10 minutes.
Do not use your calculator.
Write down the answers only.

1. How many eggs are there in 8 dozen?

2. What is the change from £1 after buying 2 grapefruits at 32 pence each?

3. Write in figures 'Two million, fifty-four thousand and six'.

4. If £6 was equally divided among 4 children, how much would they each receive?

5. What do you get when you take 12 from 100 and divide the result by 11?

6. A water-tank holding 36 litres of water lost one-quarter of it through a leak. How much was left?

7. In one carton there are 50 packets of sweets. How many packets are there altogether in 12 cartons?

8. A train which was due at 4.57 p.m. arrived 20 minutes late. At what time did it arrive?

9. If 1 kg of a mixture costs 23 pence, what will 100 kg cost?

10. What is the smallest number into which 5, 6 and 10 divide exactly?

11. If 5 similar books weigh 3.5 kg, what will 2 of them weigh?

12. A purse contained 4 pound coins and 4 fifty-pence coins. How much money was left after spending £2.99?

13. Give an approximate answer to 41×69.

14. What is left when 0.05 is subtracted from 1?

15. What fraction of 1 metre is 60 cm?

Exercise A2 Multi-choice Exercise

Select the correct answer to each question.

1. The number of centimetres in 1 kilometre is

   A 10   **B** 10^2 **C** 10^3 **D** 10^4 **E** 10^5

2. If $a = 3$, $b = -2$, $c = 5$, the value of $4a^2 - 3bc$ is

    A -6 **B**   6   **C**   66   **D**   144   **E**   174

3. A medicine spoon holds 5 ml. How many spoonfuls are there in a bottle containing $\frac{1}{4}$ litre of medicine?

    A   5   **B**   20   **C**   50   **D**   200   **E**   500

4. In the diagram, b equals

    A $40°$ **B** $70°$ **C** $100°$

    D $110°$ **E** $140°$

    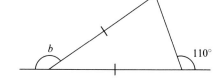

5. For what value of x is the expression $13x - 7$ equal to the value of the expression $5x + 11$?

    A $\frac{2}{9}$ **B** $\frac{1}{2}$ **C**   1   **D** $2\frac{1}{9}$ **E** $2\frac{1}{4}$

6. In standard index form, 128 000 is

    A 1.28×10^{-5} **B** 1.28×10^3 **C** 1.28×10^4

    D 1.28×10^5 **E** 128×10^3

7. The size of angle a is

    A $55°$ **B** $65°$ **C** $70°$

    D $80°$ **E** $85°$

    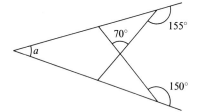

8. The value of 12^0 is

    A   0   **B**   1   **C** $\frac{1}{12}$ **D** -12 **E**   12

9. In the diagram, $\angle DBC$ is bisected by BE. The value of x is

    A   32   **B**   58   **C**   61

    D   122   **E**   151

    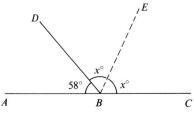

10. The bar chart shows how some money is divided among 3 departments A, B, C. The bar A is 11.2 cm long, B is 9.6 cm and C is 4.2 cm. If the total amount is £125, how much is B's share?

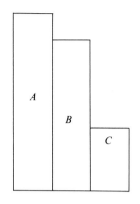

    A £21   **B** £41$\frac{2}{3}$ **C** £48

    D £56   **E** £96

11. The approximate value (estimated to 1 significant figure) of $\dfrac{14.98 \times 0.619}{3100}$ is

    A 0.003   **B** 0.08   **C** 0.03   **D** 0.8   **E** 0.3

12. A man buys a television set which costs £378. He pays an initial payment of $\frac{1}{3}$ of the cost and arranges to pay the rest in 20 equal monthly instalments. The monthly instalment is

    A £5.40   **B** £12.60   **C** £17.40   **D** £18   **E** £20

13. The size of angle a is

    A 32°   **B** 48°   **C** 58°

    D 68°   **E** 80°

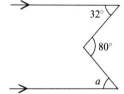

14. $2\frac{1}{2} - 1\frac{1}{3} + \frac{1}{4}$ is equal to

    A $\frac{2}{3}$ **B** $\frac{11}{12}$ **C** $1\frac{1}{3}$ **D** $1\frac{5}{12}$ **E** $2\frac{1}{12}$

15. A bag of sugar contained 1 kg and after using some to bake a cake it contained 0.85 kg. How many grams of sugar had been used?

    A 0.015   **B** 0.15   **C** 1.5   **D** 15   **E** 150

16. How many axes of symmetry has an equilateral triangle?

    A 0   **B** 1   **C** 2   **D** 3   **E** 6

17. Which of the numbers 61, 63, 65, 67, 69 are prime?

    A 61 only   **B** 61 and 67   **C** 61 and 69

    D 61, 63, 67 and 69   **E** 61, 67 and 69

18. 20 people went together to an exhibition. There were x adults, for whom the entrance fee was £3 each, and the rest were children who were charged £2 each. The total cost was £52.
An equation for finding x is

   A $3x + 40 = 52$ **B** $3x = 52 - 2x$ **C** $52 - 3x = 20 - x$

   D $3x + 2(20 - x) = 52$ **E** $2x + 3(20 - x) = 52$

19. It is 5.15 p.m. and my train is due at 1850 according to the timetable. How long have I to wait?

   A 25 min   **B** 35 min   **C** 1 hr 25 min   **D** 1 hr 35 min   **E** 2 hr 35 min

20. In the pie chart, the angle representing B should be

   A 90°   **B** 105°   **C** 120°

   D 150°   **E** 175°

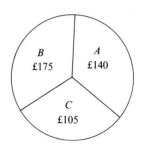

21. The prime factors of 1000 are

   A $2^2 \times 5^3$ **B** $2^3 \times 5^3$ **C** $2^3 \times 5^2$ **D** 8×125

   E $10 \times 10 \times 10$

22. A woman buys 5 kg of potatoes at p pence per kg and 2 cauliflowers at q pence each. The change from £5, in pence, which she should receive, is

   A $5 - 5p + 2q$ **B** $5 - 5p - 2q$ **C** $500 - 5p + 2q$

   D $500 - 5p - 2q$ **E** $500 - 10pq$

23. Which of these numbers has a value nearest to 30?

   A 2^5 **B** 3^3 **C** 4^3 **D** 5^2 **E** 6^2

24. What extra fact is sufficient to prove that $\triangle ABC \equiv \triangle DEF$?

   A $AC = DF$ **B** $AB = DF$

   C $AB = EF$ **D** $BC = DF$

   E $\angle A = \angle D$

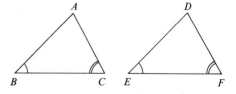

25. Mr Sumner's car will run for about 40 miles on one gallon of petrol, and petrol costs £1.60 per gallon. For a journey of 450 miles the cost of the petrol will be approximately

   A £6.40   **B** £18   **C** £44   **D** £64   **E** £72

26. The angles of a triangle are $(x + 5)°$, $(2x - 35)°$, $(2x + 10)°$. Which of the following accurately describes the triangle?

   A   isosceles triangle   **B**   equilateral triangle

   C   right-angled triangle   **D**   right-angled and isosceles triangle

   E   none of these

27. If a team of 8 volunteers estimate that it will take 12 hours for them to do a certain project task, how long should it take them if two people drop out of the scheme, and the remainder all work at the same rate?

   A   9 hours   **B**   12 hours   **C**   14 hours   **D**   15 hours

   E   16 hours

28. In $\triangle ABC$, the mid-point of BC is M, and $MA = MB = AB$. The size of $\angle BAC$ is

   A   More than 60° but less than 90°

   B   Exactly 90°

   C   Between 90° and 120°

   D   Exactly 120°

   E   More than 120°

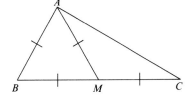

29. Which amount is nearest to £1?

   A   £0.89   **B**   £1.11   **C**   eleven 10 p coins   **D**   forty-four 2 p coins

   E   four 20 p coins and eleven pence

30. A watch loses 5 seconds every hour. It is correct on Monday at 9.00 a.m. What time does it show at 9.00 a.m. on Tuesday?

   A   8.58   **B**   8.59   **C**   9.00   **D**   9.01   **E**   9.02

Exercise A3   Revision

1. Find the total cost of 4 kg of sugar at 48 p per kg, $\frac{1}{4}$ kg of cheese at £3.52 per kg, $\frac{1}{2}$ kg of apples at 54 p per kg and 2 dozen eggs at 85 p per dozen. How much change would there be from a £10 note?

2. Simplify

   1 $2x^2 - 6x + 4 + 3x^2 + x - 2 + 5x - 4x^2$

   2 $2x^3 \times 4x^5$

   3 $3(x + 2y) + 2(x - 3y)$

   4 $6x^6 \div 2x^2$

   5 $3x^3 + 5x^3$

3. How many

1	cm in 1 metre	**6**	pence in £1
2	m in 1 km	**7**	mm in 1 metre
3	seconds in 1 minute	**8**	minutes in 1 hour
4	g in 1 kg	**9**	mm^2 in $1\,cm^2$
5	cm^3 in 1 litre	**10**	cm^3 in $1\,m^3$?

4. These flags have been rotated with • as centre of rotation. In each case 1 is rotated into 2. Estimate, then measure, the angle of rotation. If it is anticlockwise give it as positive, e.g. $+30°$, if it is clockwise give it as negative, e.g. $-30°$.

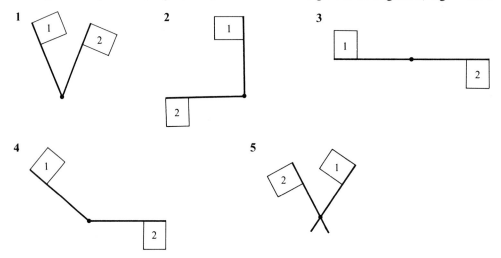

5. **1** Express 96 in its prime factors.
    2 A number expressed in its prime factors is $2 \times 3 \times 5^2$. What is this number?
    3 Which numbers between 40 and 50 are prime?

6. **1** If 1 franc is worth p pence, how many pence will f francs be worth?
    2 If x kg of potatoes are bought for y pence, what is the price per kg?
    3 The sum of two numbers is 12. One of them is x. What is the other? What is their product?
    4 Elaine is 3 years younger than Eric. If Eric is x years old, how old will Elaine be next year?
    5 A man earned £x per month and his wife earned £y per week. What were their total earnings in a year?

7. In congruent triangles ABC and DEF, $\angle A = \angle F$ and $\angle B = \angle E$. Name the three pairs of equal sides.

8. Find the values of

1 $1\frac{3}{4} + 4\frac{5}{6}$ **3** $2\frac{2}{3} \times 2\frac{1}{4} \times \frac{5}{6}$ **5** $(3\frac{1}{4} + 1\frac{1}{3}) \times 1\frac{1}{5}$

2 $3\frac{1}{10} - 2\frac{3}{5}$ **4** $2\frac{1}{12} \div 1\frac{1}{4}$

9. The rainfall records for a town in England for one year were as given in this bar diagram.

   1 Which was the wettest month and how much rain fell then?
   2 Which was the driest month and how much rain fell then?
   3 In which month was the rainfall double that of the preceding month?

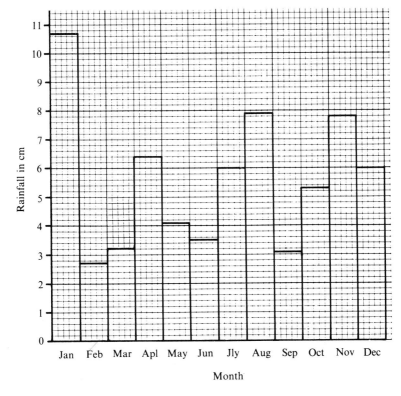

10. Simplify

1 $5 - 0.27$ **6** $3.6 \div 40$

2 0.49×1000 **7** $0.56 \div 0.7$

3 $0.63 \div 100$ **8** $\dfrac{0.3 \times 0.42}{0.7}$

4 0.6×0.04

5 0.3^2 **9** 4.6×0.11

      10 $4.83 \div 2.1$

11. **1** If 20 fence-posts cost £48, what would be the cost of 25 posts?

    2 It is estimated that 5 men can lay a pipeline in 16 days. To do the work in 10 days, how many extra men should be used (assuming that all men work at the same rate)?

12. Find the size of angle d.

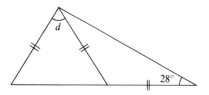

13. Simplify

    1 $x^3 \times x^4 \div x^6$

    2 $(x^3)^2$

    3 $x^6 \div x^3$

    Find the value of

    4 11^0

    5 10^{-1}

14. Write these numbers correct to 2 decimal places.

    1 5.628

    2 3.2296

    3 37.283

    4 0.0976

    5 0.0628

15. **1** Which is the largest number which divides into both 60 and 132?

    2 When boxes are stacked in piles of 5 there are 2 left over. When they are stacked in piles of 8 there are still 2 left over. If the number of boxes is between 50 and 100, how many are there?

Exercise A4   Revision

1. Write down any number less than 10, add 3 to it and square the result. Then add 1 and multiply by 10. Subtract 100 and divide by the number you started with. Add 5 and then divide by 5. Subtract 9 and halve the result. Subtract the number your started with. What is your answer?

2. The table shows the dinners ordered for the 1st year forms at a school, for a week in September.

	1P	1Q	1R	1S	Total
Mon	35	28	22	25	110
Tues	34	28	18	26	
Wed	33		21	26	104
Thur	33	21			
Fri		26	22		106
Total for week	166		105	131	

Copy the table and fill in the missing figures, including the total number of dinners ordered for the week by all the 1st year forms.

1   On which day were the least dinners ordered?
2   If the dinners cost 60 p each, what was the total cost of the dinners ordered for the week by form 1Q?

3. If $a = 3$, $b = 4$ and $c = 0$, find the values of

1   $ab + 2bc$
2   $2b^2 + a^3$
3   $3c(a + b)$
4   $\dfrac{2a + 3b + 4c}{2a - b}$
5   $\sqrt{a^2 + b^2}$

4. Find the size of angle a.

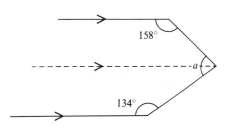

5. Find the approximate value (to the nearest whole number) of $\sqrt{3.92 \times 9.08}$. Use your calculator to find the value correct to 3 significant figures.

6. A new road is being paid for by four towns A, B, C and D. Town A pays $\frac{1}{5}$ of the cost and B and C each pay $\frac{1}{3}$ of the cost. What fraction of the cost does D pay? What does the road cost if D pays £40 000?

7. State whether it is a reflection, rotation or translation which transforms

    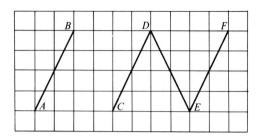

    1   *AB* into *CD*
    2   *AB* into *DC*
    3   *AB* into *ED*
    4   *AB* into *EF*
    5   *CD* into *ED*
    6   *CD* into *FE*

    On sketch-diagrams show any centres of rotation or axes of reflection.

8. Construct a triangle *ABC* with *BC* = 7 cm, ∠*B* = 95° and ∠*C* = 40°. Bisect ∠*A*, letting the bisector cut *BC* at *D*. Measure the length of *BD*, to the nearest mm.

9. A man worked 48 hours in a week. For the first 40 hours he was paid £2.50 an hour. For the rest he was paid at the overtime rate of £3.75 an hour.

    1   What were the man's wages that week?
    2   How many hours altogether had he worked in a week when he earned £137.50?

10. A group of people were asked how they prefer to spend their leisure time, choosing from reading (R), playing sports (S), watching television (T), other activities (U). The results were as follows:

    R T T S T R T R T S R T R S T
    U T R U R T S U U S S T U T T
    T T T T R R T R S U S T R U S
    T R T U R T R R U T R T U S U

    Tally these results and show them on a bar chart or pictogram.

11. The electricity bill for a certain householder was worked out as follows:-
    a standing charge of £5.50 per quarter plus a cost of 4.6 pence per unit used. The meter reading was 32340, and the previous reading was 31740. How many units had been used, and what was the total cost for that quarter?

12. Find the size of angle *b*.

    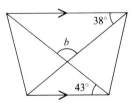

13. Work through this flowchart. What does your answer represent?

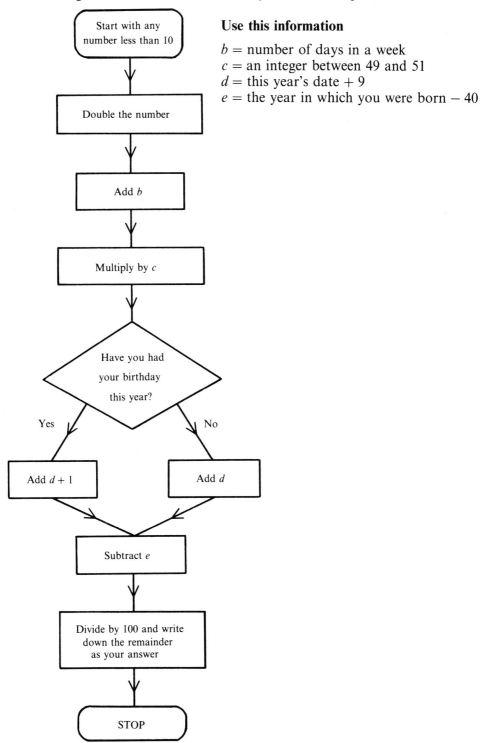

Use this information

b = number of days in a week
c = an integer between 49 and 51
d = this year's date + 9
e = the year in which you were born − 40

14. 1 If $s = ut + \frac{1}{2}ft^2$, what is the value of s when $u = 9$, $f = 10$, $t = 4$?

2 If $I = \dfrac{PRT}{100}$, what is the value of I when $P = 750$, $R = 8$, $T = 4$?

3 If $g = \dfrac{v - u}{t}$, find t when $v = 90$, $u = 20$ and $g = 10$.

4 If $S = 90(2n - 4)$, find n when $S = 720$.

5 If $a = \dfrac{b(100 + c)}{100 - c}$, find b when $a = 9$ and $c = 20$.

15. The following information is given by a travel-agent for holidays in Spain.

Prices in £ per person from London	Departure commencing between			Single room supplements per person per night
	1 May–18 Jun	19 Jun–9 Jly	10 Jly–26 Aug	
Hotel Marti 11 days (10 nights)	155	181	213	£1.20
12 days (11 nights)	162	189	223	
15 days (14 nights)	184	214	251	
Hotel Parki 15 days (14 nights)	202	234	274	£1

Supplements for flights from:	11 days	12 days	15 days (dep. Mon)	15 days (dep. Sat)
Glasgow	£49	£47	£39	£57
Manchester	£31	£33	£23	£39

1 Mr and Mrs Dee are going on their honeymoon for 12 days, departing Saturday, 4th July, flying from Manchester. They want a double room. Which hotel must they stay at? Find the total cost.

2 Three friends are going for 15 days holiday, flying from Glasgow, departing on Saturday, 13th June. They each want single rooms and will stay at the Hotel Parki. Find the cost for each person, and the total cost.

3 Mr and Mrs Ede and their 7-year old daughter Mary want an 11-days holiday, flying from London and departing on Saturday, 8th August. (Mary will occupy a bed in her parents' room and there is a $\frac{1}{5}$ reduction in cost for her.) Find the total cost.

To the student:

2   Independent work

The next exercise, and the similar exercises in the other Miscellaneous Sections give several suggestions for projects, practical work or investigations which could be done either individually or by a group working together. It is not intended that anyone should do all of them, so a choice should be made, depending on your interests.

Some ideas **may** be suitable for the practical work or investigational work needed for the school-based part of the examination but it is advisable to check first with your own Examination Board's regulations if you wish any work to count towards your final grade.

Only brief details have been given here because too much detail would reduce the value of independent work. Financial information can be found from newspapers, magazines, catalogues, brochures, and by asking family and friends. Mathematical facts can be found from maths magazines and books in the library.

These lists are only suggestions, and you should think of other ideas for other investigations.

Making a booklet about a topic

Present your work in an attractive way. Use file paper of a suitable size. Use unlined paper for pages which include drawings or plans. Squared paper or graph paper may also be appropriate for some sections. Use thin cardboard to strengthen the covers, and design the front cover with a neat title and possibly some illustration. Keep the pages in the booklet with file tags or ribbon.

A Maths Scrapbook

Smaller topics could go all together in a Maths Scrapbook which can have different pages for different investigations. It can be a ready-made book where you stick your writings onto the background, or it can be a made-up booklet as before. Make a suitable mathematical design for the front cover. Look out for any mathematical articles, jokes or cartoons you find in magazines, etc. and put these in your book.

Planning an investigation

Plan ahead to decide what you are going to do. Keep a proper record of your progress and include a summary of it.

These points are useful guidelines:

1   Before you begin, say what you are trying to find.
2   Then say what you actually do to find it.
3   Give your results. (If there is a long list of data, record it separately at the end. Summarise your results here in a table.)
4   Say what you can deduce from your results.
5   If you have used any books, give their titles and authors. If you have had ideas or help from anyone, say what this help was.

Exercise A5   Practical work and Investigations

1. **A holiday abroad.**

   Plan a holiday abroad for your family. (It is an imaginary holiday so you can decide for yourself the type of holiday you want and how much you want to spend on it.)
   Get details of costs from travel agents' brochures. (The old ones for last year that they no longer want will do.) Don't forget costs of things such as passports, travel to the airport, excursions, extras like postcards and presents, money for snacks and drinks. Make a list of all the costs.
   Plan a timetable for the holiday, starting from the time you must leave home. Find your destination in an atlas. How far from home is it, and in roughly what direction? What sort of weather do you expect? What is the usual temperature at the time of year when you will be going?
   Plan the list of things to take. Find out the weight of luggage you are allowed, and whether you are limited to 1 suitcase. Give some idea of the things you plan to do while on holiday. Is it to be a lazy fortnight on the beach or a more energetic holiday? Are you going sightseeing, and if so, where?
   Find out the rate of exchange and make a conversion table for use while you are away, e.g. 10 pts = 5 p, 20 pts = 10 p, and so on.
   There are other details you can add to make your booklet more interesting. Illustrate it with pictures and a map.

2. **Banking**

   Many people have a bank account nowadays. Many firms pay wages directly into the employees' bank accounts as this is safer and quicker than paying by cash.
   Find out

   1 the names of the biggest banks in the country, and which of them have branches in your district.
   2 The types of bank account they offer, and the advantages and disadvantages of each, e.g. which accounts include a cheque book, and which pay interest. Do the banks charge you for having an account?
   3 How to write a cheque, and what a cheque stub is.
   4 The procedure for paying money into your account.
   5 What a bank statement is.
   6 What a cheque card is, and the conditions of use. What you should do if you lose it.
   7 What a credit card is, and the conditions of use.
   8 How to use an autobank machine.
   9 The usual banking hours in your district.
   10 What other services the banks offer.
   11 Some banks offer special terms for students. Find out about these.
   12 When you have decided which bank to choose, what is the procedure for opening an account?

3. **Tests of divisibility**

The tests for prime numbers 2, 3 and 5 have been given earlier. It is useful to know the checks for other small numbers.

Investigate divisibility by 4. Do these numbers divide exactly by 4?
34, 134, 234, 48, 148, 248. Can you find a test for checking if a number greater than 100 is divisible by 4?

Investigate divisibility by 6. Do these numbers divide by 2, 3, 6?
22, 27, 30, 134, 135, 138. Can you find a test for checking if a number is divisible by 6?

Here are some numbers which divide by 9. Add up their digits.
738, 2007, 53415, 87651. Can you find a test for checking if a number is divisible by 9?

Divisibility by 11

Alternate figures add up to the same total or there is a difference of 11 (or 22, 33, . . .) between the totals. For example, for 28 413, alternate figures are 2, 4, 3 with total 9; and 8, 1 also with total 9; so the number is divisible by 11. For 616, the totals of alternate figures are 12 and 1. There is a difference of 11 so the number is divisible by 11.

Test this rule with other numbers.

What are the tests for checking if a number is divisible by 10, 25 or 15?

For divisibility by 7, use your calculator to find several 3-figure numbers which are divisible by 7. For each number, e.g. 469,

1	add all the figures together	$4 + 6 + 9 = 19$
2	add the first two figures together	$4 + 6 = 10$
3	write down the middle figure	$\underline{6}$
4	add all these totals together	$\underline{35}$

Repeat for other numbers. What do you notice? Can you investigate for 4-figure numbers, or larger numbers?

4. **Moebius bands**

These are long strips of paper glued together at the ends to form a loop. Some of the strips have a twist, or several twists, put in them before they are glued. Make one each with 0 twists, 1 twist, 2 twists, etc. For each loop, investigate whether it is one-sided or two-sided, and how many edges it has. Continue your investigations by seeing what happens when you cut each strip lengthways down a centre line. It is interesting to try to predict the result in advance. Investigate sides and edges again, and the lengths of the new strips in comparison with the original. Finally, make new strips which you can cut lengthways by a cut which is $\frac{1}{3}$ of the width across. Investigate the results.
Moebius (or Mobius) was a Mathematician who lived in the 19th century. Can you find out anything about him?

5. **'Casting out nines'**

This is an extra check for a multiplication or addition sum. It is not a foolproof check but it will often indicate an error, and it is an interesting method to learn. First, we must learn how to reduce a number to a 1-figure number by adding its digits, and if necessary adding again.

e.g.   for $5813 \rightarrow 5 + 8 + 1 + 3 = 17 \rightarrow 1 + 7 = 8$

$492567 \rightarrow 4 + 9 + 2 + 5 + 6 + 7 = 33 \rightarrow 3 + 3 = 6$

To save time, any 9 or figures which add up to 9 can be crossed out first without affecting the result, as long as we leave the last 9 if there is no other number, so as not to be left with nothing.

e.g. for 5813, cross out 8 and 1 which make 9.

$5813 \rightarrow 5 + 3 = 8$, (or we could have crossed out 5 and 3 and 1 instead, leaving 8).

492567. Cross out 9, 4 and 5, 2 and 7, leaving 6.

918. Cross out 9, **or** 1 and 8, but not both, leaving 9, because we don't want to be left with 0.

Now, to check multiplication, e.g. $5813 \times 1967 = 11634171$

$\qquad\qquad\qquad\qquad\qquad\qquad\qquad\quad \downarrow \qquad \downarrow \qquad\quad \downarrow$

Reduce the numbers to single figures. 8   5   6

Make a cross

Put the two figures of the question in a and b.
Put the answer figure in c.
Multiply the figures in a and b, reduce this answer and put it in d.
$8 \times 5 = 40 \rightarrow 4 + 0 = 4$

If the numbers in c and d are not the same, as here, the answer is wrong. It should have been 11434171, so $c = 4$. This gives

and here $c = d$, so the answer satisfies the check. (However this does not definitely prove that the answer is correct, as other answers could also satisfy the check.)

Practise using this method with other numbers.

How can this method be used to check addition?

6. **The Sieve of Eratosthenes**

Write down the numbers 2 to 50 inclusive. Draw a circle round 2 and then cross out every other number which divides by 2. The 1st number not circled or crossed out is 3. Draw a circle round 3 and then cross out every other number which divides by 3. The next number not crossed out or circled is 5. Draw a circle round 5 and then cross out every other number which divides by 5. The next number not crossed out is 7. Draw a circle round 7 and then cross out every other number which divides by 7. Now draw a circle round all the remaining numbers which are not crossed out. The circled numbers are the prime numbers. Write them down in a list.

Why was it sufficient to stop at 7? If we had made a list up to 125 what other number would need to be crossed out?

This method can be used to find the prime numbers up to any large number. It is useful to set the numbers down on squared paper in neat columns and then a pattern can be seen as you cross out the numbers.

Set out in columns of 10,   1   2   3   4   5   6   7   8   9 10

                         11 12 13 14 15 16 17 18 19 20

                         21 22 ·   ·   ·

or try other columns, especially columns of 6.   1   2   3   4   5   6

                                 7   8   9 10 11 12

                             13 14 15 16 17 18

                             19 20 ·   ·   ·

1 is a special number, so mark it in a different way. It is not counted as a prime number although it has no factors other than itself. This method is known as 'The Sieve of Eratosthenes'. See if you can find out anything about Eratosthenes (or Erathostenes), who lived a long time ago.

7. **'Russian multiplication' or 'Peasants' multiplication'**

e.g. To multiply 1653 by 937. This method only uses the 2 times table.

	937	1653
Halve the 1st number	468	3306
each time, ignore $\frac{1}{2}$'s	234	6612
	117	13224
Double the 2nd number	58	26440
each time.	29	52896
	14	105792
Cross out the rows	7	211584
where the number in	3	423168
the 1st column is even	1	846336
		1548861

Halve the 1st number each time, ignore $\frac{1}{2}$'s

Double the 2nd number each time.

Cross out the rows where the number in the 1st column is even

Stop when you reach 1

Add up this column, ignoring the crossed-out numbers. This gives the answer.

Try using this method with other numbers.

8. **Cubes**

(a) Work out the cubes from 1^3 to 10^3.
Copy and complete this pattern.

natural numbers	sum	cubes of natural numbers	sum
1	1	1^3	1
$1 + 2$	3	$1^3 + 2^3$	9
$1 + 2 + 3$	6	$1^3 + 2^3 + 3^3$	36
$\cdots$		$\cdots$	
$1 + 2 + \cdots + 10$	55	$1^3 + 2^3 + \cdots + 10^3$	

What do you notice about the connection between the 2nd and 4th columns?
Double the numbers in column (2) and divide each by the largest number of the
same row in column (1). What do you notice? Can you use this to find a formula
for

(1) $1 + 2 + 3 + \cdots + n$.
(2) $1^3 + 2^3 + 3^3 + \cdots + n^3$?

(b) Several cubes of edge 1 cm are stacked together to form a larger cube. This
larger cube is then painted on the outside. Thus the small cubes may have some
of their faces painted. Make a table of results for the small cubes.

Edge of large cube	Number of small cubes	Number with these faces painted			
		0 faces	1 face	2 faces	3 faces
2 cm	8	0	0	0	8
3 cm	27				
4 cm					
5 cm					
$\cdots$					

Do you notice any patterns? What would be the results for a large cube of edge
10 cm?

9. **Sevenths**

Work out the recurring sequence of decimals for $\frac{1}{7}$, $\frac{2}{7}$, $\frac{3}{7}$, $\frac{4}{7}$, $\frac{5}{7}$, $\frac{6}{7}$.
Investigate the patterns formed.
Also try adding the 1st and 4th figures, the 2nd and 5th, the 3rd and 6th.
Add the 1st 2 figures as a 2-figure number, with the 3rd and 4th, and 5th and
6th.
Add the 1st 3 figures as a 3-figure number with the last 3 figures as a 3-figure
number.
Investigate the decimals for the thirteenths, $\frac{1}{13}$, $\frac{2}{13}$, etc.
You could also investigate the seventeenths, but the sequence is too long to get
it all displayed on your calculator. You can find it in stages, however.

10. **For the Computer Programmer**

If you have the use of a computer at home or at school, and have learnt how to
make programs for it, then you may like to make some programs to link with
mathematical ideas.

If you are a beginner, start with simple programs. e.g. You could make a
program to improve your mental arithmetic. Get the computer to display
$\boxed{A \times B =}$, where A and B are random numbers between 1 and 12. You input
the answer. The computer checks whether the answer equals AB and tells you
whether you are right or wrong. Then you can improve the program so that a
score is kept of how many you get right, or by adding a time limit within which
you must answer, or by changing $\times$ to $+$ or $-$ in a random order.

Having made one program you will then think of ideas for other programs. Keep
the listings of all programs. As your skill develops you may be able to improve
your earlier work.

Here are some suggestions for programs linking with the work of previous
chapters:

1 To test whether any number is a prime number.
2 To find all prime numbers up to a fixed number.
3 To find the prime factors of any number.
4 To find all the factors of any number.
5 To draw a bar chart for given data.
6 To draw a straight line graph for given data.
7 To make a conversion table, e.g. to convert gallons into litres.

About Chapters 6 to 10

First, there is a chapter on Probability, which is an interesting branch of Mathematics.
You will understand it better if you do some of the experimental work first, so try to
find time for this, even if it is not part of your examination.

Then there are further chapters in Geometry and Statistics, covering the next stages
of these subjects.

The work on algebraic graphs is introduced in Chapter 10.

As before, you will find a more challenging exercise at the end of each chapter, and
a Miscellaneous Section B after Chapter 10.

6 Probability

Experimental Probability

Probability is the likelihood of an event happening, for example, a trial being successful. It is measured on a numerical scale from 0 to 1 and can either be given as a fraction, e.g. $\frac{3}{4}$, or as a decimal, e.g. 0.75.

If we have a number of beads in a bag, some red and some blue, but otherwise identical, and we pick one out at random (i.e. without looking), record its colour, replace it in the bag and give the bag a shake to mix the beads up again, and keep repeating this, then after a few trials (say 10) we can work out the fraction

$$\frac{\text{number of trials giving a red bead}}{\text{total number of trials}}.$$

These are the results from one such experiment when the bag contained more red beads than blue ones.

number of trials (n)	number of red beads (r)	fraction $\dfrac{r}{n}$	$\dfrac{r}{n}$ to 2 decimal places
10	5	$\frac{5}{10}$	0.50
25	16	$\frac{16}{25}$	0.64
50	29	$\frac{29}{50}$	0.58
100	62	$\frac{62}{100}$	0.62
200	120	$\frac{120}{200}$	0.60
300	182	$\frac{182}{300}$	0.61
500	305	$\frac{305}{500}$	0.61
1000	596	$\frac{596}{1000}$	0.60

Here are the first 100 results, worked out after every 10 trials, plotted on a graph.

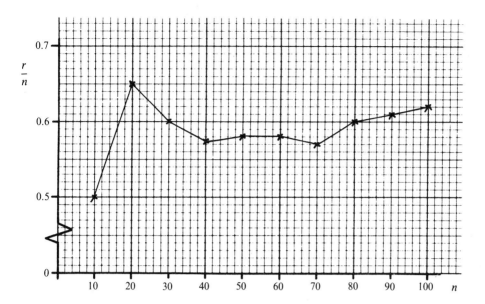

Although the results may be erratic after only a few trials they settle down around 0.6 so that in the long run red appears in 0.6 of the trials.

The probability of a red bead $= \dfrac{\text{number of red beads drawn out}}{\text{total number of beads drawn out}} = 0.6$

We can only use this definition of probability if we do enough trials to show that the fraction is settling down to a steady value. If the event was unpredictable the fraction would not settle down and we could not find a value for the probability.

When we know the probability of an event happening we can use its value to predict the likelihood of a future result. That is why Probability is linked to Statistics. Government departments, business firms, industrialists, scientists, medical researchers and many other people and organisations use the figures from past events to predict what is likely to happen in the future, and thus they can plan ahead. For example, Insurance Companies use their knowledge of past claims to predict future ones, and they can then decide what premiums they must charge. If you want to gamble on a sporting event it is useful to estimate the probability of winning. You might then realise that you are unlikely to win in the long run and decide not to waste your money on the bet.

In many cases we can find the probability by common-sense reasoning. For instance, if we had said that the bag of beads contained 60 red and 40 blue beads you could have reasoned that since $\frac{60}{100}$ of the beads were red, the probability of a red bead $= 0.6$, without doing the experiment.

Later we shall **calculate** probabilities, but before doing that it is interesting to do a few experiments, and later on you can compare the results with calculated probabilities and see how close they are.

Here are some suggestions for experiments. All the trials should be done randomly and fairly. Toss a coin properly. Give a die (dice) a good shake before rolling it out onto a flat surface. Shuffle a pack of cards properly, for most experiments you should take out the jokers first so that the pack contains the 52 cards of the 4 suits. If you have not got proper equipment it is often possible to think of a substitute. If you can combine other people's results with yours to give more trials, do so. Keep a record of your results to use again later.

Exercise 6.1

1. Toss a coin 200 times. Record your results in order, in a grid of 10 columns by 20 rows. Put H for head and T for tail.

    The grid starts like this:

H	H	T	H	T	T	H			

Before you begin, estimate how many heads you are likely to get.
Make a table similar to this one and fill it in.

number of tosses (n)	number of heads (h)	fraction $\dfrac{h}{n}$	$\dfrac{h}{n}$ to 2 decimal places
1			
2			
3			
4			
5			
10			
20			
50			
100			
150			
200			

From your results, what value would you give for the probability of a toss showing a head?

2. Throw a die 400 times. Record the number which lands face upwards, in a grid of 20 columns by 20 rows.

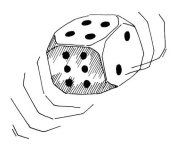

Make a table similar to this and fill it in.

number of throws (n)	number of 6's (s)	fraction $\dfrac{s}{n}$	$\dfrac{s}{n}$ to 2 decimal places
10			
20			
50			
100			
200			
300			
400			

From your results, what value would you give for the probability of a throw showing a six?

3. Put 10 similar drawing-pins into a cup and holding it approximately 20 cm above a table, gently tip the drawing-pins out so that they land on the table. They come to rest point upwards, like this , or on their side, like this . Count and record how many land point upwards. Repeat the experiment 50 times. Find the total number point upwards after 1, 5, 10, 20, 30, 40 and 50 goes.

Make a table similar to this and fill it in.

total number tipped out (n)	number point upwards (s)	fraction $\dfrac{s}{n}$	$\dfrac{s}{n}$ to 2 decimal places
10			
50			
100			
200			
300			
400			
500			

If the results are settling down to a certain value this gives the value of the probability that a drawing-pin in this type of experiment will land point upwards. (There is no theoretical way of checking this result.)
The height through which the drawing-pins fall may affect the result. You could investigate this by repeating the experiment from different heights. Different makes of drawing-pins may also give different results.

4. Shuffle a pack of cards and pick out 3 cards.
    Record as *P* if they contain at least one
    picture-card (i.e. Jack, Queen or King).
    Record as *N* if there is no picture card.
    Replace the cards, shuffle and repeat 100 times
    altogether.
    Before you begin, estimate how many times *P*
    will occur.

    Find the fraction $\dfrac{\text{number of times } P \text{ occurs}}{\text{total number of trials}}$ as

    a decimal to 2 decimal places.
    From your results, what value would you give
    for the probability that of three cards drawn at random, at least one card is a
    picture-card?

5. Collect 200 single-figure random numbers by taking the last figure of a list of
    phone numbers out of a random page of a directory. (If a firm has consecutive
    numbers listed, only use the first one.) Record these numbers in a grid, as in
    question 1.
    Before you begin, estimate how many of each number 0 to 9 you expect to get.

    Count up your results and give them in a table.
    (The frequency is the number of times that number
    occurs.)
    Now add up the frequencies of the odd numbers.

    Find the fraction $\dfrac{\text{number of odd numbers}}{\text{total number of numbers}}$ as a

    decimal to 2 decimal places.
    From your results, what value would you give for the
    probability that a number picked at random from the
    numbers 0 to 9 is odd?

number	frequency
0	
1	
2	
3	
4	
5	
6	
7	
8	
9	

6. Instead of tossing coins again, use the results of question 1 in pairs, as if you had
    tossed two coins together, so that the possible results are *HH, HT, TH, TT*.
    If you had 200 single results you will have 100 results for pairs. Count the number
    of heads in each pair and put your results on a tally chart. Before you begin
    estimate how many of each you will get.

heads	tally marks	frequency (f)
0		
1		
2		
		100

    What is the most likely result? What are your estimates for the probabilities of
    0 heads, 1 head, 2 heads?

7. Use a set of dominoes going up to double six.
    (If you have no dominoes, label cards 0–0,
    0–1, up to 0–6; then 1–1, 1–2, up to 1–6; then
    2–2, etc, ending 6–6. There are 28 cards
    altogether.)
    Pick out a domino at random and record the
    total score. Replace and repeat 200 times.
    The scores range from 0 to 12. Make a tally
    chart of the results.
    What is the estimated probability of getting a score of 6 if a domino is picked at
    random?

8. Ask as many people as you can on what day of the week their birthday falls this
    year. Tally the results. What is the estimated probability that if a person is chosen
    at random, his/her birthday is on a Saturday?

Theoretical Probability

Probability or chance is the likelihood of an event happening.

A probability of 0 means that there is no chance of the event happening.

A probability of 1 means that it is certain that the event will happen.

A probability of $\frac{1}{2}$ means that there is a 50-50 chance of the event happening. In the
long run, $\frac{1}{2}$ of the trials will give successful results.

A probability of $\frac{2}{3}$ means that in the long run $\frac{2}{3}$ of the trials will give successful results.
The nearer the value of the probability is to 1, the more chance there is of a successful
outcome.

The nearer the value of the probability is to 0, the less chance there is of a successful
outcome.

If a trial has a number of **equally likely outcomes** and of these certain ones are
successful then

$$\text{Probability (or chance) of a successful outcome} = \frac{\text{number of successful outcomes}}{\text{total possible outcomes}} = \frac{s}{n}$$

Example 1

Find the probability of a tossed coin showing heads.

There are 2 equally likely outcomes, heads or tails, and of these 1 outcome,
heads, is successful.

$$\text{Probability of heads} = \frac{s}{n} = \frac{1}{2}$$

Example 2

Find the probability of a number picked at random from the numbers 1 to 10
being divisible by 4.

There are ten equally likely outcomes of which two (4 and 8) are successful.

$$\text{Probability of picking a number divisible by 4} = \frac{s}{n} = \frac{2}{10} = \frac{1}{5}$$

Use of Sample spaces

Example 3

Five discs numbered 1 to 5 are placed in a bag and one is drawn out at random and not replaced. A second disc is then drawn out at random.

1   What is the probability that the second disc has a number higher by at least 2 than the first disc?
2   What is the probability that the total of the two numbers is 6?

Set down the possible equally likely results in a diagram called a sample space.

		1st disc				
		1	2	3	4	5
2nd disc	1		·	·	·	·
	2	·		·	·	·
	3	·	·		·	·
	4	·	(a)	·		·
	5	·	·	·	·	

A dot represents one of the equally likely outcomes, e.g. dot (a) represents the outcome that the first disc is 2 and the second disc is 4. There are 20 dots so there are 20 equally likely outcomes. (It might be more useful to write the actual outcomes e.g. (2, 4), or the total score, instead of just dots.)

We will mark in some way all the outcomes where the second disc has a number higher by at least 2 than the first disc, and in a different way where the total of numbers is 6. (Normally these would go on the original diagram but here to make it clearer we have two new diagrams.)

1

		1st disc				
		1	2	3	4	5
2nd disc	1		·	·	·	·
	2	·		·	·	·
	3	⊡	·		·	·
	4	⊡	⊡	·		·
	5	⊡	⊡	⊡	·	

⊡ represents a successful outcome.

There are 6 successful outcomes.

2

		1st disc				
		1	2	3	4	5
2nd disc	1		·	·	·	⊙
	2	·		·	⊙	·
	3	·	·		·	·
	4	·	⊙	·		·
	5	⊙	·	·	·	

⊙ represents a successful outcome.

There are 4 successful outcomes.

1   The probability that the 2nd disc has a number higher by at least 2 than the

first disc $= \dfrac{s}{n} = \dfrac{6}{20} = 0.3$

2   The probability that the total of the two numbers is $6 = \dfrac{s}{n} = \dfrac{4}{20} = 0.2$

The OR rule

If there are two outcomes A or B of an experiment, either of which can occur, but not both together, then

Probability of A or B occurring = probability of A occurring + probability of B occurring.

In symbols this is written as

$P(A \text{ or } B) = P(A) + P(B)$

This rule also applies to more than two outcomes.

The total probabilities of all possible outcomes add up to 1.

Example 4

There are a number of red, white and blue beads in a bag. The probability of picking a red bead is $\frac{1}{3}$ and the probability of picking a blue bead is $\frac{1}{5}$.

1   What is the probability of picking a bead which is red or blue?
2   What is the probability of picking a white bead?

1   $P(\text{red or blue}) = P(\text{red}) + P(\text{blue}) = \frac{1}{3} + \frac{1}{5} = \frac{8}{15}$
2   $P(\text{red}) + P(\text{white}) + P(\text{blue}) = 1$
$$P(\text{white}) = 1 - P(\text{red}) - P(\text{blue}) = 1 - \frac{1}{3} - \frac{1}{5} = \frac{7}{15}$$

Example 5

In a pack of 52 cards one card is drawn at random. What is the probability that it is   1   a heart   2   an ace   3   an ace or a heart?

1   $P(\text{heart}) = \frac{13}{52} = \frac{1}{4}$
2   $P(\text{ace}) = \frac{4}{52} = \frac{1}{13}$
3   It would be wrong to use the OR rule because the two events, ace and heart, can occur together with the ace of hearts. Instead, find the number of successful outcomes. There are the 13 hearts, including the ace, and the other 3 aces, making 16 successful outcomes altogether.

$$P(\text{ace or heart}) = \frac{s}{n} = \frac{16}{52} = \frac{4}{13}$$

The AND rule

If one experiment has an outcome A and another experiment has an outcome B, and both experiments are carried out, then

Probability of A and B occurring = probability of A occurring $\times$ probability of B occurring

In symbols this is written as

$P(A \text{ and } B) = P(A) \times P(B)$

This rule also applies to more than two events.

The outcome B is usually independent of the result of outcome A, for example if one experiment involves tossing a coin and the other involves throwing a die. Occasionally, the probability of the outcome for one of the experiments depends on the outcome of the other, for example if two cards are drawn from a pack and the first card is not replaced before the second one is drawn.

Example 6

If two dice are thrown, find the probability of getting two sixes.

The 1st experiment is tossing the 1st die. $P(\text{six}) = \frac{1}{6}$

The 2nd experiment is tossing the 2nd die. $P(\text{six}) = \frac{1}{6}$

$P(\text{two sixes}) = P(\text{six}) \times P(\text{six}) = \frac{1}{6} \times \frac{1}{6} = \frac{1}{36}$

(This result can also be found using a sample space diagram.)

Example 7

If there are 10 beads in a bag of which 3 are blue, and 2 are picked out at random and not replaced, what is the probability of getting 2 blue ones?

$P(\text{1st blue}) = \frac{3}{10}$

$P(\text{2nd blue}) = \frac{2}{9}$, provided that the 1st was blue.

$P(\text{both blue}) = P(\text{1st blue}) \times P(\text{2nd blue}) = \frac{3}{10} \times \frac{2}{9} = \frac{1}{15}$

A coin or die has no memory so the probabilities are not affected by any previous tosses. Suppose a fairly-tossed coin has come down heads 5 times in succession. The 6th toss is not affected by the previous results and the probability of it being a head is still $\frac{1}{2}$.

But the probability of getting 6 heads in succession is

$P(\text{head}) \times P(\text{head}) \times P(\text{head}) \times P(\text{head}) \times P(\text{head}) \times P(\text{head}) = \frac{1}{2} \times \frac{1}{2} \times \frac{1}{2} \times \frac{1}{2} \times \frac{1}{2} \times \frac{1}{2}$

$$= \frac{1}{64}$$

Tree diagrams

Example 8

In a bag there are 5 red discs and 3 blue ones. If two discs are picked out at random (and not replaced), what is the probability of getting one of each colour?

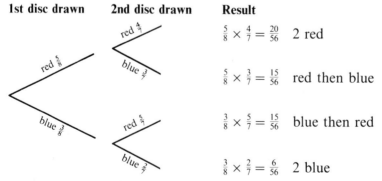

1st disc drawn	2nd disc drawn	Result		
red $\frac{5}{8}$	red $\frac{4}{7}$	$\frac{5}{8} \times \frac{4}{7} = \frac{20}{56}$	2 red
	blue $\frac{3}{7}$	$\frac{5}{8} \times \frac{3}{7} = \frac{15}{56}$	red then blue
blue $\frac{3}{8}$	red $\frac{5}{7}$	$\frac{3}{8} \times \frac{5}{7} = \frac{15}{56}$	blue then red
	blue $\frac{2}{7}$	$\frac{3}{8} \times \frac{2}{7} = \frac{6}{56}$	2 blue

Note that the probabilities for the 1st branch **and** then the 2nd branch were multiplied.
Note as a check that the total probabilities add up to 1.
Probability of one of each colour:

$P(\text{red then blue } \mathbf{or} \text{ blue then red}) = P(\text{red then blue}) + P(\text{blue then red})$

$$= \frac{15}{56} + \frac{15}{56} = \frac{15}{28}$$

Example 9

A coin is tossed 3 times in succession. What is the probability of getting at least one head?

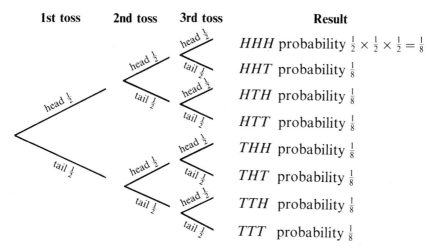

The only result without at least 1 head is TTT, with probability $\frac{1}{8}$.

The probability of getting at least 1 head is $1 - \frac{1}{8} = \frac{7}{8}$

(This could also be found by adding the probabilities of the 1st 7 results.)

Example 10

A man has four possible routes home from work. For the 1st part of the journey he can either go by train or by bus. The probability that he will go by train is $\frac{2}{3}$.

After he gets off the train he can either walk or catch a bus. The probability that he will walk is $\frac{3}{4}$.

If the 1st part of his journey is by bus then he completes his journey by taxi, with probability $\frac{1}{5}$, or by walking.

What is the probability that he walks part of the way home?

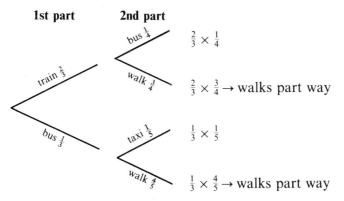

The probability that he walks part of the way home $= (\frac{2}{3} \times \frac{3}{4}) + (\frac{1}{3} \times \frac{4}{5}) = \frac{23}{30}$

Exercise 6.2

1. A fair die is thrown once. What is the probability of getting

    1 a three,
    2 a square number?

2. 20 discs, numbered from 1 to 20, are placed in a bag and one is drawn out at random. What is the probability of getting a disc with

    1 a number greater than 15,
    2 a number which includes the digit 1,
    3 a number which is divisible by 3?

3. In a fairground game a pointer is spun and you win the amount shown in the sector where it comes to rest. Assuming that the pointer is equally likely to come to rest in any sector, what is the probability that

    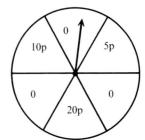

    1 you win some money,
    2 you win 20 p?

4. In a tombola game, $\frac{7}{8}$ of the counters are blank. The rest have a number on them and they win a prize. If you take a counter out of the drum at random what is the probability that you win a prize?

5. If you choose a card at random from a pack of 52 playing-cards, what is the probability that it is

    1 an ace,
    2 a diamond,
    3 a red card with an even number?

6. A letter is chosen at random from the 11 letters of the word MATHEMATICS. What is the probability that it is

    1 the letter M,
    2 a vowel,
    3 a letter from the second half of the alphabet?

7. A bag contains 6 coloured discs. One disc is pulled out, its colour noted and then it is returned to the bag. After 120 draws the results are Yellow 44 times, Red 19 times, Blue 57 times. How many counters of each colour do you think are in the bag?

8. The students in a school club belong to two forms 5X and 5Y.

	5X	5Y
girls	12	16
boys	8	14

    If from this club one member is chosen at random, what is the probability that it is

    1 a boy,
    2 a member of 5Y,
    3 a girl from 5X?
    4 If a girl has to be chosen at random what is the probability that she is from 5X?

9. Raffle tickets are sold from books of three different colours, blue, green and pink. The probability that the winning ticket is blue is $\frac{1}{3}$ and the probability that the winning ticket is green is $\frac{2}{5}$. What is the probability that the winning ticket is pink?

10. In a pack of playing-cards, the 2 of diamonds and the 2 of hearts have been removed. If you choose a card at random from the remaining cards, what is the probability that it is

   1 a diamond,
   2 a two,
   3 the 2 of diamonds?

11. There are 7 beads in a bag, 4 red, 1 white, 2 blue. One is taken out at random and replaced, and then another one is taken out. What is the probability that

   1 the 1st one is red,
   2 the 2nd one is blue,
   3 the 1st one is red and the 2nd one is blue?

12. Hank usually has lunch at Dan's cafe. The probability that sausage and mash is on the day's menu is $\frac{2}{3}$. The probability that there is apple pie on the menu is $\frac{3}{4}$, quite independently of whether there is sausage and mash or not. Hank's favourite meal is sausage and mash followed by apple pie.
What is the probability that he can have this today?

13. On this spinner, the probability of getting any number from 1 to 5 is equally likely.

   1 If Betty spins twice, what is the probability that she scores a 5 and then a 4?
   2 What is the probability that she scores the same number twice in succession?

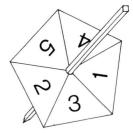

14. In Mr Wright's job if extra work comes in during the afternoon he has to work late. The probability that he has to work late on any one evening is $\frac{1}{8}$. What is the probability that he will have to work late this Friday and also next Friday?

15. Ronnie's bus ticket always has a different 4-figure number on it.

   1 What is the probability that the number on this morning's ticket has a unit figure of 7?
   2 What is the probability that he gets a ticket with a unit figure of 7 on the way to school and also on the way home from school?

16. A card is drawn from a full pack of 52 cards and a second card is drawn from another full pack. What is the probability that

   1 both cards are hearts,
   2 both cards are red ones?

17. In a computer game the probability of scoring a hit is $\frac{2}{5}$. What is the probability that the first two players both score hits?

18. A large batch of red tulip bulbs has been accidentally mixed with some yellow tulip bulbs, so that the probability of picking a red bulb is $\frac{2}{3}$.

    1 What is the probability of picking a yellow one?
    2 If I buy 4 bulbs which are picked out at random, what is the probability of getting 4 red ones?

19. It is estimated that the probability that Rajesh will win in the 100 m race is $\frac{1}{4}$, and that he will win in the javelin event is $\frac{1}{3}$. What is the probability that he wins both events?

20. A pack of 52 cards is split into two piles with the Kings, Queens and Jacks in the first pile and the rest of the cards in the second pile.

    1 If a card is drawn at random from the 1st pile what is the probability that it is the Queen of hearts?
    2 If a card is drawn at random from the 2nd pile what is the probability that it is an ace?
    3 If you take one card from each pile what is the probability that you get the Queen of hearts and an ace?

21. A box contains 2 red, 3 yellow and 5 green sweets. One is taken out at random, and eaten. A second sweet is then taken out.

    1 If the 1st sweet was green, what is the probability that the 2nd sweet is also green?
    2 If the 1st sweet was not red, what is the probability that the 2nd sweet is red?

22. Two dice are thrown together. Make a sample space diagram of the equally likely results. What is the probability
    1 that the sum of the two numbers is greater than 10,
    2 that the sum of the two numbers is 7,
    3 of a double (the two dice showing the same number),
    4 of both dice showing numbers less than 3?

23. There are six cards numbered 1 to 6. One card is selected at random and not replaced, and then a second card is selected. Make a sample space diagram of the equally likely results. What is the probability
    1 that the sum of the two numbers is greater than 10,
    2 that the sum of the two numbers is 7,
    3 that the product of the two numbers is odd?

24. A coin and a die are tossed together. What is the probability of getting
    1 a head on the coin and a six on the die,
    2 a head on the coin or a six on the die (or both)?

25. Two cards are drawn from a pack of 52 cards. What is the probability that the second card is from the same suit as the first
    1 if the 1st card is replaced before the 2nd card is drawn,
    2 if the 1st card is not replaced before the 2nd card is drawn?

26. Write down a list of all possible results if a coin is tossed 4 times in succession, e.g. *HHHH, HTHH, HHHT*, . . .
What is the probability of getting

1   4 heads,
2   3 or more tails,
3   exactly 2 heads and 2 tails?

27.   A bag contains 8 blue marbles and 2 red marbles. Two marbles are drawn at random. Show the probabilities on a probability tree.

1st draw   **2nd draw**

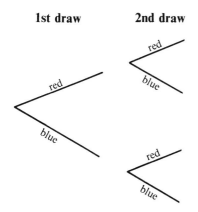

What is the probability of getting

1   2 red marbles,
2   1 marble of each colour,
3   2 blue marbles?

28.   The probability that Simon is late for school on a Monday morning is $\frac{1}{5}$. If he is late on Monday, the probability that he is late on Tuesday is $\frac{1}{10}$, but if he is on time on Monday the probability that he is late on Tuesday is $\frac{1}{5}$. Show this information on a tree diagram.
What is the probability that

1   Simon is late on both mornings,
2   Simon is late on one of the two mornings?

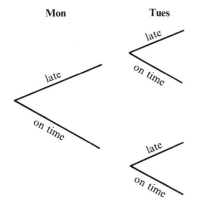

Exercise 6.3

1. 200 discs numbered 1 to 200 are placed in a bag and one is drawn out at random. What is the probability of getting a disc with a number which is a square number?

2. On the way to work Mrs Cole passes through three sets of traffic lights. The probability that the first set is green when she gets to them is $\frac{2}{3}$, the probability that the second set is green is $\frac{3}{4}$ and the probability that the third set is green is $\frac{1}{2}$. Show the probabilities (for green or not green) on a probability tree. What is the probability that

    1 she finds all three sets of lights green as she gets to them,
    2 she has to stop at at least two of the three sets of lights?

3. A regular triangular pyramid (tetrahedron) has its four faces numbered 1, 2, 3, 4 and it is used as a die by counting as the score the number on the bottom face. Draw up a sample space showing the outcomes when this die is thrown twice. Find the probability that

    1 in each of the two throws the score is 4,
    2 in the two throws the sum of the scores is 4,
    3 in the two throws the product of the scores is 4.

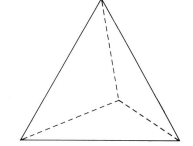

4. Three competitors Alan, Bob and Charles enter for the high jump and the long jump in the school sports. The chances of each of them winning these events are estimated as follows:

	Alan	Bob	Charles
High jump	$\frac{2}{5}$	$\frac{3}{10}$	$\frac{1}{10}$
Long jump	$\frac{1}{3}$	$\frac{1}{2}$	$\frac{1}{12}$

    What is the probability that

    1 Alan wins both events,
    2 Bob wins the high jump and Charles wins the long jump,
    3 both events are won by other competitors?

5. Two dice are thrown together. Draw up a sample space showing the total scores.

    1 List in a table the probability of scoring each total from 2 to 12.
    2 What is the most likely total score?
    3 What is the chance of getting this score three times in successive throws?

6. Yasmin and Zelda play two sets of tennis. The probability of Yasmin winning the 1st set is $\frac{2}{3}$. If she wins the 1st set, the probability of her winning the 2nd set is $\frac{2}{3}$, but if she loses the first set the probability of her losing the 2nd set is $\frac{1}{2}$. (There are no drawn sets.)
Draw up a probability tree for the two sets. What is the probability of

    1   Yasmin winning both sets,
    2   Zelda winning both sets,
    3   the girls winning one set each?

7. Find the theoretical results for the experiments you carried out in Exercise 6.1 (except for questions 3 and 4) and compare your experimental results with these.

PUZZLES

23. In the 'Tower of Hanoi' puzzle, there are 8 discs of different sizes on 1 peg, with two empty pegs.

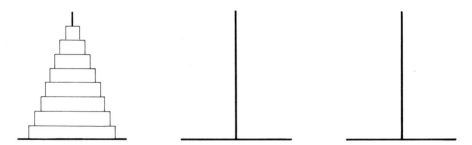

The game is to transfer all the discs to one of the empty pegs.
Only one disc can be moved at a time. A disc can only be placed on an empty peg or onto a larger disc, never onto a smaller one.
Make your own version of this game using circles of cardboard, and see how many moves are needed. You may prefer to discover the pattern of moves by starting with less than 8 discs. Notice the moves of the smallest disc.
The legend has it that there is such a peg with 64 discs on it. At the rate of 1 move per second, how long will it take to move all 64 discs?

24. Mine cost 52p, my neighbour's cost 26p and I got some for my friend who lives at the far end of the road, and they cost 78p. What was I buying in the hardware shop?

25. Nine people, Andrew, Bilkish, Craig, Dhiren, Edith, Faruk, Graham, Helen and Iqbal share a prize of £450 amongst themselves.
Bilkish gets £1 more than Andrew, Craig gets £1 more than Bilkish, Dhiren gets £1 more than Craig, and so on. How much does Iqbal get?

26. If it takes a clock 6 seconds to strike 6, how long does it take to strike 12?

7 *Quadrilaterals*

Quadrilaterals

The sum of the angles of a quadrilateral is 360°.

Trapezium

One pair of parallel sides

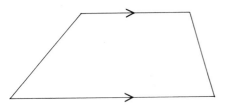

If the other 2 sides are equal it is an isosceles trapezium.

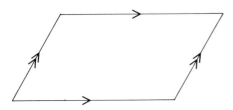

Kite

Two adjacent sides are equal and the other two adjacent sides are equal.

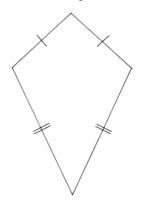

Parallelogram

Opposite sides are parallel

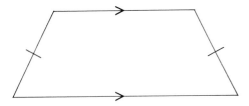

Opposite sides are equal
Opposite angles are equal

Rectangle

It is a parallelogram with one angle a right angle

Opposite sides are parallel and equal
All angles are right angles

CHAPTER 7

Rhombus

It is a parallelogram with one pair of adjacent sides equal

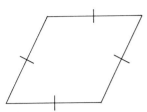

Opposite sides are parallel
All sides are equal
Opposite angles are equal

Square

It is a rectangle and a rhombus

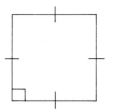

Opposite sides are parallel
All sides are equal
All angles are right angles

Diagonals

Isosceles trapezium

Diagonals are equal (but do not bisect each other).

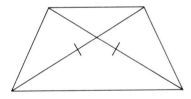

Kite

One diagonal is a line of symmetry. It bisects the other diagonal at right angles.

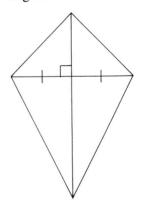

Parallelogram

Diagonals bisect each other.

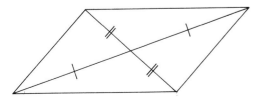

Rectangle

Diagonals bisect each other.
Diagonals are equal.

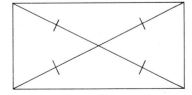

Rhombus

Diagonals bisect each other at right angles.
They also bisect the angles of the rhombus.

Square

Diagonals bisect each other at right angles.
Diagonals are equal.
Diagonals make angles of 45° with the sides of the square.

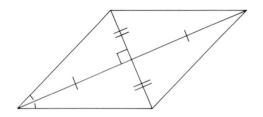

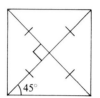

Example

Symmetrical properties of a parallelogram.

The parallelogram has no axes of symmetry, but it has a point of symmetry at O, the mid-point of AC.
If the parallelogram is rotated about O through 180°, then
AD is rotated into CB, so $AD = CB$,
AB is rotated into CD, so $AB = CD$,
$\angle B$ is rotated into $\angle D$, so $\angle B = \angle D$,
$\angle BAD$ is rotated into $\angle DCB$ so $\angle BAD = \angle DCB$,
OB is rotated into OD so $OB = OD$. Also, since the rotation is through 180°.
BOD is a straight line, and is the other diagonal.
This has shown that, in a parallelogram,
    opposite sides are equal,
    opposite angles are equal,
    the diagonal bisect each other.

Exercise 7.1

1. Draw sketch diagrams of these figures and mark on your drawings any lines or points of symmetry.

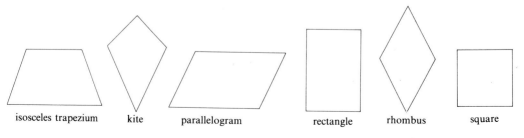

isosceles trapezium   kite   parallelogram   rectangle   rhombus   square

2. Of the figures parallelogram, rhombus, rectangle and square,

    1 which have diagonals which bisect each other,

    2 which have diagonals which bisect the angles of the figure,

    3 which have diagonals which are equal?

3. What is the order of rotational symmetry of

    1 a rectangle,   **2** a square?

4. Three angles of a quadrilateral are 50°, 75° and 123°. Find the size of the 4th angle.

5. Two angles of a quadrilateral are 72° and 118° and the other two angles are equal. What size are they?

6. Find the sizes of the marked angles.

    1 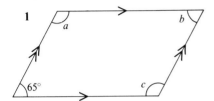   **2**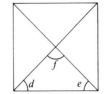

    (this is a square)

7. Two angles of a trapezium are 106° and 93°. Find the size of each of the other two angles.

8. $ABCD$ is a kite with $AB = BC$ and $AD = DC = $ diagonal AC. $\angle ABC = 80°$. Find the size of $\angle BAD$.

9. What sort of triangles are these?

    1 $\triangle ABC$, where $ABCD$ is a rectangle.

    2 $\triangle PQR$, where $PQRS$ is a square.

    3 $\triangle XYZ$, where $WXYZ$ is a rhombus.

10. $ABCD$ is a trapezium with $AD \,||\, BC$ and diagonals cutting at X.

    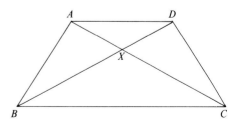

    1 If $BX = XC$, which angles are equal to $\angle XBC$?

    2 Explain why $AX = XD$.

    3 Name a pair of congruent triangles.

    4 Show that $\angle BAC = \angle CDB$.

11. *ABCD* is a rectangle and *M* and
     N are points on *AB* and *DC* such
     that *AM = DN*.
     Which triangle is congruent to Δ*AMC*?

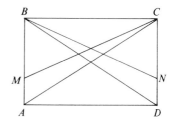

12. *ABCD* is a square. ∠*XAY* = 90°.

     1   If Δ*ADY* is rotated about *A*
         anticlockwise through 90°,
         what are the new positions of
         point *D*, the line *DY*, the point
         Y?

     2   Name a length equal to *AX*.

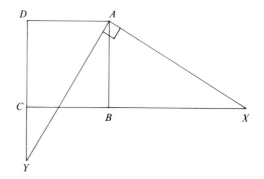

13. 1   In this parallelogram, name
         the point of symmetry.

     2   Name triangles congruent to
         Δ*ABX*,   Δ*BXC*,   Δ*ABC*,
         Δ*ABD*.

     3   Name an angle equal to
         ∠*DAB*.

     4   Name lengths equal to *AX*,
         and *BX*.

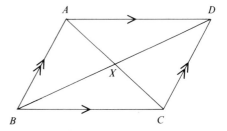

14. 1   In the rhombus *ABCD*, the diagonals intersect at *E*. Describe a single
         transformation which maps (i) Δ*ABE* into Δ*CDE*, (ii) Δ*ABE* into Δ*CBE*.

     2   In the parallelogram *ABCD*, the diagonals intersect at *E*. Describe a single
         transformation which maps Δ*ABD* into Δ*CDB*.

15. Four rods are placed together to make the outline of a plane shape.

     1   If the rods are, in order, 4 cm, 6 cm, 4 cm and 6 cm, what two possible shapes
         can be made?

     2   If the rods are, in order, 4 cm, 4 cm, 6 cm and 6 cm, what shape is made?

     3   If all the rods are 8 cm long, what two possible shapes can be made?

16. Draw an accurate, full-size drawing of this figure.
Join AD and measure it to the nearest mm.
What sort of figure is $ABCD$?

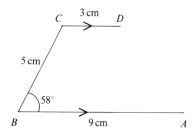

17. Draw a triangle ABC with $BC = 6$ cm, $\angle B = 70°$, $\angle C = 55°$.
Find, using compasses, a point D to complete the quadrilateral $ABCD$ such that $AD = CD = 8$ cm.
Measure the length of AC and the angle ADC.
If the quadrilateral has a line of symmetry show it on your diagram by a dotted line.

18. Draw accurately a parallelogram $ABCD$ with $AB = 9$ cm, $BC = 6$ cm and $\angle ABC = 42°$. Draw its diagonals and measure the acute angle between them.

19. Construct the quadrilateral $ABCD$ in which $AB = 4$ cm, $BC = 6$ cm, $CD = 5$ cm, $\angle B = 60°$ and $\angle C = 90°$. Measure $\angle A$, and the length of AD.

20. Construct a square $ABCD$ with side $AB = 5$ cm. Join its diagonals and let them meet at X. Measure AC and BD, and also measure the sizes of the angles at X.

Exercise 7.2

1. If 3 angles of a quadrilateral are $x°$, $2x°$ and $3x°$, write down a formula for the size of the 4th angle.

2. The angles of a quadrilateral, in order, are $3x°$, $4x°$, $5x°$, $6x°$. Find x, and the sizes of the angles. What sort of quadrilateral is it?

3. $ABCD$ is a parallelogram.

   1 What is the size of $\angle A$?
   2 Find the size of $\angle AYX$.
   3 What sort of triangle is $\triangle AYX$?

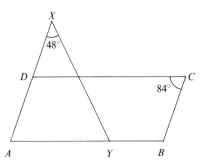

4. In these rectangles, find the sizes of a and b.

1
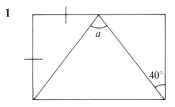

2
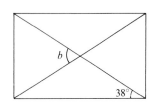

5. *ABCD* is a square.
   Δ*CDE* is an equilateral triangle.

   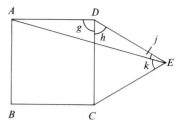

   1 Explain why *AD* = *DE*.
   2 What sort of triangle is Δ*ADE*?
   3 Find the sizes of angles *g*, *h*, *j* and *k*.

6. The diagonals *AC* and *BD* of a parallelogram *ABCD* are 8 cm and 10 cm long respectively, and intersect at an angle of 56°. Construct the parallelogram. Estimate and then measure the lengths of *AB* and *AD* and the size of ∠*DAB*.

7. For each part of this question, sketch a quadrilateral *ABCD* and mark on it the information given, then say whether it is necessarily a trapezium, parallelogram, rectangle, rhombus or square.

   1 *AB* // *CD*, *AB* = *CD*.

   2 ∠*B* = ∠*C* = 90°.

   3 *AB* // *CD*, *AD* // *BC*, *AC* = *BD*.

   4 *AC* and *BD* are axes of symmetry.

8. Write down two equations, one involving *x*, the other involving *y*, and solve them. Hence find the numerical values of the lengths of the sides of this parallelogram.

   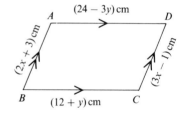

9. If Δ*ABC* is reflected in the line *BC*, with *A* reflected into a point *D*, what sort of quadrilateral is *ABDC*, with the following conditions:

   1 if *AB* is not equal to *AC*, and ∠*A* is an obtuse angle,
   2 if *AB* = *AC*, and ∠*A* is an obtuse angle,
   3 if *AB* = *AC*, and ∠*A* is a right angle?

10. If Δ*ABC* is rotated about *M*, the mid-point of *BC*, through 180°, so that *B* is rotated onto *C*, *C* onto *B*, and *A* onto a point *D*, what sort of quadrilateral is *ABDC*, with the following conditions:

   1 if *AB* is not equal to *AC*, and ∠*A* is an obtuse angle,
   2 if *AB* is not equal to *AC*, and ∠*A* is a right angle,
   3 if *AB* = *AC*, and ∠*A* is an obtuse angle,
   4 if *AB* = *AC*, and ∠*A* is a right angle?

8 Polygons. Solid figures

Polygons

Regular Polygons

A regular polygon has all sides equal and all angles equal.

Number of sides	Name	Each interior angle	Each exterior angle
3	equilateral triangle	60°	120°
4	square	90°	90°
5	regular pentagon	108°	72°
6	regular hexagon	120°	60°
7	regular heptagon	$128\frac{4}{7}°$	$51\frac{3}{7}°$
8	regular octagon	135°	45°
n	n-sided regular polygon	$\left(180 - \dfrac{360}{n}\right)°$	$\left(\dfrac{360}{n}\right)°$

Regular polygons

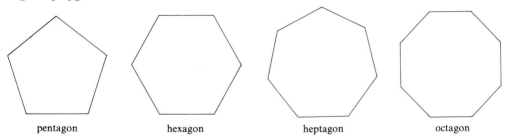

pentagon   hexagon   heptagon   octagon

Exterior angles of a convex polygon are the angles formed when each side is produced in order.

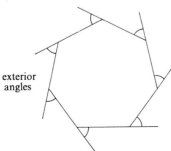

exterior angles

The sum of the exterior angles is 360°.

To find the sizes of angles in a regular polygon

Example 1

Find the angles of a regular octagon.

To find the size of an exterior angle, divide 360° by 'number of sides'.
Exterior angle of regular octagon = 360° ÷ 8 = 45°
An interior angle and an exterior angle together make 180°, so
Interior angle of regular octagon = 180° − 45° = 135°

Example 2

Find the angles of a regular 24-sided polygon.

Sum of exterior angles = 360°
Each exterior angle = 360° ÷ 24 = 15°
Each interior angle = (180 − 15)° = 165°

Example 3

A regular polygon has interior angles of 160°. How many sides has it?

Each exterior angle = (180 − 160)° = 20°
Sum of exterior angles = 360°
Number of exterior angles = 360 ÷ 20 = 18
The polygon has 18 sides.

Non-regular polygons have the same angle-sums as regular polygons with the same number of sides.
e.g. A regular hexagon has interior angles of 120° so the sum of the interior angles of any hexagon is 6 × 120° = 720°.
A regular octagon has interior angles of 135° so the sum of the interior angles of any octagon is 8 × 135° = 1080°.

For a polygon of n sides the sum of the interior angles is $(180n - 360)°$.
The sum of the exterior angles of any convex polygon is 360°.

Exercise 8.1

1. Sketch these figures and mark any lines or points of symmetry: equilateral triangle, square, regular pentagon, regular hexagon, regular heptagon, regular octagon.
   Copy and complete this table.

name of figure	number of axes of symmetry	Has it a point of symmetry?	order of rotational symmetry
equilateral triangle			
square			
. . .			

Is there a pattern in your answers?

2. 1   A regular polygon has 10 sides. What is the size of (i) an exterior angle, (ii) an interior angle?

    2   A regular polygon has 20 sides. What is the size of an interior angle?

3. 1   A regular polygon has exterior angles of 30°. How many sides has it?
    2   A regular polygon has interior angles of 135°. (i) What is the size of an exterior angle? (ii) How many sides has it?
    3   A regular polygon has interior angles of 170°. How many sides has it?

4. *ABCD* is part of a regular pentagon. *PCBQ* is part of a regular octagon. State or find the sizes of ∠*BCD* and ∠*BCP* and hence find the size of angle *a*.

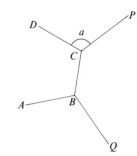

5. *ABCD* is a square and *ABPQR* is a regular pentagon.

    1   What kind of triangle is Δ*RAD*?

    2   State or find the sizes of ∠*BAR* and ∠*BAD* and hence find the size of ∠*RAD*.

    3   Find the size of ∠*DRA*.

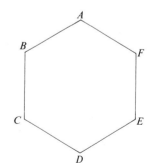

6. Sketch this regular hexagon and join points as necessary.
    What sort of quarilaterals are

    1   *ABCD*,   2   *ABDE*?

    What sort of triangles are

    3   Δ*ABC*,   4   Δ*ABD*,   5   Δ*ACE*?

7. Three regular polygons fit exactly together at a point *P*.

    1   If they all have the same number of sides, what are the sizes of the angles at *P*? What sort of polygons are they?
    2   If one polygon is a square and the other two have an equal number of sides, what are the sizes of the angles of *P*? What sort of polygons are they?

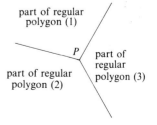

8. In this regular 12-sided polygon with centre O, find the sizes of angles a, b, c.

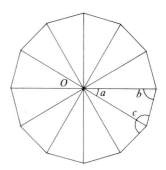

9. *ABCDE* is a non-regular pentagon. The dotted line is a line of symmetry. $\angle B = 90°$, $\angle C = 110°$. Find the size of angle *BAE*.

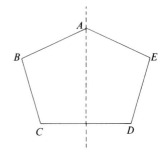

10. *ABCDEF* is a non-regular hexagon. The dotted lines are axes of symmetry. If $\angle A = 140°$, find the sizes of angles B, C, D, E, F.

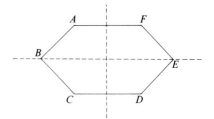

11. **To construct a regular pentagon *ABCDE***

    Method 1.

    Draw $AB = 6\,\text{cm}$, make angles of $108°$ for $\angle BAE$ and $\angle ABC$.
    Mark off $6\,\text{cm}$ on these lines for points E and C.
    To find D, with compasses centre C, draw an arc of radius $6\,\text{cm}$, with centre E draw an arc of radius $6\,\text{cm}$, to meet the first arc at D.
    Join CD and ED.

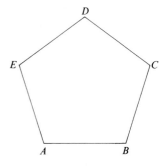

    Check the accuracy of your drawing by measuring angles C, D and E, which should all be $108°$.
    Measure the distance from A to D. (You can also measure the other 4 diagonal lengths of the pentagon, which should all be equal.)

CHAPTER 8

Method 2.

Starting at a point *O*, draw 5 lines *OA*, *OB*, *OC*, *OD* and *OE*, each 5 cm long, with an angle of 72° between each one and the next. Join *AB*, *BC*, *CD*, *DE*, *EA* and measure these lines (which should be equal in length).

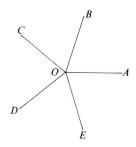

12. **To construct a regular hexagon *ABCDEF* of side 6 cm.**

Method 1.

Draw *AB* = 6 cm, make angles of 120° for ∠*BAF* and ∠*ABC*.
Mark off 6 cm on these lines for points *F* and *C*.
Make angles of 120° at *F*, for ∠*AFE*, and at *C*, for ∠*BCD*.
Mark off 6 cm on these lines for points *E* and *D*.
Join *ED*.
Measure angles *FED* and *CDE*, which should be 120°.
Measure the distances from *A* to *D*, *B* to *E*, *F* to *C*.

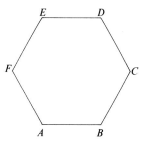

Method 2, is similar to method 2 for a pentagon, shown above. Make angles of 60° between the lines.

Method 3.

With compasses mark a centre *O* and draw a circle, radius 6 cm.
Take 1 point on the circumference to be *A*.
With compasses, radius 6 cm, centre *A*, mark off an arc to cut the circumference at *B*.
Repeat with centre *B* to get point *C*.
Continue this method to get points *D*, *E* and *F*.
As a check, *FA* = 6 cm.
Join the sides *AB*, *BC*, *CD*, *DE*, *EF* and *FA*.

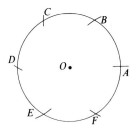

13. 1 What is the sum of the angles of a pentagon? Four of the angles of a pentagon are 75°, 110°, 124° and 146°. Find the size of the fifth angle.

   2 What is the sum of the angles of a hexagon? Five of the angles of a hexagon are 108°, 106°, 115°, 120° and 124°. Find the sixth angle.

   3 What is the sum of the angles of an octagon? Five of the angles of an octagon are each 130°, two other angles are 140° and 155°. Find the size of the remaining angle.

   4 Five of the exterior angles of a hexagon are 45°, 55°, 60°, 65° and 85°. Find the sixth exterior angle.

   5 Nine of the ten angles of a decagon are each 150°. What are the sizes of their exterior angles? Find the size of the tenth exterior angle and hence find the size of the tenth interior angle.

Solid figures

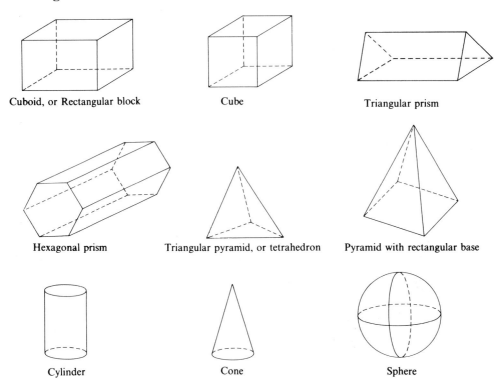

Cuboid, or Rectangular block   Cube   Triangular prism

Hexagonal prism   Triangular pyramid, or tetrahedron   Pyramid with rectangular base

Cylinder   Cone   Sphere

Nets of solid figures

These are the patterns which when cut out and folded will make the solid figures.

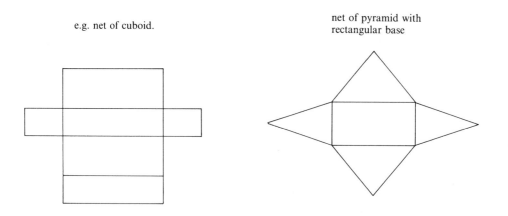

e.g. net of cuboid.

net of pyramid with
rectangular base

There are other arrangements possible, to make the same solid figures.

Exercise 8.2

1. Count the number of faces, edges and vertices (corners) on several solid figures. Copy and complete this table.

    F = number of faces, E = number of edges, V = number of vertices.

	F	E	V	$F + V - E$
cuboid triangular prism tetrahedron . . .				

    The relationship between F, E and V applies to all solids with plane faces (i.e. no curved faces).

    If a solid figure has 15 plane faces and 12 vertices, how many edges will it have?

2. The net of a cube can be arranged in several different ways. Which of these drawings of arrangements of six equal squares, if cut out and folded, would make a cube?

    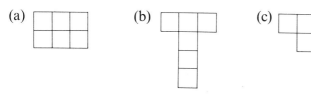

    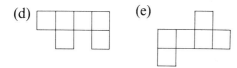

3. A solid consists of a triangular pyramid fitted exactly on top of a triangular prism. State how many faces, edges and vertices the solid figure has.

    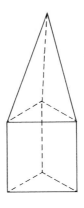

4. This net can be folded to make a triangular prism.
   Which letter(s) will point A join?

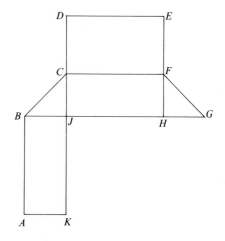

5. **1** The circular cylinder has an axis of symmetry. Sketch 3 other solid figures which have an axis of symmetry.

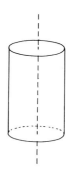

   2 The cylinder has a plane of symmetry. How many planes of symmetry has a cuboid?

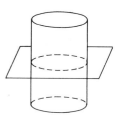

6. The curved surface of a cone is made from a sector of a circle. Draw a circle centre O, radius 8 cm. Cut out the sector AOB, bend it round and join OA to OB. (The shape of the cone will depend on the size of $\angle AOB$.)
   What shape is needed to make the curved surface of a cylinder?

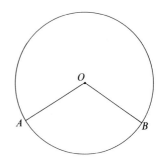

Exercise 8.3

1. Sketch the regular pentagon *ABCDE* and join points as necessary.

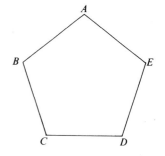

   1 What is the size of ∠*A*?

   2 What sort of triangle is Δ*BCD*?

   3 What is the size of ∠*CBD*?

   4 What is the size of ∠*ABD*?

   5 What sort of figure is *ABDE*?

   6 If *CE* cuts *BD* at *K*, what sort of figure is *ABKE*?

2. Here are 2 flow charts for finding the size of each interior angle of a regular polygon.

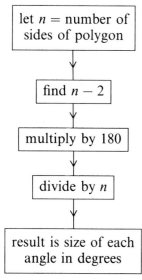
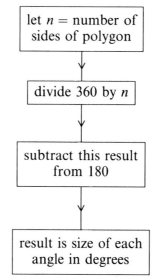

   Use each flow chart to find the size of an interior angle in

   1 a hexagon   **2** a regular 20-sided polygon.

   Which flow chart do you prefer to use?

3. The diagram shows part of a regular polygon. If it has 10 sides, find the size of angle *a*.

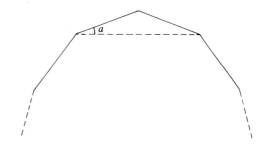

4. Three regular polygons with a sides, b sides and c sides respectively meet at a point P.

    What is the exterior angle of a polygon with a sides?

    What is the exterior angle of a polygon with b sides?

    What is the exterior angle of a polygon with c sides?

    The sum of these three exterior angles is 180°.

    Find an equation connecting a, b and c, and simplify it to show that

    $$\frac{1}{a} + \frac{1}{b} + \frac{1}{c} = \frac{1}{2}.$$

    If $b = 12$ and $c = 6$, use this equation to find a.

    If one polygon has 12 sides and another has 6 sides, what sort of polygon is the third one?

part of polygon
with a sides

part of polygon
with c sides

P

part of polygon
with b sides

5. Sketch a regular pentagon $ABCDE$ and draw all its diagonals. (A diagonal is a line which joins two non-adjacent points, e.g. AC and AD are diagonals.)
    How many diagonals are there?
    Sketch a regular polygon with 10 sides. From one point, how many diagonals can be drawn? To find the total number of diagonals, multiply this number by 10, because you can draw diagonals from each of the 10 points, then divide by 2 because using this method you have counted every diagonal twice.
    Can you find a formula for the number of diagonals of a regular polygon with n sides?
    If so, use your formula to find the number of diagonals of a regular polygon with 20 sides.

6. Find the value of x in each figure. The dotted lines are axes of symmetry.

1

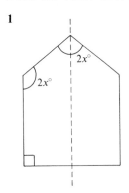

2

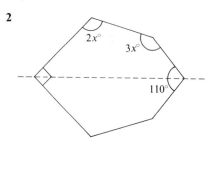

7. Two square pyramids with congruent square bases have their bases glued together to make a solid figure with 8 triangular faces (an octahedron). How many edges and vertices does this solid figure have?

8. If small triangular pyramids are sliced off all the corners of a cube, how many faces, edges and vertices has the remaining solid?

9. If the ends of a triangular prism are equilateral triangles and the other faces are rectangular, how many planes of symmetry has the prism?

10. If the ends of a hexagonal prism are regular hexagons and the other faces are rectangles, the line joining the centres of the hexagons is an axis of symmetry. If the solid is rotated about this line, what is the order of rotational symmetry?

PUZZLES

27. Start from ∗, going horizontally or vertically (not diagonally), and spell out the names of 7 plane figures.

T	A	N	T	R	I	X	A
N	G	O	R	T	A	E	G
E	G	O	A	E	N	H	O
P	R	L	P	L	G	M	N
M	A	E	E	Z	I	U	Q
A	L	L	A	R	E	A	U
R	A	*P	L	S	T	D	R
E	R	A	U	Q	A	L	I

28. Alan, Bob and Charles are allowed to pick apples in an orchard. Alan picks 7 sackfuls containing 16 kg each, Bob picks 7 sackfuls containing 14 kg each, Charles has smaller sacks and he picks 10 sackfuls holding 9 kg each. They had agreed beforehand that they would share the fruit equally. How can they do this without opening any of the sacks?

29. There are three married couples having dinner together.
George is older than Michelle's husband.
Frank's wife is older than Nadia.
Lynnette's husband is older than George.
Michelle is not Edward's wife.
The oldest man is married to the youngest woman.
The oldest woman paid the bill. Who was this?

9 Averages

When statistical data has been collected, we often need to find an average measurement. There are several kinds of average. Here we will use the mean, the median and the mode.

1 **The mean** $= \dfrac{\text{the total of the items}}{\text{the number of items}}$

The formula is written as $\bar{x} = \dfrac{\Sigma\, x}{N}$,

where $\bar{x}$ (read as x bar) is the symbol for the mean,
Σ, the Greek capital letter sigma, means 'the sum of', so $\Sigma\, x$ means the sum of the x-values, and
N is the number of items.

2 **The median.** When the items are arranged in order of size, the median is the value of the middle item, or the value halfway between the middle two if there is an even number of items.

3 **The mode** is the value which occurs most often. (Sometimes a set of values will not have a mode, as there may not be any value which occurs more often than any of the others.)

Example 1

Numbers of members of a club attending the meetings

Week number	1	2	3	4	5	6	7	8	9	10	Total
Attendance	20	19	24	22	20	23	20	28	24	20	220

The mean attendance $\bar{x} = \dfrac{\Sigma\, x}{N} = \dfrac{220}{10} = 22$

The median

(Arrange the items in order of size.)

| 19 | 20 | 20 | 20 | 20 | 22 | 23 | 24 | 24 | 28 |

↑
middle

The median is halfway between 20 and 22, i.e. 21.
(Half the values are less than 21 and half are greater than 21.)

The mode

The value which occurs most often is 20 (as there were 4 weeks when 20 members were present), so the mode is 20.
Summary:- Mean = 22, median = 21, mode = 20.

All these averages can be used in different circumstances, although the most usual one is the mean, as this is the one which involves all the values. If one of the values is very high or low compared to the others, this will affect the mean and in this case the median might be a better average to use. The mode is the simplest average to find, but generally it is not as useful as the other two. However, if a trader was selling, for instance, women's slippers, he would find it useful to know the mode size of women's feet, as he could then stock most of that size and less of other sizes.

Example 2

In a class test, the marks were

| 5 | 10 | 25 | 25 | 25 | 30 | 30 | 30 | 30 | 35 |

The mean mark is 24.5
The median mark is 27.5
The mode mark is 30
The fairest average to quote here is the median. Half the students have less than 27.5 and half have more. The mean has been distorted by the two low values, and only two students have marks less than the mean. The mode is not a representative average, as only 1 student has a better mark.

It can sometimes be misleading if an average is used without saying which one it is. For instance, in a wages dispute, the workers could quote the lowest of the mean, median or mode wage as the 'average' wage, to support their case for better wages. The management could reply by quoting one of the other averages.
As a simple example, suppose a child got £1 pocket money and he did a survey with another 7 of his friends and the 8 amounts were £1, £1, £1, £1, £2, £2, £2, £10.

The mean amount $= \dfrac{£20}{8} = £2.50$. The child could quote this to his parents as the

'average' amount when he asked for a bit more. But the mean has been distorted by the high value of £10, so it is not very representative. In fact his parents could point out that he was getting the 'average' amount already, as the mode is £1. But the median amount is £1.50, (half get more, half get less,) and this seems the fairest average to use in this case.

If the word 'average' is used without specifying which one in an arithmetical question, it refers to the mean.

Example 3

Find the mean and median of these ages:

12y 4m,   5y 7m,   4y 3m,   8y 5m,   7y 9m.   (Ages in years and months.)

y	m
12	4
5	7
4	3
8	5
7	9
38	4

$$\text{Mean age} = \frac{\Sigma \, x}{N}$$

$$= \frac{38y \, 4m}{5} = 7 \text{ years 8 months}$$

(If using a calculator remember to deal with the months and years separately.)

For the median, arrange the ages in order of size.

4y 3m,   5y 7m,   7y 9m,   8y 5m,   12y 4m.

$\uparrow$

middle

The median age is 7 years 9 months.

In your answers, remember to give the unit of measurement. Here the ages are in years and months. Check that your answer seems to be reasonable. Do not give too many decimal places. If the data is accurate to the nearest whole number then it is reasonable to give the averages to 1 decimal place.

Example 4

After 5 tests Kevin has an average of 13 marks. In a 6th test he scores 19 marks. What is his new average mark?

(Do **not** just find the average of 13 and 19 as this is wrong. You must find the total of the marks first, before finding the average.)

In the 1st 5 tests Kevin scored $13 \times 5 = 65$ marks
In the 6th test he scored $\underline{19}$ marks
Total of marks $= 84$ marks

$$\text{Average mark} = \frac{\Sigma \, x}{N} = \frac{84}{6} = 14 \text{ marks}$$

Frequency Distributions

Discrete data (i.e. the variables are numbers, not measurements)

Formula for the mean $\bar{x} = \dfrac{\Sigma \, fx}{\Sigma \, f}$

where $\Sigma \, f$ is the total of the frequencies and $\Sigma \, fx$ is the total of the fx values.

Example 5

The numbers of children in 50 families (with at least 1 child) are as follows:

4 5 2 2 3 4 4 3 5 4 7 3 3 4 2 2 2 2 2 6

3 2 3 3 1 2 3 2 2 6 5 5 3 2 4 4 2 4 1 2

2 2 1 3 3 2 2 4 5 3

Tally chart

Number of children	Number of families	f
1					3
2	ⅢⅢ ⅢⅢ ⅢⅢ |||	18
3	ⅢⅢ ⅢⅢ ||	12
4	ⅢⅢ ||||	9
5	ⅢⅢ	5
6				2
7			1
		50

(Remember the 5th tally mark goes through the other 4.)

Histogram	**Vertical line graph**
Children in 50 families	**Children in 50 families**

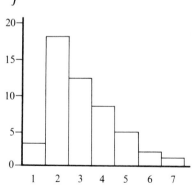

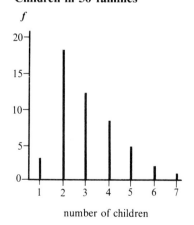

A histogram is similar to a vertical bar chart with no gaps between the bars. A vertical line graph is similar to a vertical bar chart with thin bars and large equal gaps between them.

Averages

Mode There are 18 families with 2 children, so the mode is 2.

Median If the numbers were arranged in order of size

1 1 1 2 2 2 . . . 5 6 6 7

the middle value would be halfway between the 25th and 26th numbers, and these are both 3, so the median is 3.

Mean Write down a frequency table and add a column for fx. Find the sums of the columns f and fx.

x	f	fx
1	3	3
2	18	36
3	12	36
4	9	36
5	5	25
6	2	12
7	1	7
	50	155

(1×3)
(2×18)

$$\bar{x} = \frac{\Sigma\, fx}{\Sigma\, f} = \frac{155}{50} = 3.1$$

The mean number of children per family is 3.1

If you are using your calculator to find the numbers in the fx column, add them into the memory as you go along, then to get the total of that column you only have to press the 'recall memory' key. But do a check in case you have missed some out. Does the answer **look** right? Looking at the distribution we would expect the average number of children to be somewhere between 2 and 4, and for any answer less than 2 or more than 4 it would be advisable to check your working.

Combining means

Example 6

If the mean amount spent on travelling to work by 6 girls was 40 p, and the mean amount spent on travelling to work by another 4 girls was 50 p, what was the mean amount for the 10 girls together?

Do **not** just average 40 p and 50 p, because 45 p is not the correct answer. Always find the total amount, then find the mean.
The total amount for the 1st 6 girls is   40 p × 6 = 240 p
The total amount for the other 4 girls is 50 p × 4 = 200 p
The total amount for the 10 girls is   440 p
The mean amount is $\frac{440}{10}$ p = 44 p

Example 7

There are 100 workers in a firm and their mean wage was £115 per week. If everyone received a £5 per week pay-rise what would the new mean wage be? (You would probably guess that it would be £120 and this is correct.)

The previous total of wages was £115 × 100 = £11 500
The extra total of wages is   £5 × 100 =   £500
The new total is   £12 000

The new mean wage $= \dfrac{£12\,000}{100} = £120$

Dispersion

The average (mean, median or mode) gives us a general idea of the size of the data, but two sets of numbers can have the same mean but be very different in other ways. The other main statistic we find is a measure of dispersion (or spread).
There are several measures of dispersion, of which we will consider the range.

The range is the simplest measure of dispersion to find.

Range = highest value − lowest value

The range only uses the extreme values so it is not always very representative.

Example 8

The numbers of members of a club attending a meeting in different weeks. The numbers have been arranged in order of size.
Case (a).   19, 20, 20, 20, 20, 22, 23, 24, 24, 28.
Case (b).   8, 11, 13, 15, 18, 23, 30, 32, 34, 36.

The mean in each case is 22 but there is a much bigger dispersion in case (b).

Range in (a) = 28 − 19 = 9
Range in (b) = 36 − 8 = 28

Exercise 9.1

1.   Find the mean and median of these sets of numbers.

   1   4   5   5   7   7   8   9   10   12   15   17

   2   12   20   31   35   39   48   55   71   85

   3   2   14   5   12   7

   4   25   53   37   17   62   93   41   27   33   19

   5   1.5   1.7   1.8   1.9   2.0   2.0   2.1   2.2

2. Find the median and mode of these sets of numbers.

    1   4   5   5   7   7   7   8   9   9   10   12   12   12   12   13

    2   26   27   29   25   31   33   27   32   28   27   33

    3   3   5   1   6   2   5   4   8   1   5   2   5

        7   2   1   5   4   3   6   9   4   1   6   7

3. Find the mean of

    1   59.2,   90.0,   75.8,   32.6.

    2   £985,   £863,   £904,   £967,   £868.

    3   1 hr 20 min,   2 hr 30 min,   1 hr 45 min,   3 hr 10 min,   2 hr 8 min,

        1 hr 13 min.

    4 $1\frac{1}{4}$, $2\frac{1}{3}$, $3\frac{1}{2}$.

    5   2.5 kg,   3.4 kg,   2.7 kg,   1.9 kg,   4.0 kg.

4. **1**   The weights in kg of 10 children are

        54,   52,   62,   49,   61,   56,   51,   64,   54,   67.

        Find the mean and the median weights.

    2   The ages of 5 boys are

        12 y 1 m,   12 y 5 m,   13 y 7 m,   11 y 2 m,   11 y 7 m.

        Find the mean age.

    3   The weights of 10 helpings of potatoes (to the nearest 10 g) are

        150 g,   170 g,   190 g,   160 g,   180 g,   140 g,   170 g,   170 g,   150 g,

        160 g.

        Find the mean weight.

    4   The temperature in a city each day of a summer week was (in °C)

        22   22   23   24   23   20   20

        Find the mean temperature.

    5   The times taken by 6 girls on a training run were

        10 min 20 sec,   9 min 5 sec,   11 min 45 sec,   12 min 0 sec,   8 min 30 sec

        10 min 50 sec.

        Find the mean time taken.

5. Find the range for the sets of numbers in question 1 on the previous page.

6. Find the range of the data in question 3 above.

7. A cricketer had an average of 30 runs (per innings) after playing 10 innings. In his next innings he was out after scoring 52 runs. What was his new average?

8. The average age of 6 boys is 8 years 2 months, and the average age of 5 others is 9 years 1 month. Find the average age of the 11 boys.

9. The average weight of 5 packages is 8.6 kg. The average weight of 4 of them is 9.6 kg. What does the 5th package weigh?

10. 12 kg of pet food at 7 p per kg are mixed with 18 kg of pet food at 10 p per kg. What is the cost of 1 kg of the mixture?

11. In a class there are 8 boys in set 1 and 12 boys in set 2. In a test the set 1 boys' average mark is 65 and the set 2 boys' average mark is 60. Find the average mark for the whole class.

12. A dealer bought 90 cases of goods at £10 per case and a second lot of 70 cases at £6 per case. What was the average price per case?

For the frequency distributions in questions 13 to 16,

  1 Draw a histogram or a vertical line graph of the distribution,

  2 Find the mean, median and mode of the distribution.

13. Number of people per household in a sample of 50 households.

size of household	1	2	3	4	5	6
number of households	10	18	9	7	4	2

14. Number of goals scored by 30 teams in a league.

goals	0	1	2	3	4	5
f (number of teams)	8	9	5	4	2	2

15. Number of heads when 8 coins were tossed together 60 times.

number of heads	0	1	2	3	4	5	6	7	8
f (number of times)	1	2	7	15	17	11	5	2	0

16. Number of pupils per class in 30 classes in a school.

number in class	29	30	31	32	33
f (number of classes)	6	10	5	5	4

17. A girl plays a computer game in which she can score from 0 to 10 in each game. The scores she achieved in several games are shown here. Find the mean score.

Score	0	1	2	3	4	5	6	7	8	9	10
Frequency	2	3	0	4	3	8	5	9	3	1	2

18. The goals scored by 20 football teams were as follows:
     8 teams scored no goals, 4 teams scored 1 goal each, 3 teams scored 2 goals, 1
     team scored 3 goals, 3 teams scored 4 goals, 1 team scored 5 goals.
     What is the average number of goals scored per team, by the 20 teams?

19. In a year-group of 60 pupils, the number of subjects each pupil passed in an
     examination, was as follows:

     5 8 8 7 8 7 6 4 8 7 8 7 7 8 5 6 6 3 6 6
     8 7 9 5 7 8 7 7 8 6 7 9 4 7 8 9 6 5 9 8
     3 8 7 4 5 8 4 5 6 9 9 9 9 7 8 8 5 6 7 6

     Tally the results to form a frequency distribution. Draw a histogram or a vertical
     line graph of the distribution. Find the mean, median and mode of the number
     of subjects passed.

20. The number of matches in 50 boxes of matches was as follows:

     34 36 40 37 37 38 37 42 36 41 37 38 38 39 39 37 36
     41 36 39 37 32 36 38 37 38 40 41 37 38 38 33 34 35
     37 41 40 37 42 39 35 35 37 32 37 35 37 41 41 41

     Make a tally chart and frequency distribution table of the data.
     Draw a histogram or a vertical line graph of the distribution.
     What is the mode of the distribution?
     Find the mean number of matches per box.

Exercise 9.2

1. In one group of children (group A) the marks in a test were 2, 3, 4, 4, 5, 5, 5,
    6, 7, 8.
    In a second group (group B) the marks in the same test were 3, 5, 5, 5, 6, 6, 6,
    6, 7, 7.

    1   Find the mean, median and mode of the marks of group A.
    2   Find the mean, median and mode of the marks of group B.
    3   Find the range of marks for each of the two groups.
    4   Which group had the greater mean mark?
    5   Which group had the greater range of marks?

2. The 1971 census recorded 7.45 million people living in Greater London in 2.65
    million households. Find the mean number of people per household.
    The figures for the North-west region of England were 6.74 million people and
    2.27 million households. Were there more people per household in London or
    in the North-west region?

3. At a seaside resort there was a mean amount of 3 hours of sunshine per day for
    the 6 days Monday to Saturday of a certain week. On the Sunday there were 10
    hours of sunshine. What was the mean amount of sunshine per day for the whole
    week?

4. If 6 bars of chocolate cost 15 pence each, and 4 bars of chocolate cost 20 pence
    each, what is the average price per bar?

5. 7 men earn £120 per week each, 4 men earn £100 per week each, and one man earn £80. What is the average wage of all these men?

6. The average age of 12 girls is 8 years and the average age of 8 boys is 10 years 6 months. What is the average age of all the children together?

7. A school had 1029 pupils and 70 teachers. What was the mean number of pupils per teacher? The next year the school increased its intake and had an extra 60 pupils. To keep approximately the same mean number of pupils per teacher, how many extra teachers were needed?

8. The number of seeds germinating in 40 pots when 6 seeds were planted in each pot was as follows:

number of seeds	0	1	2	3	4	5	6
frequency (number of pots)	0	1	3	12	10	11	3

    Find the mean, median and mode of the distribution.
    If you pick a pot at random from this batch what is the probability that it will have 4 or more germinating seeds?

9. Here is a flow chart.

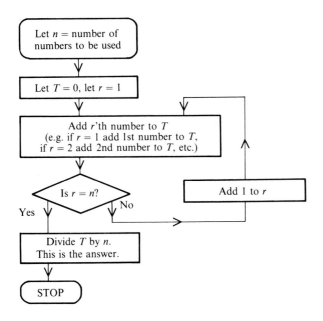

    Use the set of numbers 6, 8, 12, 15, 17 in this flow chart.
    What is the answer?
    What does the answer represent?

10. The number of goals scored in the 1st 4 divisions of the football league were written down in order as they were heard on the radio.
     Results:

     ```
     0  2  0  2  2  2  0  3  1  4  1  0  1  0  2  1  4  1  5  1  5  0  3
     2  2  1  1  4  2  0  3  0  1  1  2  1  0  1  1  2  2  1  2  0  1  1
     1  2  0  0  2  2  1  2  0  3  2  0  1  0  0  0  1  0  1  2  1  0  2
     2  3  0  2  0  3  1  1  2  1  2  2  2  1  3
     ```

     Make a frequency table to show these results.
     Draw a histogram or a vertical line graph of the distribution.
     Find the mean, median and mode number of goals scored.

11. Throw two dice and note the total score shown, and repeat this 180 times. (If you have already recorded the results of throwing 1 die, as in Exercise 6.1, question 2, use the results in pairs, as if you had thrown two dice together.

     e.g. if the results were 1 6   5 5   4 6   6 2   . . .

          the scores are   7   10   10   8   )

     Before you begin it is interesting to estimate the most likely score (the mode) and the average score (the mean).
     Make a frequency table of the results. Draw a histogram or a vertical line graph of the distribution, and find the mean and mode scores.
     (You can compare your results with the theoretical frequencies. As in Exercise 6.3, question 5, find the theoretical probabilities of scoring each total from 2 to 12. Multiply each of these by 180, the total number of throws in this experiment, to get a list of theoretical frequencies. Your experimental results should not match completely.)

12. Use 5 cards with numbers 1, 2, 3, 4, 5 printed, one number on each. Draw 3 cards at random and add the numbers together to get the 'score'. Mix the cards again and repeat this several times, putting the scores in a tally chart.
     Make a frequency distribution of the results and show this in a histogram or a vertical line graph. Find the mode, median and mean scores.
     Make a list of all the possible different outcomes of the experiment, with their 'scores', e.g. 1, 3, 4; score 8. (Disregard the order so that 3, 1, 4 is not counted as a different outcome.) Since these are equally likely outcomes you can find the theoretical probability of each score. Multiply each probability by the number of times you did your experiment to get a theoretical frequency distribution. Compare this with your experimental results.

13. **Collect other data** suitable for finding averages and making frequency distribu-tions. Some suggestions are:
     The shoe sizes of boys or girls in your class.
     The number of pets kept by a sample of children.
     The number of children in a sample of families.
     The number of goals scored in football matches by home teams, compared with the number of goals scored by away teams.
     The number of passengers in cars.
     The number of customers entering a shop in 1-minute intervals, compared at different times of the day.

10 Graphs

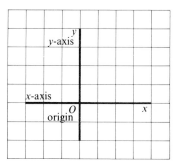

Coordinates

A point on a graph can be specified by giving its coordinates, i.e. its x-value and its y-value.

Example 1

Point A has x-value 1 and y-value 2. This can be written as the point (1, 2).

A is (1, 2)
B is (−2, 1)
C is (0, −3).

Copy this diagram and plot the point $D(3, -2)$.

Join AB, BC, CD and DA.

What sort of figure is $ABCD$?

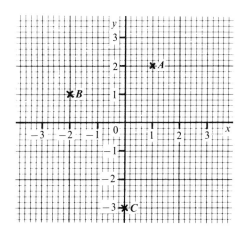

Straight line graphs

Example 2

For this question, use graph paper with x from -1 to 3 and y from -3 to 9 using scales of $1\,\text{cm}$ to 1 unit on both axes.

1   This is a pattern of numbers connecting x and y.

x	-1	0	1	2	3
y	-1	0	1	2	3

To represent this pattern on graph paper, plot the points $(-1,\ -1)$, $(0,\ 0)$, $(1,\ 1)$, $(2,\ 2)$, $(3,\ 3)$.
These points lie on a straight line. Draw it.
The connection in the pattern between y and x is $y = x$.
So $y = x$ is the equation of the line.

2   Here is another pattern of numbers.

x	-1	0	1	2	3
y	-2	0	2	4	6

To represent this, plot the points $(-1,\ -2)$, $(0,\ 0)$, $(1,\ 2)$, $(2,\ 4)$, $(3,\ 6)$ on the same graph as before, and draw the straight line through these points.
The equation of the line is $y = 2x$.
It is a steeper line than the other one.
The gradient (or slope) of $y = x$ is 1.
The gradient of $y = 2x$ is 2.

$$\text{Gradient} = \frac{\text{increase in } y}{\text{increase in } x}$$

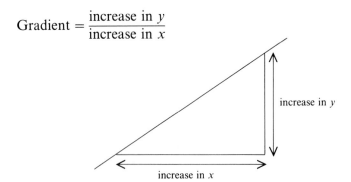

3   Make patterns for $y = 3x$, and $y = \tfrac{1}{2}x$, and plot these lines on your graph.

Example 3

For this question use graph paper with x from -1 to 3 and y from -4 to 5, using equal scales on both axes.
Plot the points representing this pattern, and draw the line.

x	-1	0	1	2	3
y	1	2	3	4	5

The equation of this line is $y = x + 2$
Draw the line $y = x$ on the same graph.
These lines are parallel, both with gradient 1. $y = x + 2$ cuts the y-axis at $(0, 2)$, but $y = x$ passes through the origin $(0, 0)$.
Make a pattern for the line $y = x - 3$, and plot this line on the same graph.

In general, the graph with equation $y = mx + c$, where m and c are numbers, is a straight line with gradient m, and it cuts the y-axis at the point $(0, c)$.

Example 4

Draw the graph of $y = 5 - 2x$.

Find the values of y when $x = -1, 0$ and 3.
When $x = 0$, $y = 5 - (2 \times 0) = 5$
When $x = 3$, $y = 5 - (2 \times 3) = 5 - 6 = -1$
When $x = -1$, $y = 5 - (2 \times (-1)) = 5 + 2 = 7$

Here are these results in a table.

x	-1	0	3
y	7	5	-1

Draw axes with x from -1 to 3 and y from -1 to 7.
Plot the points $(-1, 7)$, $(0, 5)$, $(3, -1)$ and draw the line.
It slopes downwards because its gradient is negative. (Its gradient is -2.)
(It is unnecessary to plot many points when you know the graph is a straight line. Two points are sufficient but a third point is also useful as a check on accuracy.)

Simultaneous equations

Example 5

Use a graphical method to solve the simultaneous equations $x - 3y = -9$ and $8x + 6y = 3$.

$x - 3y = -9$ can be rearranged as $3y = x + 9$, i.e. $y = \frac{1}{3}x + 3$
$8x + 6y = 3$ can be rearranged as $6y = -8x + 3$, i.e. $y = -\frac{4}{3}x + \frac{1}{2}$
Find the y-values when $x = -3, 0, 3$.

For $y = \frac{1}{3}x + 3$

x	-3	0	3
y	2	3	4

For $y = -\frac{4}{3}x + \frac{1}{2}$

x	-3	0	3
y	$4\frac{1}{2}$	$\frac{1}{2}$	$-3\frac{1}{2}$

Draw the x-axis from -3 to 3 and the y-axis from -4 to 5.
Plot the points for each line and draw the lines on the graph.
Label each one with its equation.
All the points on the 1st line will satisfy the equation $x - 3y = -9$. For example, the point $(2, 3\frac{2}{3})$ satisfies this equation.
All the points on the 2nd line will satisfy the equation $8x + 6y = 3$. For example the point $(1, -\frac{5}{6})$ satisfies this equation.
To solve the equations **simultaneously** means finding a solution which satisfies both equations, so the equations are satisfied simultaneously at the point which lies on both lines. Draw dotted lines from this point to both axes, to read off the coordinates.
The point is $(-1\frac{1}{2}, 2\frac{1}{2})$.
The solution of the equations is $x = -1\frac{1}{2}, y = 2\frac{1}{2}$.

To find the gradient of a line drawn on a graph

Choose 2 points A and B on the line, a reasonable distance apart.

Gradient of $AB = \dfrac{\text{increase in } y}{\text{increase in } x}$

$$= \dfrac{y\text{-coordinate of } B - y\text{-coordinate of } A}{x\text{-coordinate of } B - x\text{-coordinate of } A}$$

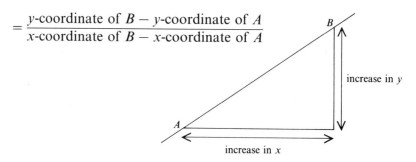

(e.g. in the diagram)

$$\text{gradient of } AB = \frac{7.8 - 2.2}{5 - 1} = \frac{5.6}{4} = 1.4$$

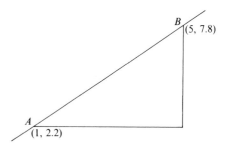

If the line slopes the other way the gradient will be negative.

$$\text{e.g. gradient of } AC = \frac{-5.4 - 2.2}{5 - 1} = \frac{-7.6}{4}$$

$$= -1.9$$

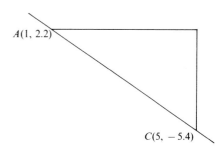

Exercise 10.1

1. Draw axes for x and y from -8 and 8 using equal scales on both axes.

   1 Plot points $A(0, 1)$, $B(6, 4)$, $C(8, 8)$, $D(2, 5)$. Join AB, BC, CD, DA.
     What sort of quadrilateral is $ABCD$?
     Mark the point of symmetry, E, and state its coordinates.

   2 Plot points $F(-8, 5)$, $G(-6, 2)$, $H(-3, 4)$. Join FG and GH.
     Find a point J such that $FGHJ$ is a square. Complete the square.
     What are the coordinates of J?
     Draw the axes of symmetry of the square on your diagram. How many axes of symmetry are there?

   3 Plot points $K(-7, -6)$, $L(-4, -8)$, $M(-1, -6)$, $N(-4, -4)$.
     Join KL, LM, MN, NK.
     What sort of quadrilateral is $KLMN$?
     What are the equations of its axes of symmetry?

2. Find the gradients of the lines
   AB, CD, EF, GH.

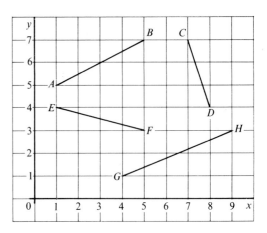

3. Draw the x-axis from − 3 to 5 using 2 cm to 1 unit, and draw the y-axis from − 4 to 12 using 1 cm to 1 unit.
   Plot the lines represented by these patterns.

   1

x	− 3	− 1	1	3	5
y	− 4	0	4	8	12

   2

x	− 3	− 1	1	3	5
y	12	10	8	6	4

   3 Make a similar pattern for the equation $y = x - 1$ and draw this line on the graph.

   4 Make a similar pattern for the equation $y = 12 - 3x$ for $x = 0, 1, 2, 3, 4, 5$ and draw this line on the graph.

   5 Find the coordinates of the point where the lines $y = x - 1$ and $y = 12 - 3x$ intersect.

   6 Draw the line $x = -2$ on the graph. Find the coordinates of the point where this line intersects the line drawn in part **2**.

4. Draw the x-axis from 0 to 10 and the y-axis from 0 to 8 using equal scales on both axes.
   Plot points A(6, 3) and B(10, 5), and join AB.
   Plot the point C(9, 7) and join BC.
   Find the point D such that ABCD is a rectangle. Join AD and DC.
   What are the coordinates of D?
   Join BD.
   What is the equation of the line BD?

5. Draw the x-axis from -2 to 6 and the y-axis from -10 to 20.
    If $y = 3x - 2$, find the values of y when $x = -2$, 0 and 5.
    For the graph of $y = 3x - 2$ plot 3 points and join them with a straight line.
    What is the gradient of this line?
    Where does the line cut the y-axis?

6. Draw the x-axis from -6 to 8 and the y-axis from -8 to 8.
    Plot the points $A(5, 3)$ and $B(2, 6)$. Join AB and find the gradient of this line.
    Plot the points $C(-4, -2)$ and $D(-2, 4)$. Join CD and find the gradient of this line.
    Plot the point $E(2, -6)$. Through E draw a line with gradient 3.
    Plot the point $F(-6, 2)$. Through F draw a line with gradient -1.

7. Draw the x-axis from -1 to 3 and the y-axis from -8 to 13.
    Draw the lines AB, $y = 3x - 5$ and CD, $y = 9 - 4x$.
    Use your graph to solve the simultaneous equations $y = 3x - 5$, $y = 9 - 4x$.

8. Draw x and y axes from 0 to 8.

    1   To draw the graph of $2x + 3y = 6$.

        If $x = 0$, what is the value of y? Mark the point corresponding to these values
        on the graph.
        If $y = 0$, what is the value of x? Mark the point corresponding to these values
        on the graph.
        Join these two points.

    In a similar way, draw the graphs of

    2   $5x + 4y = 20$,

    3   $8x + 5y = 40$,

    4   $6x + 7y = 42$.

    From your graphs find the solution of the simultaneous equations $6x + 7y = 42$,
    $8x + 5y = 40$.

Exercise 10.2

1. Draw the x-axis from -6 to 10 and the y-axis from -4 to 11 using equal scales
    on both axes. Draw triangles labelled A to F by plotting and joining the 3 points
    given in each case.
    Triangle A (2, 6), (2, 9), (3, 10)
    Triangle B (5, 3), (6, 6), (7, 6)
    Triangle C (9, 0), (6, -2), (6, -3)
    Triangle D (-5, 7), (-3, 10), (-2, 10)
    Triangle E (-5, 4), (-2, 4), (-1, 5)
    Triangle F (-4, -2), (-4, -3), (-1, -1)
    Which pairs of triangles are congruent?

2. Find the gradient of the line AB.

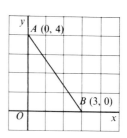

3. Draw axes with x from -4 to 4 and y from -12 to 24.
    Use a scale of $2\,cm$ to 1 unit on the x-axis and a scale of $1\,cm$ to 2 units on the y-axis.
    Draw the graph of $y = 3x + 2$, by finding values of y when $x = -4, 0$ and 4 and plotting the three points.
    Also draw the graph of $y = 16 - 2x$ in a similar way.
    Using your graphs, solve the simultaneous equations $y = 3x + 2$ and $y = 16 - 2x$.

4. For prizes for a children's party Mrs Davies decides to buy packets of sweets at $8\,p$ each and bars of chocolate at $16\,p$ each.
    If she buys x packets of sweets and y bars of chocolate, what is the total cost?
    She needs 25 prizes altogether. Write down an equation using this fact.
    On graph paper draw x and y axes from 0 to 40. Draw the graph of the equation.
    Mrs Davies decides to spend £3.20 on the prizes. Write down another equation using this fact, simplify it, and draw its line on your graph.
    How many packets of sweets and bars of chocolate does she buy?

5. Draw the x-axis from 0 to 5 and the y-axis from 0 to 3. Draw the straight line which passes through $(1, 2)$ and $(5, 3)$. Find the gradient of the line and the coordinates of the point where the line meets the y-axis.

6. Two rolls of carpet are together worth £600. The first roll contains x metres costing £10 per metre, and the second contains y metres costing £8 per metre.
    Write down an equation connecting x and y.
    In this equation, if $x = 0$, what is the value of y? If $y = 0$, what is the value of x?
    Draw the x-axis from 0 to 60 and the y-axis from 0 to 80. Draw the line representing your equation on the graph.
    If the second roll of carpet is $12\,m$ longer than the first, write down another equation connecting x and y. Draw its line on the graph.
    Solve the equations simultaneously to find how much carpet there is in each roll.

7. A firm employs skilled workers and trainee workers. The skilled workers are paid £30 per day and the trainees are paid £15 per day.
    If altogether there are 30 workers, of whom x are skilled and y are trainees, write down an equation involving x and y.
    Draw x and y axes from 0 to 40 and draw the line of the equation on the graph.
    If the daily wage bill is £600 write down a second equation, simplify it, and draw its line on the graph.
    Solve the equations simultaneously to find how many workers there are in each category.

8. Find the gradients of the lines (1), (2), (3), (4), (5).

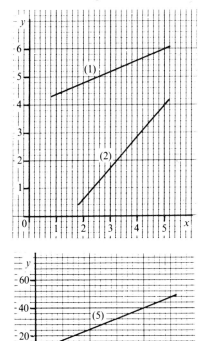

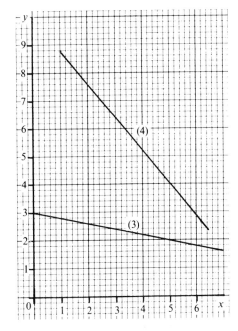

PUZZLE

30. This map shows the roads where Jenny lives. How
     many different routes are there for her to cycle from
     home to school, (never going Northwards, of course)?

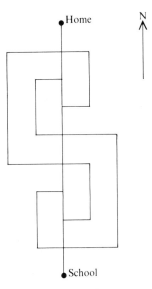

Miscellaneous section B

Exercise B1   Aural Practice

If possible find someone to read these questions to you.
You should do all of them within 10 minutes.
Do not use your calculator.
Write down the answers only.

1. How many hours are there from 8 a.m. to 11 p.m.?
2. I bought 4 similar tins of peas and received 52 pence change from £1. How much did one tin of peas cost?
3. Which is larger, $\frac{1}{3}$ or $\frac{3}{10}$?
4. How many 10 pence coins are worth £5?
5. A girl was 3 years old in 1985. When will she be 18 years old?
6. How many more 3's than 4's are there in 36.?
7. What is 5 less than one-quarter of 44?
8. A boy jogs $1\frac{1}{2}$ km every evening. How far does he go in a week?
9. If 22 cm was cut from 1 metre of ribbon, how much was left?
10. Three parcels weigh 3 kg, 5 kg and 10 kg. What is their average weight?
11. Two angles of a triangle are 30° and 70°. What size is the third angle?
12. A man is normally paid £4 per hour. How much does he earn for 5 hours work on a Sunday when he is paid at 'double time'?
13. If the time is 'a quarter past three in the afternoon', write this in figures using the 24-hour clock system.
14. What is one-quarter of one-half?
15. Find the total cost of 10 pencils at 7 pence each and 10 notebooks at 13 pence each.

Exercise B2   Multi-choice Exercise

Select the correct answer to each question.

1. Which of the following has no axis of symmetry?

   A   right-angled isosceles triangle   **B**   equilateral triangle

   C   square   **D**   rhombus   **E**   parallelogram

2. If oranges are packed 150 to a box, 12 boxes are needed. How many boxes are needed if they are packed 200 to a box?

   A   6   **B**   9   **C**   12   **D**   15   **E**   16

3. Which of the following is the closest approximation to $\sqrt{\dfrac{15.9 \times 20.1}{3.95}}$?

    A 9   **B** 12   **C** 30   **D** 80   **E** 6400

4. The line $y = 2x - 3$ passes through the point

    A $(0, -3)$ **B** $(-3, 0)$ **C** $(3, 0)$ **D** $(-3, 3)$

    E $(3, -3)$

5. 50 metres, as a fraction of $1\frac{1}{2}$ km, is

    A $\frac{1}{3}$ **B** $\frac{1}{10}$ **C** $\frac{1}{30}$ **D** $\frac{1}{50}$ **E** $\frac{3}{100}$

6. A die is thrown twice. What is the probability that both scores are greater than 4?

    A $\frac{1}{3}$ **B** $\frac{2}{3}$ **C** $\frac{1}{4}$ **D** $\frac{1}{9}$ **E** $\frac{4}{9}$

7. In a cuboid, the number of faces + the number of edges =

    A 12   **B** 14   **C** 18   **D** 20   **E** 24

8. In this parallelogram, the value of x is

    A 26   **B** 28

    C 30   **D** 35

    E 44

    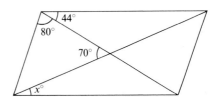

9. What is the value of $\dfrac{3x - 1}{3x + 4}$ when $x = -3$?

    A -2 **B** -1.6 **C** $\frac{8}{13}$ **D** 1.6   **E** 2

10. The mean of this frequency distribution is

    A 1   **B** 1.3   **C** 2

    D 2.5   **E** 3.9

    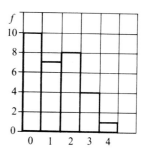

11. The value of x is

    A 19   **B** 26   **C** 32

    D 52   **E** 64

    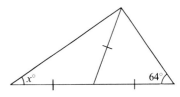

12. $3d^3 + 3d^3 =$

    A $6d^3$　　　　**B** $9d^3$　　　　**C** $6d^6$　　　　**D** $9d^6$　　　　**E** $9d^9$

13. The weight of 1 cm³ of water is 1 g. What is the weight, in kg, of 5 litres of water?

    A 0.005　　　**B** 0.05　　　**C** 0.5　　　**D** 5　　　**E** 50

14. Which of these triangles are congruent to each other?

    A I and II only

    B I and III only

    C II and III only

    D I, II and III

    E no two of them

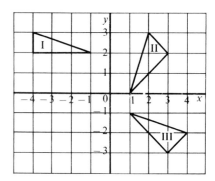

15. Three lines have lengths $(x + 6)$ cm, $(2x - 7)$ cm and $(6x - 5)$ cm. The average length, in cm, is

    A $3x - 2$　　　　**B** $3x + 2$　　　　**C** $3x - 6$　　　　**D** $9x - 6$

    E $9x + 6$

16. The gradient of the line RS is

    A $\frac{1}{2}$　　　**B** 1　　　**C** -1

    D -2　　　**E** 2

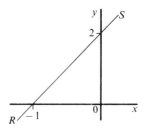

17. In the first half of a season, a junior football team played 12 matches and scored an average of 3.5 goals per match. How many goals must they score in the remaining 8 matches to bring their average up to 4 goals per match over the whole season?

    A 32　　　　**B** 36　　　　**C** 38　　　　**D** 40　　　　**E** 48

18. In this quadrilateral, the size of angle a is

    A 98°　　　　**B** 110°　　　　**C** 115°

    D 130°　　　　**E** 140°

19. If Denise travels to work by train it is quicker, but costs her three times as much as if she travelled by bus. She decides that she could save £300 a year by going by bus. The cost of travel by bus for the year would be

A £100   **B** £150   **C** £200   **D** £300   **E** £600

20. *ABCD* is a square and *ABEFG* is a regular pentagon. The size of $\angle BEC$ is

A 54°   **B** 72°   **C** 75°

D 81°   **E** 90°

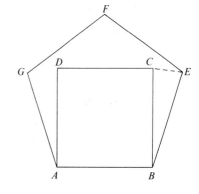

21. $1\frac{5}{8} \times 1\frac{3}{5}$ is equal to

A $1\frac{3}{8}$ **B** $2\frac{3}{8}$ **C** $2\frac{3}{5}$ **D** $2\frac{8}{13}$ **E** $3\frac{9}{40}$

22. If the point *P* with coordinates $(-3, 5)$ is reflected in the line $y = 1$ its image point is

A $(-3, 5)$ **B** $(-3, -3)$

C $(3, -5)$ **D** $(3, 5)$

E $(5, 5)$

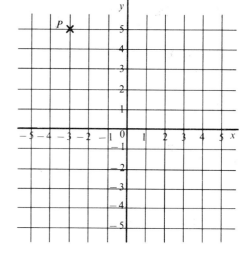

23. The gradient of the line joining the points $(-1, 2)$ and $(5, -1)$ is

A -2 **B** -1

C $-\frac{1}{2}$ **D** $-\frac{1}{4}$

E $\frac{1}{2}$

24. Which one of the following statements referring to a parallelogram is **not** correct?

    A opposite angles equal   **B** sum of angles = 360°

    C opposite sides equal   **D** opposites sides parallel

    E diagonals equal

25. In standard index form, 0.000 81 is

    A 8.1×10^{-4} **B** 8.1×10^{-3} **C** 8.1×10^4

    D 0.81×10^{-3} **E** 81×10^5

26. The value of x is

    A 32   **B** 43   **C** 47

    D 58   **E** 137

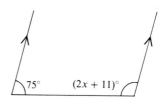

27. Two of the sides AB, DC of a regular octagon $ABCDEFGH$ when extended meet at K. The size of $\angle BKC$ is

    A 45°   **B** 60°   **C** 90°   **D** 120°   **E** 135°

28. A stallholder had 200 kg of potatoes to sell but $\frac{1}{4}$ were bad and $\frac{1}{5}$ of the remainder were too small for sale. What quantity were fit for sale?

    A 30 kg   **B** 40 kg   **C** 110 kg   **D** 120 kg

    E 160 kg

29. The mean of the numbers 6, 5, 8, 11, 7, 6, 13 is

    A 6   **B** $6\frac{1}{2}$ **C** 7   **D** 8   **E** 11

30. The median of the numbers 6, 5, 8, 11, 7, 6, 13 is

    A 6   **B** $6\frac{1}{2}$ **C** 7   **D** 8   **E** 11

Exercise B3   Revision

1. From this list of numbers:

   15   21   24   27   31   34   44   47   51   57

   1 Find the largest prime number.
   2 Find two numbers whose product is 765.
   3 Find two numbers whose sum is 104.
   4 Find two numbers which as numerator and denominator of a fraction reduce to $\frac{2}{3}$.
   5 Find two numbers which as numerator and denominator of a fraction simplify to 1.8.

2. Name the solid figures with the shape of

    1 a cricket ball,
    2 a tin of soup,
    3 a clown's hat,
    4 a match box,
    5 a child's building block.

3. The probability of Amy winning a prize in a raffle is $\frac{7}{100}$, the probability of Barbara winning it is $\frac{1}{20}$ and the probability of Charles winning it is $\frac{2}{25}$. What is the probability that none of them will win it?

4. $ABCD$ is a square, BEC is an isosceles triangle and $\angle CED = \angle AEB = 90°$. $\angle BEC = 42°$. Find the size of $\angle CDE$.

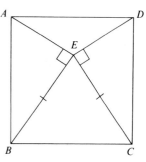

5. Find the mean, the median and the mode of this set of numbers.

    1   2   2   2   5   7   8   10   14   17   20

6. In the diagram, AD bisects $\angle BAC$. Find the size of $\angle C$.

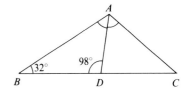

7. Express in standard index form

    1   687   2   528 000   3   0.23

8. Solve the equations

    1   $2x - 11 = 55$ 4 $5x + 5 = 3x + 17$

    2   $3x + 8 = 15$ 5 $3(x + 2) + 6(2x - 3) = 30 + x$

    3   $3x - 4 = x + 7$

9. Two sides of a regular pentagon are produced to meet at a point P. Find the size of $\angle P$.

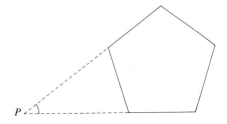

10. If $x = -4$, find the values of

    1 $2(x + 3) + 3(x - 1)$ **4** $x^3 - x$

    2 $2x^2 + 2x$

    3 $(x - 3)(x + 1)$ **5** $\dfrac{3x - 2}{3x + 2}$

11. Rearrange these formulae to give x in terms of the other letters.

    1 $y = mx + c$

    2 $y = \sqrt{x} - 3$

    3 $a = b - cx$

    4 $y = x^2 + 4$, where x is positive.

12. Find the values of

    1 $1\frac{1}{6} + (\frac{2}{3} \times 2\frac{1}{4})$

    2 $(1\frac{1}{6} \div \frac{2}{3}) + 2\frac{1}{4}$

    3 $1\frac{1}{6} - \frac{2}{3} + 2\frac{1}{4}$

13. One of the numbers 5,   6,   7,   8,   9,   10,   11,   12   is drawn at random. What is the probability that it is a factor of 60?

14. A trader buys 20 sacks of potatoes at £5 a sack and 100 sacks of potatoes at £3.80 a sack. What is the average price per sack of potatoes?

15. In the following lists, where values are given for $x = -2, 0, 1$ and 3, find the connection between y and x, in the form $y = mx + c$, where m and c are numbers.

1 x	y	2 x	y	3 x	y	4 x	y	5 x	y
-2	2	-2	-1	-2	-3	-2	5	-2	-3
0	0	0	0	0	-1	0	3	0	1
1	-1	1	$\frac{1}{2}$	1	0	1	2	1	3
3	-3	3	$1\frac{1}{2}$	3	2	3	0	3	7

On graph paper, draw axes for x from -2 to 3 and for y from -3 to 7.
For each list, plot the points on the graph and join them with a straight line.
Label each line with its equation.

Exercise B4   Revision

1. These diagrams represent the nets of solid figures. Give the names of the solid figures.

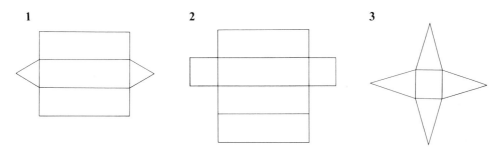

2. Find the size of angle *c*.

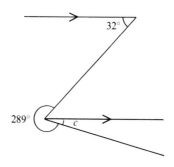

3. What fraction is £4.80 of £7.50?

4. A baby was weighed at the Health Clinic every month and the results for the first year were as follows:

Age in months	1	2	3	4	5	6	7	8	9	10	11	12
Weight in kg	4.5	5.0	6.0	6.5	7.0	7.5	8.0	8.5	9.0	9.2	9.4	9.5

Show this information on a graph.

5. A certain estate of 660 hectares consists of ploughed land, pasture land and woodland. This is represented in the pie chart shown.

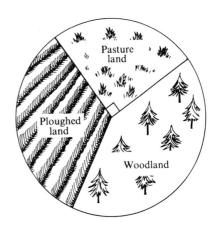

1   The angle in the pasture land sector is 90°. How many hectares are pasture land?

2   There are 220 hectares of ploughed land. The angle in this sector has not been drawn accurately. What should it be?

3   What fraction of the estate is woodland?

6. Find the size of angle *a*.

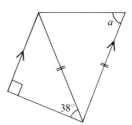

7. Three men weigh 60 kg, 58 kg and 68 kg. What is their average weight? A fourth man joins them and the average weight of all four is 64 kg. What does the fourth man weigh?

8. Construct a quadrilateral *ABCD* as follows:
    Draw a line *AC*, 10 cm long.
    Draw the perpendicular bisector of *AC*, cutting *AC* at *M*.
    Find points *B* and *D* on the bisector, such that *BM* = *MD* = 3 cm.
    Join *AB*, *BC*, *CD*, *DA*.
    Measure *AB*, to the nearest mm.
    Measure ∠*ABC*.
    What sort of quadrilateral is *ABCD*?

9. Alan plays a game where he can either win, draw or lose. The probability of him winning is $\frac{1}{3}$, the probability of him drawing is $\frac{1}{2}$. What is the probability of him losing?
    Show the results of two games on a tree diagram and find the probability that he wins at least 1 of the two games.

10. A plumber does three repair jobs as follows:- the first from 9.35 a.m. to 11.15 a.m., the second from 11.45 a.m. to 12.50 p.m. and the third from 2.05 p.m. to 3.50 p.m. Find the average time taken for a job.

11. This table shows the number of children in 100 families.

Children in family	0	1	2	3	4	5	6
Number of families	15	20	30	21	8	5	1

    Draw a histogram or vertical line graph to illustrate the data.
    Find the mean, median and mode number of children per family.

12. *ABCDEFGH* is a regular octagon, whose point of symmetry is *O*.

    1   What is the size of ∠*AOB*?
    2   What is the size of ∠*ABC*?
    3   If *AC*, *CE*, *EG* and *GA* are joined, what sort of quadrilateral is formed?

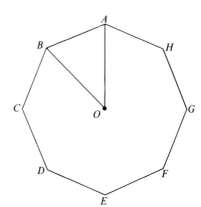

13. Simplify

   1 $3(x + 2y) - 2(x - 3y)$ 4 $(-2x)^2 + 3x^2$

   2 $x(x - 2y) + y(x - y)$ 5 $\dfrac{(-3x) \times (-4x)}{(-6x)^2}$

   3 $2x - (3x - 2y)$

14. Identify whether the quadrilateral $ABCD$
is necessarily a parallelogram, trapezium,
rectangle, square or rhombus, if it has the
following properties.

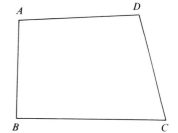

   1 $AD \parallel BC$.
   2 $AB = DC$ and $AD = BC$.
   3 $\angle A = \angle C$ and $\angle B = \angle D$.
   4 Angles A, B, C, D are right angles.
   5 $AB = BC = CD = DA$.

15. In a road survey, the cars passing a certain point in 1 minute intervals were
counted, for 30 minutes. Here are the results.

   9 11 3 15 11   1 13 12 1 10 15 0 9 11 0
 10 5 5 4 5 11 7 13 7 9 12 5 9 10 6

Show the results in a tally chart in classes 0–3, 4–7, 8–11, 12–15.

Exercise B5   Practical work and Investigations

1. Motoring

How much does it cost to run a car?
Imagine that you are planning to buy a car and want to see how much it will cost
you.
Decide what make of car you want, and whether you will buy a new one or a
secondhand one. Find the cost of the car, or of a bank loan to buy the car, or
the hire-purchase payments. Find other costs, such as road tax, insurance. For
the cost of petrol, find out how many miles per gallon your car should do on
average, decide how many miles you will travel in a year, (ask other drivers how
many miles they do), and work out the cost of the petrol. There are other costs
such as oil, car cleaning, repairs and replacements, garage rent, parking fees,
membership of a motoring association, MOT if the car is over 3 years old, and
so on. Make an estimate of these. Find the estimated total cost for a year, and
see from this how much you will need per week.
Illustrate your booklet with a picture of the car.
If you prefer you can imagine you are buying a motor bike instead of a car.

Other ideas:
Find a list of 'stopping distances' from the highway code booklet and plot these
on a graph, drawing 2 curves, one for dry conditions and one for wet conditions.

Look at second-hand values for cars as advertised in the local newspaper, and
for different makes draw graphs showing the average prices of cars 1 year old,
2 years old, and so on. After a few years you may want to sell your car. Do some
models seem to retain their values more than others?

2. **Probability of winning in competitions**

There are many competitions in newspapers, magazines and leaflets available in shops. Other competitions such as raffles are organised to raise money for Charities. Examples:

1   If there are 8 items which you have to put in order of merit, find how many different entries are possible. Often the winning entry depends on the judge's opinion, so assume that all entries are equally likely to win. What is the probability that your entry is the correct one?

2   If there are 8 questions each with possible answers A, B, C, D, how many possible combinations of answers are there? If you choose answers at random, what is the probability that your entry is the correct one?

3   Premium Bonds are a form of gambling where you do not lose your original investment, but instead of earning interest on it the interest is paid out in prizes to the winners. You can get a leaflet from the Post Office which gives details about how the scheme works, and from this you can work out your chances of winning a prize.

4   You may like to try to work out the probability of winning on various 'fairground' games, or other forms of gambling such as the football pools, poker or roulette. But note that the promoter arranges things so that he makes a profit in the long run.

3. **Geometrical models**

There are 5 regular solids so you could begin by making these.
Equilateral triangles stuck together, 3 at a point, will make a regular tetrahedron.
Equilateral triangles stuck together, 4 at a point, will make a regular octahedron.
Equilateral triangles stuck together, 5 at a point, will make a regular icosahedron.
Why are these the only regular solids which can be made with equilateral triangles?
Another regular solid is made with squares. What is it?
The 5th regular solid is made by sticking together regular pentagons. It is a dodecahedron.

If you have the plans of the nets of these solids you can make them from their nets. Put a tab on each alternate edge of the net. Score all lines before you bend them.

There are 13 semi-regular solids, made with combinations of regular polygons. You could try to make these.
With 6 squares and 8 equilateral triangles, with the same length of edge, putting 2 of each alternately at each point, you get a cuboctahedron. With 18 squares and 8 triangles, with 3 squares and 1 triangle meeting at a point, you can make a rhombicuboctahedron. With 6 squares and 32 triangles, with 4 triangles and a square meeting at a point, you can make a snub cube. Other solids use different combinations of equilateral triangles, squares and regular pentagons, hexagons, octagons and decagons. Can you discover them all?

There are 4 other regular solids called the Kepler-Poinsot Polyhedra, which are interesting models.

To make the great stellated dodecahedron, first make a regular icosahedron as a base. Then make 20 triangular pyramids to stick on the 20 faces of the icosahedron. The long slant edges of these pyramids must be 1.62 times the length of the base edges, which are the same length as the edges of the icosahedron. If you are interested in making maths models you can find details of many others from library books.

4. **Shapes in Everyday Life**

Make a booklet about these, illustrated with drawings, pictures, postcards and photographs.

Ideas:

symmetry in nature, and in man-made objects,

triangles—pylons, etc.

circles—wheels, drainpipes,

shapes in nature—spirals in snails, jellyfish, pattern on a sunflower centre, cone of a volcano,

shapes in building—unusual modern designs, bridges, the Pyramids, radio telescopes (paraboloid), cooling towers (hyperboloid), spheres of the early warning system.

Your booklet can include all of these, arranged in different sections, or you may choose to concentrate on one aspect such as symmetry.

5. **History of numbers and calculation**

Counting can be traced back to very ancient times, and yet it is only a few years ago that modern calculators and computers were invented. You could make a topic booklet about this, including early methods of writing numbers in different parts of the world, and methods of calculation such as the abacus, Napier's bones and logarithms, and ending with a section on the development of the computer.

6. **History of measurement**

It is interesting to find out about the measures which were used long ago in Britain. Land is still measured in acres. An acre is the area of land that could be ploughed in a day, in the days when oxen were used for ploughing.

If you have an interest in another country, maybe you could find out about how its system developed.

In France at the time of the Revolution, the old measures were abolished and the Metric System adopted. This is now used worldwide for scientific work and is being introduced gradually into Britain.

You could make a topic booklet about measurements. You could include weights as well. You could also find out about the measurement of time, and about coinage, or these could be topics in themselves.

7. Regular Polygons

1   Investigate the number of diagonals for polygons with 3, 4, 5, . . . sides. Find a formula for the number of diagonals of an n-sided polygon.

2   When all the diagonals are drawn, how many regions are there inside the polygon?

3   Paper knots. Use strips of paper of uniform width. Practise with narrow strips first. Tie an ordinary knot to get a pentagon. Go round an extra turn to get a heptagon. Tie a reef knot in two strips of paper for a hexagon. By bending the paper in a different way you get an octagon.

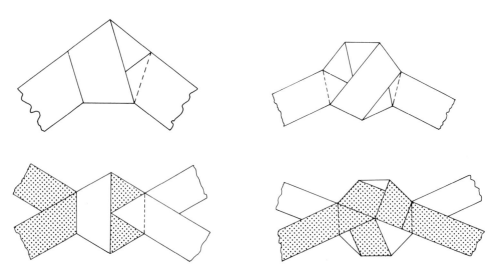

4   You probably can construct a hexagon using ruler and compasses. Here is how to find the arc length to construct a regular pentagon or decagon, without measuring the angles.

Draw a circle centre C, radius r and mark a point A on the circumference. Construct a tangent at A. Mark a point D on the tangent such that $AD = \frac{1}{2}r$. (Measure or bisect AC to get this length.) With centre D, radius DC, mark a point E on the tangent on the other side of A to D. Then AE is the radius you need to step out arcs on the circle to make the vertices of a regular decagon. Joining alternate arcs will give a pentagon.

5   Draw a regular pentagon and join its diagonals. Find in the figure an acute-angled isosceles triangle, an obtuse-angled isosceles triangle, an isosceles trapezium, a rhombus, a kite, a pentagon. Find non-regular polygons with different numbers of sides. How many triangles are there altogether in the figure?

Do a similar investigation for a regular hexagon and a regular octagon.

8.   **Pentominoes and hexominoes**

Pentominoes are arrangements of 5 equal squares which join together with edges
of adjacent squares fitting exactly together, such as

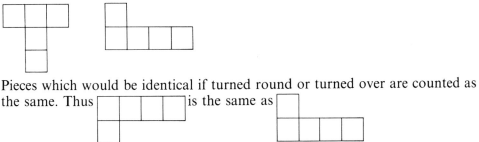

Pieces which would be identical if turned round or turned over are counted as
the same. Thus 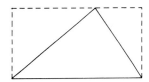 is the same as

There are 12 different pieces. Find them. Some of them will form the net of an
'open' cube. Which ones? The 12 pieces can be fitted together to form various
rectangles. Make some cardboard pieces and investigate.
Hexominoes consist of 6 squares joined together. Investigate these shapes and see
how many you can find. Some of them will form the net of a cube. Which ones?
Which pieces can be used to make tessellations?

9.   **Areas**

When we measure area we compare it with a unit area.
We can use the area of a square of side 1 cm for the unit.
This is called 1 square centimetre and written 1 cm^2.

Cut out 12 such squares out of cardboard. Together they make an area of
12 cm^2. By arranging them together, find some shapes which have an area of
12 cm^2. You can cut up some of the squares to make more interesting shapes.
Three of these shapes are rectangles. What are the measurements of rectangles
which have an area of 12 cm^2? If you had more squares, say 20 squares, what
sizes of rectangles could you make? Can you find the formula for the area of a
rectangle?

Cut out a rectangle 2 cm long by 1 cm wide. Its area is 2 cm^2. Divide it into 2
triangles by cutting along a diagonal. What is the area of each triangle?
Put the 2 triangles together. What other shapes can be made, as well as the
original rectangle? What are the areas of these shapes? Can you find the
formulae for the areas of these shapes, by seeing how they are made from the
right-angled triangles?

To find the area of a general triangle, enclose it in
a rectangle, then cut out the two extra triangles and
rearrange them to fit on the top of the original
triangle. Thus the original triangle is half the area of
the enclosing rectangle. Will this help you to find
the formula for the area of a triangle?

To find the area of a parallelogram, cut off one end, put it onto the other end, and what shape do you get? Will this help you to find the formula for the area of a parallelogram?

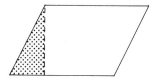

If we are measuring larger areas we will compare them with $1\,m^2$ or $1\,km^2$. Imagine you are making a square with edge 1 m with your squares of edge 1 cm. How many will you need? This tells you how many cm^2 make $1\,m^2$. Similarly, how many m^2 are there in $1\,km^2$? How many mm^2 are there in $1\,cm^2$?

Areas of irregular shapes

One way to estimate these areas is to draw them on a squared grid and count the squares.
For those squares on the boundary, where more than half the square is included in the area, count it as a whole one, and where less than half the square is included, do not count it at all. This method will give an approximate value for the area.
In the diagram,

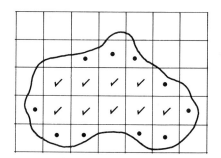

Whole squares . . . 9
Boundary squares counted . . . 10
Other boundary squares not counted.
Total area 19 squares.
If each square has edge 1 cm, area = $19\,cm^2$.
If the squares are larger, e.g. edge 5 cm, their areas are $25\,cm^2$, so area = $19 \times 25\,cm^2 = 475\,cm^2$.
If the squares are smaller, e.g. edge 2 mm, their areas are $4\,mm^2$, so area = $19 \times 4\,mm^2 = 76\,mm^2 = 0.76\,cm^2$.

Can you think of other ways to estimate such areas?

10. **For the Computer Programmer**

More suggestions:
1   Probability. Make programs to generate random numbes for the simulation of throwing dice, tossing coins, etc.
2   Get large numbers of results for the throws of 2 dice, with the totals worked out and a frequency distribution table made.
3   Investigate the number of throws needed to get a six, when throwing a die. Find the average number of throws needed.
4   A program to find the mean of a set of numbers.
5   A program to find the mean of a frequency distribution.
6   A program to draw graphs of linear functions.
7   A program to draw a histogram for given data.
8   A program to find the size of the interior angle of a regular polygon, for any number of sides.

To the student:

3   Improving your work

Check your handwriting and if necessary, improve it. It must be legible even when you are working quickly. Badly written work means that you confuse 6 with 0 or b, 2 with z, 5 with s, and so on. Show minus signs clearly. Do not alter figures, e.g. a 2 into a 3, by overwriting. Cross the 2 out and write the 3 nearby. Do not change + into − except by crossing it out and re-writing clearly. + which might mean either + or − cannot be marked as correct because you have not made it clear which it is. Altered figures cannot be marked as correct. So always make clear alterations.

Try to work at a reasonable speed. If you tend to work slowly, try to speed up, because in an examination you must give yourself a reasonable chance of completing the paper to gain good marks. When you are doing a question, concentrate completely on it so that you immediately think about the method, start it quickly, and continue working it out without a pause until you finish it. Work out any simple arithmetic in your head so that you do not break your concentration, and waste time, by pressing calculator keys. (You could do a check later, using the calculator, if you want to.)

Make sure that you use brackets correctly. $180 - 30 + 40$ is not the same as $180 - (30 + 40)$. The first expression equals 190, the second one equals 110. Be careful when you work out algebraic expressions or equations, especially those involving brackets.

Sketch diagrams, or rough plans of what you are going to do, are very useful even if they are not required as part of the answer.

When you have found an answer, consider if it is reasonable, especially if you have pressed calculator keys to get it. Look at the relative sizes of lengths or angles on the diagram, which should give a general idea even if the diagram is not drawn to an exact scale. A man earning £12 000 per year would not pay £30 000 per year in tax! It would also be rather unlikely, though not impossible, for him to pay only £30 in tax. A circle with radius 10 cm cannot have a chord of length 24 cm. (Why?) If the answer to a simple algebraic equation is an awkward number such as $x = -3\frac{10}{71}$, this **could** be correct, but it is more likely that you have made a mistake. When you have found an answer, give it correct to a suitable degree of accuracy, e.g. to 3 significant figures, and don't forget the units, e.g. £, cm, m², kg, where necessary.

About Chapters 11 to 15

The work on Algebra, Geometry and Statistics is taken further with brackets, fractions, formulae and more graphs in Chapter 13, circles in Geometry in Chapter 11, and grouped data in Statistics in Chapter 14. The areas and volumes of all figures are linked together in Chapter 12, and percentages are introduced in Chapter 15. Percentages are used so much in our lives that this is a very important chapter with interesting and useful applications.

11 Circles

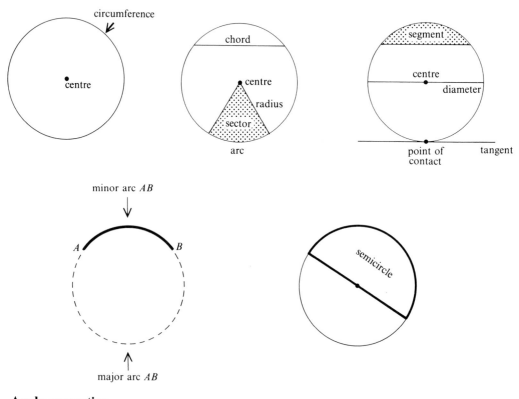

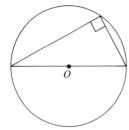

Angle properties

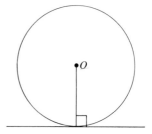

The angle in a
semicircle is a
right angle.

The angle between a tangent
and the radius to the point
of contact is a right angle.

Chord property   **Tangents from an external point**

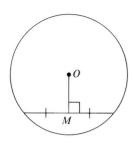

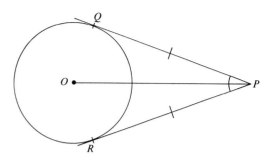

OM is an axis of symmetry. The perpendicular bisector of a chord passes through the centre of the circle.

OP is an axis of symmetry. The tangents are equal, i.e. *PQ* = *PR*. Also *OP* bisects ∠*QPR*.

Exercise 11.1

1. Sketch these diagrams and mark in the axes of symmetry.

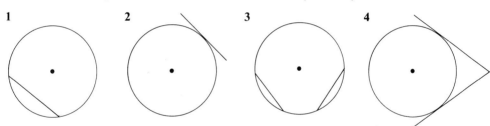

2. *TP* and *TQ* are tangents, touching the circle centre *O* at *P* and *Q*.

   1 Name the axis of symmetry.

   2 State which triangles are congruent.

   3 Name an angle equal to ∠*TOP*.

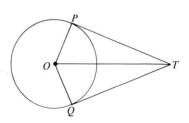

3. *AB* and *CD* are equal chords in a circle centre *O*.

   1 Copy the figure and draw in an axis of symmetry.

   2 Are triangles *AOB*, *DOC* congruent?

   3 Name an angle equal to ∠*AOB*.

   4 Can Δ*AOB* be rotated into the position of Δ*COD*?

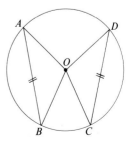

4. The two circles each have centre O. AB is a tangent to the smaller circle, touching
    at X.
    What is the size of $\angle AXO$?
    Explain why $AX = XB$.

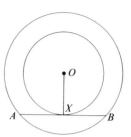

5. Find the marked angles. O is the centre of the circle. TP is a tangent touching the
    circle at P.

1

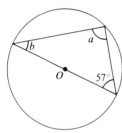

2

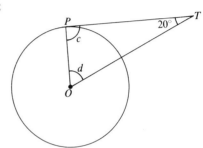

3

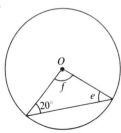

4

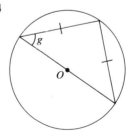

5

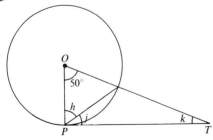

Constructions

Exercise 11.2

1. **To find the mid-point of a line *AB* or the perpendicular bisector of *AB***

   1 **By measurement.** Find the length of *AB*, divide this by 2 and measure this distance from *A* to get the mid-point.
   If you need the perpendicular bisector also, use your protractor to draw a line through this mid-point at right-angles to *AB*.

   2 **By paper folding.** You need to use thin paper such as tracing paper. Fold the paper so that *B* lies on top of *A* and make a firm crease. This crease is the perpendicular bisector of *AB* and cuts *AB* at its mid-point.

   3 **Using ruler and compasses.**

   With centre *A* and a radius more than half of *AB*, draw two arcs.

   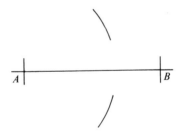

   With centre *B* and the same radius, draw two arcs to cut the first two arcs at *X* and *Y*.
   Join *XY*, cutting *AB* at *Z*.
   Then *Z* is the mid-point of *AB*, and *XZY* is the perpendicular bisector of *AB*.

   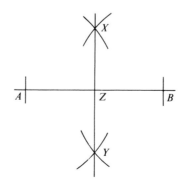

2. **To bisect an angle *ACB***

1   **By measurement.** Find the size of $\angle ACB$ with your protractor, divide this by 2 and measure this angle from *A*, turning towards *B*.

2   **By paper folding.** Fold the paper so that the line *CA* fits along the line *CB*. Make a firm crease (which goes through *C*). This crease is the bisector of $\angle ACB$.

3   **Using a ruler.** Place the edge of the ruler along *AC* with the ruler on the side of the line nearer *B*. Draw a line along the opposite edge.
Then place the edge of the ruler along *BC* with the ruler on the side of the line nearer *A*. Draw a line along the opposite edge.
If the two lines you have drawn cross each other at *Z*, join *CZ*, which is the bisector of $\angle ACB$.

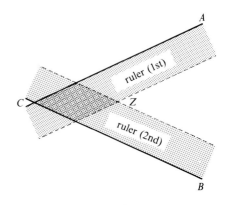

4   **Using ruler and compasses.**

With centre *C*, draw arcs to cut *CA* and *CB* at *X* and *Y*.

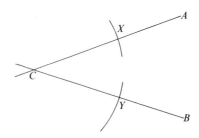

With centres *X* and *Y* in turn, and a suitable radius, draw arcs to cut at *Z*. Join *CZ*, which is the bisector of angle *ACB*.

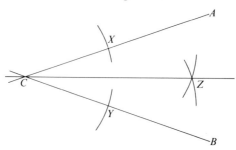

3. **To draw a perpendicular to a line *AB* from a point *C***

1 **Using a protractor.**
Place your protractor so that the
0° line passes through *C* and the
90° line lies along *AB*. Mark the
point where the 180° mark is and
after removing the protractor
join this point to *C*.
Then this line through *C* is
perpendicular to *AB*.

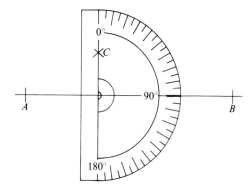

2 **By paper folding.** Fold the paper so that *AB* lies along itself and the crease passes through *C*. This crease is the perpendicular from *C* to *AB*.

3 **Using ruler and compasses.**

With centre *C* and a suitable radius, draw
arcs to cut *AB* at *X* and *Y*.

With centres *X* and *Y* in turn, draw arcs,
with the same radius for both, to cut at *Z*.
Join *CZ*, which is perpendicular to *AB*.

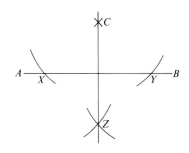

4. **To make an angle of 60°, at *P*, on the line *PQ*, using ruler and compasses.**

With centre *P* draw a large arc, to cut *PQ* at *Z*.
With centre *Z* and the same radius, draw an
arc to cut the other arc at *R*.
Join *PR*.
Then angle *RPQ* = 60°.

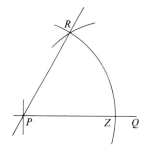

5. **To make an angle of 90°, at *C*, on the line *AB*, using ruler and compasses.**
    i.e. **To draw a perpendicular to a line *AB* from a point *C* on *AB***

With centre *C*, draw arcs to cut
AB at *X* and *Y*.

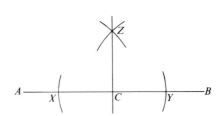

With centres *X* and *Y* in turn, and
radius slightly larger than before,
draw arcs to cut at *Z*.
Join *CZ*, which is perpendicular
to *AB*.

6. Draw a circle centre *A*, radius 4.5 cm, and
    mark a point *P* on its circumference.
    Construct the tangent to the circle with *P* as
    point of contact.

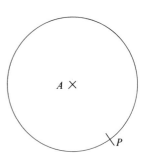

7. Construct △*ABC* with the measurements
    given.
    Measure ∠*C*.
    Bisect ∠*B*, and let the bisector cut *AC* at *D*.
    Measure *CD* to the nearest mm.

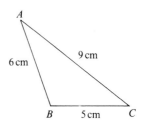

8. Draw a line *AB* of length 14 cm, and construct its perpendicular bisector, cutting
    AB at *O*.
    With centre *O*, radius 7 cm, draw a circle, cutting the bisector at *C* and *D*.
    Join *AC*, *BC*, *AD*, *BD*. Measure *AC* to the nearest mm.
    What sort of figure is *ACBD*?

9. Construct △*ABC* with the measurements
    given.
    Measure ∠*A*.
    Construct the bisector of ∠*A*, meeting *BC*
    at *D*.
    Measure *AD* to the nearest mm.

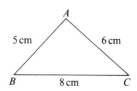

10. Using ruler and compasses, construct an angle of 60°, and then bisect it to make
    an angle of 30°.

11. Using ruler and compasses, construct an angle of 90°, and then bisect it to make an angle of 45°.

12. Construct a parallelogram $ABCD$ with $AB = 7$ cm, $AD = 4$ cm and $\angle A = 60°$. Join AC and estimate, then measure, its length.

Locus

The locus of a point is the path traced by the point as it moves so as to satisfy certain conditions.

1. The locus of a point at a fixed distance r units from a given point A is a circle, centre A, radius r.

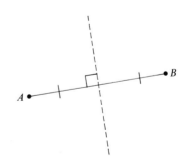

2. The locus of a point at a fixed distance r units from a given line AB is a pair of lines, each parallel to AB, and distance r from AB.

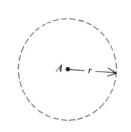

3. The locus of a point equidistant from two given points A and B is the perpendicular bisector of AB.

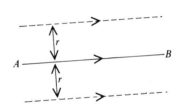

4. The locus of a point equidistant from two given lines AOB, COD is the pair of lines which bisect the angles at O.

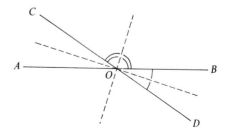

Exercise 11.3

1. Draw a triangle ABC with $AB = 8\,\text{cm}$, $BC = 9\,\text{cm}$ and $CA = 7\,\text{cm}$. Draw the locus of points inside the triangle which are (1) 5 cm from B, (2) 6 cm from C. Mark a point P inside the triangle which is 5 cm from B and 6 cm from C. Measure PA.

2. Draw a triangle ABC with $AB = 7\,\text{cm}$, $BC = 9.5\,\text{cm}$ and $\angle B = 90°$. Draw the locus of points inside the triangle which are (1) 2 cm from AB, (2) 3 cm from BC. Find a point P inside the triangle which is 2 cm from AB and 3 cm from BC. Measure PB.

3. Draw a triangle ABC with $BC = 8.5\,\text{cm}$, $\angle B = 47°$ and $\angle C = 55°$. Draw the locus of points inside the triangle which are (1) equidistant from AB and BC, (2) equidistant from B and C. Find a point P which lies on (1) and (2), and measure PB.

4. Draw a triangle ABC with $BC = 10\,\text{cm}$, $AB = 6\,\text{cm}$ and $\angle B = 55°$. Draw the locus of points inside the triangle which are (1) equidistant from AB and AC, (2) 2.5 cm from the mid-point of BC. Find a point P which lies on (1) and (2), and measure PA.

5. Draw a rectangle $ABCD$ with $AB = 6\,\text{cm}$, $BC = 8\,\text{cm}$. Draw the locus of points inside the rectangle which are (1) 2 cm from BC, (2) equidistant from A and C. Find a point P which is 2 cm from BC and equidistant from A and C. Measure PA and check by measuring PC.

6. Draw a triangle ABC with $AB = 8\,\text{cm}$, $BC = 10\,\text{cm}$ and $\angle B = 90°$. Draw the locus of points inside the triangle which are (1) 1 cm from BC, (2) equidistant from A and C, (3) 9 cm from A.
    Using these loci, mark P, a point 1 cm from BC and equidistant from A and C, and shade the region of points inside the triangle which are more than 1 cm from BC and more than 9 cm from A.

7. Draw a line AB 8 cm long. Find and shade a region within which a point P must lie if PA is less than PB and PB is less than 5 cm.

8. P is a point which moves inside the rhombus $ABCD$ so that its distance from AB is less than its distance from AD and its distance from A is greater than its distance from C. Sketch the rhombus and shade the region in which P must lie.

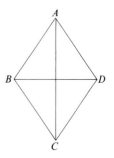

9. A circle has radius 8 cm. What is the locus of a point P which moves so that it is always 1 cm from the circumference of the circle?

Exercise 11.4

1. In the diagram, O is the centre of the circle. TP is a tangent touching the circle at P and $TP = OP$. Find,

    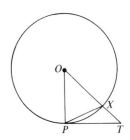

    1 the size of $\angle TOP$,
    2 the size of $\angle OPX$,
    3 the size of $\angle TPX$.

2. In the diagram, O is the centre of the circle. AD is parallel to BC. If CD is joined, what sort of figure is $ABCD$?

    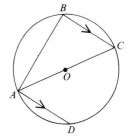

3. TP and TQ are tangents touching the circle centre O at P and Q.

    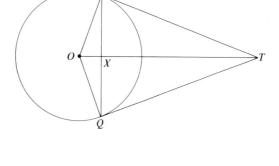

    1 Name the axis of symmetry.

    2 Name three pairs of congruent triangles.

    3 Name a line equal to PX.

    4 Name an angle equal to $\angle PXT$.

    5 What is the size of $\angle PXT$?

4. AB, CD are parallel chords of a circle centre O. OXY is perpendicular to AB and CD. Explain why $AC = BD$.

    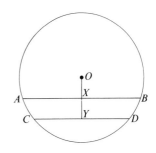

5. In the diagram, O is the centre of the circle.
    Write down an equation and solve it to find the
    value of x.

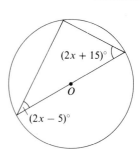

6. In the diagram, O is the centre of
    the circle and TP and TQ are
    tangents touching the circle at P
    and Q.

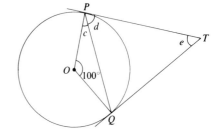

    1   What sort of triangle is $\triangle OPQ$?
    2   Find the size of angle c.
    3   Find the size of angle d.
    4   What sort of triangle is $\triangle TPQ$?
    5   Find the size of angle e.

7. In the diagram, O is the centre of the circle.
    What kind of triangles are $\triangle OAB$, $\triangle OBC$, $\triangle OAC$?
    Find the sizes of the angles of the triangle ABC.

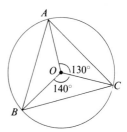

8. **To construct the circumscribed circle of a
    triangle**

    Draw an acute-angled triangle ABC.
    Draw the perpendicular bisectors of AC
    and BC to meet at O.
    With centre O, radius OA, draw the
    circle.
    (This circle is also called the circumcircle
    of the triangle.)

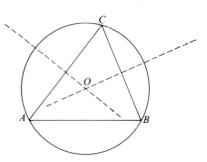

9. Construct a triangle ABC with $AB = 7\,\text{cm}$, $AC = 5\,\text{cm}$ and $\angle A = 55°$.
    Measure BC.
    Construct the circumcircle of the triangle, and measure its radius.

10. **To construct the inscribed circle of a triangle**

Draw an acute-angled triangle ABC.
Draw the bisectors of angles A and B to
meet at I.
Draw a line from I, perpendicular to AB,
meeting AB at X.
With centre I, radius IX, draw the circle.
(This circle is also called the in-circle of
the triangle.)

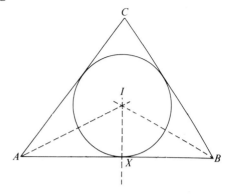

11. Construct a triangle ABC with $AB = 10$ cm, $\angle A = 47°$ and $\angle B = 57°$.
Measure AC and BC.
Construct the inscribed circle of the triangle, and measure its radius.

12. Draw a line OT 14 cm long, with mid-point M.
With centre M, draw a circle passing through O and T.
With centre O draw a circle radius 5 cm to cut the first circle at P and Q.
Join TP and TQ.
What do you notice about the lines TP and TQ?

13. Draw a triangle ABC with $AB = 8$ cm, $BC = 6$ cm and $\angle ABC = 70°$. Find

1 the locus of points inside the triangle which are 4 cm from C,

2 the locus of points inside the triangle which are equidistant from AB and BC.

Mark the region inside the triangle giving the set of points P where P is less than
4 cm from C and nearer to BC than to AB.

14.

The triangle is rotated clockwise about B until C lies on the table. Then it is
rotated clockwise about the new position of C until A lies on the table. On an
accurate drawing show the loci of C, B and A. Mark each locus clearly.

15. As the minute hand of a clock slowly rotates, an insect starts to move at a constant speed along the hand starting at the centre of the clock when the hand is pointing to 12 and moving towards the tip of the hand, reaching it when the hand again points to 12. Draw a circle of radius 6 cm to represent the clock face and draw 12 equally-spaced radii to represent the hand as it points to each number in turn. Mark the position the insect has reached on each one. Join these points with a curve to represent the path of the insect.

PUZZLES

31. How many squares of side 24 cm can be cut from a piece of paper 65 cm square?

32. Write in figures: eleven thousand, eleven hundred and eleven.

33. In a dress shop there were six dresses in the window, marked for sale at £15, £22, £30, £26, £16 and £31. Five of the dresses were sold to two customers, the second customer spending twice as much as the first one. Which dress was unsold?

34. How many mathematical words can you find reading horizontally, vertically or diagonally, in both directions?

P	Y	R	O	T	C	E	V	R	H
E	E	S	H	A	R	E	A	P	Y
Q	M	R	T	N	A	F	A	Y	P
U	N	E	C	G	O	R	N	R	O
A	O	T	A	E	G	A	G	A	T
T	G	E	M	N	N	C	L	M	E
I	Y	M	E	T	I	T	E	I	N
O	L	A	X	I	S	I	A	D	U
N	O	I	T	A	R	O	C	G	S
E	P	D	O	H	E	N	O	C	E

35. When Katie and Roger were married, they hadn't much money, and on their first wedding anniversary Roger was unable to buy his wife a decent present. So he gave her 1p, and said that it was all he could afford, but he would try to double the amount each year from then on. Sure enough, the next year he gave her 2p, and the following year 4p. Katie was quite pleased to get £5.12 this year, and says she is looking forward to their Silver Wedding anniversary when they will have been happily married for 25 years. Roger, however, doesn't seem quite so enthusiastic about this. Why?

12 *Areas and volumes*

Perimeters

The perimeter of a figure is the total length of its boundary.

Perimeter of a triangle = sum of lengths of its 3 sides

Perimeter of a rectangle = sum of lengths of its 4 sides

$$= 2 \times (\text{length} + \text{breadth}) = 2(l + b)$$

Areas

Area of a rectangle = length $\times$ breadth = lb

Area of a square = $(\text{length})^2 = l^2$

Area of a triangle = $\frac{1}{2} \times$ base $\times$ perpendicular height = $\frac{1}{2}bh$

Area of a parallelogram = base $\times$ perpendicular height = bh

Area of a trapezium = $\frac{1}{2} \times$ sum of the parallel sides $\times$ the perpendicular

distance between them = $\frac{1}{2}(a + b)h$

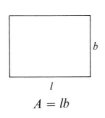

$A = lb$

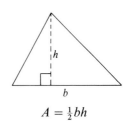

$A = \frac{1}{2}bh$

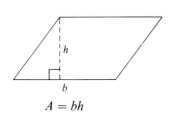

$A = bh$

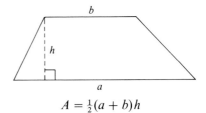

$A = \frac{1}{2}(a + b)h$

Circles

Circumference $= \pi \times$ diameter $= 2\pi \times$ radius

$C = \pi d$

$C = 2\pi r$

Area $= \pi \times (\text{radius})^2$

$A = \pi r^2$

π (pi) is an irrational number so it cannot be written as an exact decimal. It is approximately 3.14159 but for normal calculations we use 3, 3.1, 3.14 or 3.142 depending on how accurate we need to be. A useful fraction to estimate π is $3\frac{1}{7}$ $(= \frac{22}{7})$. If you use 3.14 or $\frac{22}{7}$ for π, your answer should normally be given corrected to 3 significant figures. Even if you use a more accurate value for π it would be sensible to give a final answer to 3 or 4 significant figures.

There may be a special key labelled π on your calculator.

Examples

1   Rectangle

Perimeter $= 2(l + b)$

$\qquad\qquad = 2 \times (10 + 8)\,\text{cm}$

$\qquad\qquad = 2 \times 18\,\text{cm} = 36\,\text{cm}$

Area $\quad = lb$

$\qquad\quad = 10 \times 8\,\text{cm}^2$

$\qquad\quad = 80\,\text{cm}^2$

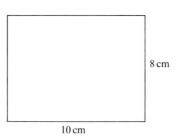

2   Triangle

Area $\quad = \frac{1}{2}bh$

$\qquad\quad = \frac{1}{2} \times 10 \times 6\,\text{cm}^2$

$\qquad\quad = 30\,\text{cm}^2$

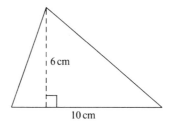

3   Parallelogram

Area $\quad = bh$

$\qquad\quad = 9 \times 5\,\text{cm}^2$

$\qquad\quad = 45\,\text{cm}^2$

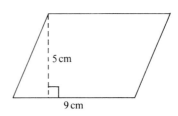

4   Trapezium

Area $= \frac{1}{2}(a + b)\,h$
          $= \frac{1}{2} \times (11 + 7) \times 8\,\text{cm}^2$
          $= \frac{1}{2} \times 18 \times 8\,\text{cm}^2 = 72\,\text{cm}^2$

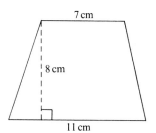

5   Circle

Find the circumference of a circle with radius 28 cm. Take π as $\frac{22}{7}$.
$C = 2\pi r$
$= 2 \times \dfrac{22}{\overset{}{\underset{7}{\cancel{7}}}} \times \overset{4}{\cancel{28}}\,\text{cm} = 176\,\text{cm}$

6   Find the area of a circle with radius 4 cm. Take π as 3.14.
$A = \pi r^2$
$= 3.14 \times 4 \times 4\,\text{cm}^2$
$= 50.24\,\text{cm}^2 \approx 50.2\,\text{cm}^2$

To find the length of an arc or the area of a sector of a circle

Length of arc $= \dfrac{\theta}{360} \times (\text{circumference}) = \dfrac{\theta}{360} \times 2\pi r$

Area of sector $= \dfrac{\theta}{360} \times (\text{area of circle}) = \dfrac{\theta}{360} \times \pi r^2$

$\theta°$ is the angle made by the arc or sector at the centre
of the circle. (θ is the Greek letter theta.)

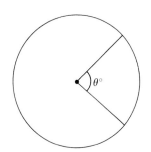

Example 7

The circle has centre O and radius 5 cm.
$\angle AOB = 36°$. Find the length of the arc AB
and the area of the sector AOB. Take π as
3.14.

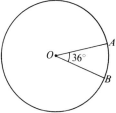

$\dfrac{\theta}{360} = \dfrac{36}{360} = \dfrac{1}{10}$, so the arc AB is $\dfrac{1}{10}$ of the circumference, and the area of the

sector AOB is $\dfrac{1}{10}$ of the area of the circle.

Circumference $= 2\pi r = 2 \times 3.14 \times 5\,\text{cm}$
Length of arc $AB = \frac{1}{10} \times 2 \times 3.14 \times 5\,\text{cm} = 3.14\,\text{cm}$
Area of circle $= \pi r^2 = 3.14 \times 5 \times 5\,\text{cm}^2$
Area of sector $AOB = \frac{1}{10} \times 3.14 \times 5 \times 5\,\text{cm}^2 = 7.85\,\text{cm}^2$

Exercise 12.1

1. Find the area of these figures.

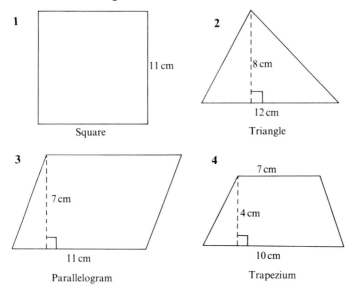

2. 1 Find the area and perimeter of a rectangular lawn 7 m long and 4 m wide.
   2 If the perimeter of a square is 36 cm, what is its area?
   3 A rectangle $9\frac{1}{2}$ cm by 6 cm is cut out of the corner of a square piece of paper of side 12 cm. What area is left? What is the perimeter of the piece that is left?
   4 There is a path 1 m wide all round a rectangular lawn of size 10 m by 8 m. Find the area of the path.

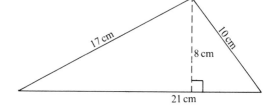

3. Find the area and the perimeter of this triangle.

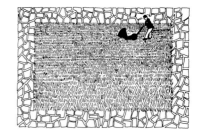

4. Find the lengths of the circumferences and the areas of these circles, giving answers corrected to 3 significant figures.

   1 Radius 14 cm. Take π as $\frac{22}{7}$
   2 Radius 6 cm. Take π as 3.14
   3 Diameter 2 m. Take π as 3.14

5. Find the area of this trapezium.

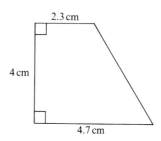

6. A room 8 m by $7\frac{1}{2}$ m contains a carpet 6 m by $5\frac{1}{2}$ m.

    1   What is the area of the uncarpeted floor?
    2   What is the cost of buying floor-covering for the uncarpeted floor at a cost of £4 per m²?

7. A floor 12 m long and 7.5 m wide is to be covered by tiles 30 cm square. How many tiles will be needed?

8. A square has a side of 1.7 cm and a circle has radius 1 cm. Which has the greater   1   perimeter,   2   area, and by how much? Take π as 3.14

9. Find the total area of the quadrilateral
    ABCD.

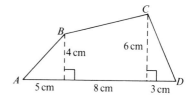

10. *O* is the centre of the circle.

    1   Find the length of the arc *AB* if the radius is 4.5 cm and ∠ *AOB* = 40°. Take π as 3.14
    2   Find the area of the sector *AOB* if the radius is 3 cm and ∠ *AOB* = 120°. Take π as 3.1

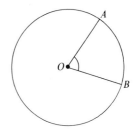

11. *ABCD* is a square. Find its area and the areas of the 3 corner triangles and hence find the area of Δ*AEF*.

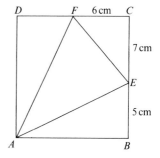

12. The circle is inscribed in a square of side 6 cm. Find the total shaded area. Take π as 3.14

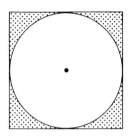

13. Draw these figures full-size

(a) a triangle base 5 cm, height 2.2 cm,
(b) a square side 2.4 cm,
(c) a parallelogram base 3.6 cm, height 1.4 cm,
(d) a circle radius 1.4 cm.
Decide by estimation which of these 4 shapes has **1** the largest area,
2 the smallest area. Calculate the areas to verify your estimate.

14. This quarter-circle (quadrant) has a radius of 7 cm. Find

1 the length of the arc AB,
2 the perimeter of the figure,
3 the area of the figure,
4 the area of $\triangle AOB$,
5 the area of the shaded segment. Take π as $\frac{22}{7}$

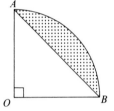

15. Find the areas of these figures, assuming that they are drawn on a grid of squares of edge 1 cm.

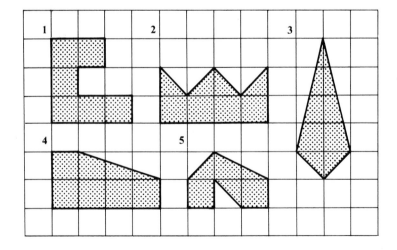

Pythagoras' Theorem

In a right-angled triangle the area of the square on the hypotenuse is equal to the sum of the areas of the squares on the other two sides.

$$a^2 = b^2 + c^2$$

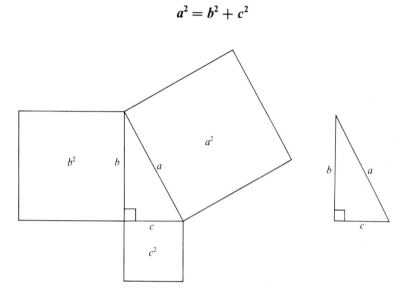

Examples

8   To find a

$$a^2 = b^2 + c^2$$
$$= 8^2 + 5^2$$
$$= 64 + 25 = 89$$
$$a = \sqrt{89}\,\text{cm}$$
$$= 9.4\,\text{cm (to the nearest mm)}$$

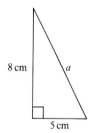

9   To find b

$$a^2 = b^2 + c^2$$
$$30^2 = b^2 + 10^2$$
$$900 = b^2 + 100$$
$$b^2 = 800$$
$$b = \sqrt{800}\,\text{cm}$$
$$= 28.3\,\text{cm (to the nearest mm)}$$

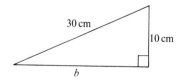

There are certain groups of numbers which give exact answers.

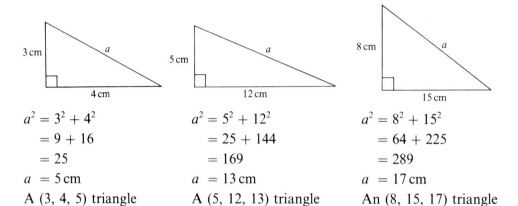

$a^2 = 3^2 + 4^2$

  $= 9 + 16$

  $= 25$

$a\ = 5\,\text{cm}$

A (3, 4, 5) triangle

$a^2 = 5^2 + 12^2$

  $= 25 + 144$

  $= 169$

$a\ = 13\,\text{cm}$

A (5, 12, 13) triangle

$a^2 = 8^2 + 15^2$

  $= 64 + 225$

  $= 289$

$a\ = 17\,\text{cm}$

An (8, 15, 17) triangle

There are many others, including multiples of these numbers such as 6, 8, 10; 10, 24, 26;   30, 40, 50; . . .

Exercise 12.2

1. Find the hypotenuse, a, in these triangles. (If the answer is not exact, give it correct to 1 decimal place.)

    1 $b = 5\,\text{cm},\quad c = 10\,\text{cm}$

    2 $b = 6\,\text{cm},\quad c = 8\,\text{cm}$

    3 $b = 1\,\text{cm},\quad c = 2\,\text{cm}$

    4 $b = 7\,\text{cm},\quad c = 4\,\text{cm}$

    5 $b = \sqrt{7}\,\text{cm},\ c = 3\,\text{cm}$

    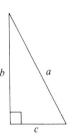

2. Find the third side in these triangles. (If the answer is not exact, give it correct to 1 decimal place.)

    1 $b = 8\,\text{cm},\quad a = 17\,\text{cm}$

    2 $b = 6\,\text{cm},\quad a = 9\,\text{cm}$

    3 $c = 24\,\text{cm},\ a = 25\,\text{cm}$

    4 $c = 5\,\text{cm},\quad a = 6\,\text{cm}$

    5 $c = \sqrt{7}\,\text{cm},\ a = \sqrt{11}\,\text{cm}$

3. **1** The longer side of a rectangular field is 40 m and a footpath crossing the field along a diagonal is 50 m long. Find the length of the shorter side of the field.

    2 Find the length of sides x and y.

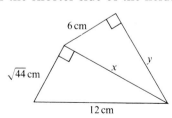

4. *AB* is a chord 24 cm long, in a circle centre *O*. The radius is 13 cm. Find the length of *OC*.

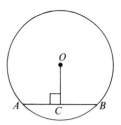

5. *O* is the centre of the circle. The tangent *PT* is 15 cm long. The radius is 8 cm. Find the length of *OP* and hence find the length of *AP*.

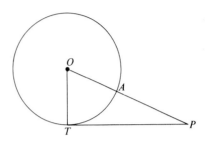

6. Find the lengths of

   1 *AB*,
   2 *BC*,
   3 *AC*.

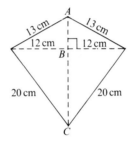

Solid figures

Cuboid Volume = length × breadth × height = lbh

Cube Volume = (length)^3 = l^3

Cylinder Volume = area of circular cross-section × height

$$= \pi \times (\text{radius})^2 \times \text{height} = \pi r^2 h$$

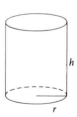

Prism Volume = area of cross-section × height

(The formula for the volume of a prism applies to any solid of uniform cross-section. The height is sometimes expressed as 'length')

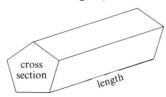

Surface areas

The surface area of a solid figure is the sum of the areas of all the faces.

A **cuboid** has 6 rectangular faces.

A **cylinder** has two circular ends and a curved surface.
The area of its curved surface = circumference × height = $2\pi rh$

Examples

10   Cuboid

   Volume = lbh

   $= 10 \times 8 \times 5 \,\text{cm}^3$

   $= 400 \,\text{cm}^3$

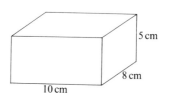

Total area of surfaces $= 2 \times [(10 \times 8) + (10 \times 5) + (8 \times 5)] \,\text{cm}^2$

$= 2 \times (80 + 50 + 40) \,\text{cm}^2 = 340 \,\text{cm}^2$

Total length of its edges $= 4 \times (10 + 8 + 5) \,\text{cm} = 92 \,\text{cm}$

11   Cylinder Radius 4 cm, height 10 cm. (Take π as 3.14.)

   Volume = $\pi r^2 h$

   $= 3.14 \times 4 \times 4 \times 10 \,\text{cm}^3$

   $= 502.4 \,\text{cm}^3 = 502 \,\text{cm}^3$ (to 3 sig. figs.)

12   Prism

   Area of triangle $= \frac{1}{2}bh$

   $= \frac{1}{2} \times 5 \times 6 \,\text{cm}^2 = 15 \,\text{cm}^2$

   Volume of prism = area of triangle × length

   $= 15 \times 10 \,\text{cm}^3 = 150 \,\text{cm}^3$

13   Cylinder Radius 5 cm, height 8 cm. (Take π as 3.14.)

   Curved surface area $= 2\pi rh$

   $= 2 \times 3.14 \times 5 \times 8 \,\text{cm}^2$

   $= 251.2 \,\text{cm}^2 = 251 \,\text{cm}^2$ (to 3 sig. figs.)

   Area of one end $= \pi r^2$

   $= 3.14 \times 5 \times 5 \,\text{cm}^2$

   $= 78.5 \,\text{cm}^2$

   Area of both ends $= 78.5 \times 2 \,\text{cm}^2 = 157 \,\text{cm}^2$

   Total surface area $= (251.2 + 157) \,\text{cm}^2$

   $= 408.2 \,\text{cm}^2 = 408 \,\text{cm}^2$ (to 3 sig. figs.)

Exercise 12.3

1. Find the volumes of these figures.

    1 A rectangular box 12 cm by 10 cm by 5 cm.
    2 A cube of edge 5 cm.
    3 A rectangular room 5 m by 4 m with height $2\frac{1}{2}$ m.
    4 A matchbox 7.5 cm by 4 cm by 1.5 cm.
    5 A case 50 cm by 30 cm by 18 cm.

2. Find the volumes of these cylinders.

    1 Radius 3 cm, height 7 cm. Take π as $\frac{22}{7}$
    2 Radius 2 cm, height 10 cm. Take π as 3.14
    3 Radius 10 cm, height 14 cm. Take π as $\frac{22}{7}$
    4 Radius 2.5 cm, height 4 cm. Take π as 3.14
    5 Radius 4 cm, height 5 cm. Take π as 3.14

3. The end of this prism is a right-angled triangle.

    1 Find the area of the triangle.
    2 Find the volume of the prism.

    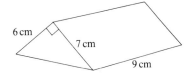

4. A room is 4 m wide, 3 m long and $2\frac{1}{2}$ m high. What is the total area of the four walls?

5. Some cylindrical tins have radius $3\frac{1}{2}$ cm and height 10 cm. Find the volume of a tin, taking π as $\frac{22}{7}$.
    The tins are packed in a rectangular box of length 28 cm, width 21 cm and height 10 cm. How many tins will fit in a box?

6. **1** If a large rectangular room has length 9 m, breadth 8 m and its volume is 360 m³, what is its height?
    2 What is the surface area of a solid cube whose volume is 27 cm³?
    3 A box measures 10 cm by 6 cm by 4 cm.

    (i) Find its volume.
    (ii) How many cubes of edge 2 cm will fit in the box?

    4 A rectangular tank is 4 m long, $2\frac{1}{2}$ m wide and 3 m deep. How many cubic metres of water does it contain when it is half-full?
    5 How many cubic metres of concrete will be needed to make a path 25 metres long, $1\frac{1}{2}$ metres wide, if the concrete is to be laid to a depth of 8 cm?

7. Find the volume of this triangular prism.

    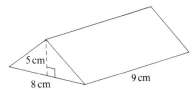

8. This sketch shows the side of a shed.

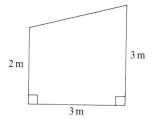

    1 Find its area.
    2 Find the volume of the shed, if it is 4 m long.

9. Find **1** the area of the curved surface, **2** the total surface area, of a cylinder with radius 2 cm, height 5 cm. Take π as 3.14.

10. This swimming pool is 1.8 m deep. Find the volume of water which it will hold.

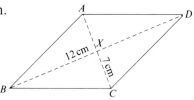

Exercise 12.4

1. How many tiles of size 9 inches square are needed to tile a wall 15 feet long to a height of 6 feet? (There are 12 inches in 1 foot.)
    If the tiles are sold in boxes of 24 how many boxes must be bought?

2. A parallelogram has base 8×10^{-2} m and height 6.5×10^{-2} m. Find its area in m^2, giving your answer in standard form.

3. In this rhombus, $AC = 7$ cm, $BD = 12$ cm.

    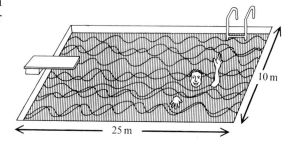

        1 What is the size of $\angle AXB$,
        2 what is the length of BX,
        3 what is the area of $\triangle ABC$?
        4 Find the area of the rhombus.

4. Draw a trapezium $ABCD$ with $AB // DC$ and $AB = 12$ cm, $\angle A = 50°$, $\angle B = 65°$, $AD = 6.2$ cm.
    By making further construction and measurement calculate the area of the trapezium.

5. Plot the points A, B, C and find the area of $\triangle ABC$ if

        1 A is $(-7, 1)$, B is $(3, 1)$, C is $(1, 6)$,
        2 A is $(-2, 5)$, B is $(1, -1)$, C is $(8, -1)$.

6. There is a circular running-track with diameter 35 m. How far has Peter run when he has made 10 complete circuits? Take π as $\frac{22}{7}$.

7. Construct a triangle ABC with $AB = 9$ cm, $BC = 7.5$ cm and $AC = 6.5$ cm. Construct and measure an additional line needed to calculate the area of $\triangle ABC$, and find this area.

8. $ABCD$ is a square of side 8 cm. Find the areas of the four triangles, and hence find the area of the quadrilateral $PQRS$.

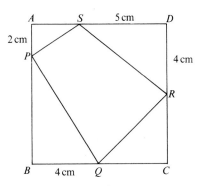

9. 1 Find the area of this parallelogram.
    2 Find the value of x.

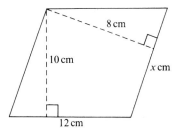

10. A circular pond of radius 18 metres is surrounded by a circular path of width 2 metres.

    1 Find the area of the pond.
    2 Find the area of the path. Take π as 3.14

11. Find 1 the area of the triangle
          2 the value of x

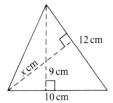

12. What fraction of the circle is the sector AOB? If the radius of the circle is 10 cm, find

    1 the length of the arc AB,
    2 the area of the sector AOB. Take π as 3.14

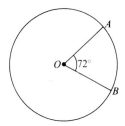

13. 1 Find the length of *AC*.
     2 Find the length of *DC*.
     3 Find the perimeter of *ABCD*.
     4 Find the area of *ABCD*.

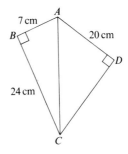

14. A patrol boat goes 8 km South, then 6 km East. Find how far it is from its starting point.

15. Plot the points $A(-1, 3)$ and $B(2, -1)$. Find the length of the line *AB*.

16. A gardener is making a rectangular concrete base for a greenhouse 5 feet wide and 12 feet long. Having measured out the edges he checks that it is truly rectangular by measuring both diagonals. How long should these diagonals be?

17. Find the lengths of

     1 *BD*, (using Δ*ABD*),
     2 *BC*,
     3 *AC*.

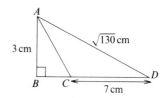

18. *AB* is a chord of length 10 cm, which moves in a circle centre *O*, radius 13 cm. *M* is the mid-point of *AB*.

     1 Find the distance *OM*.
     2 As the chord moves, what is the locus of *M*?

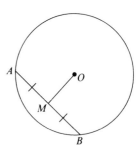

19. In the diagram, *O* is the centre of the circle and the radius is 8.5 cm. *BC* = 8 cm.

     1 What is the size of ∠*B*?
     2 What is the length of *AB*?
     3 What is the perimeter of Δ*ABC*?
     4 What is the area of Δ*ABC*?

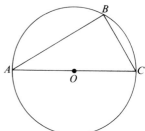

20. The circles are concentric, with centre O
    and radii 10 cm and 6 cm. Chord AB
    touches the smaller circle at C.

    1 What is the size of $\angle OCA$?
    2 Find the length of AC, and hence find
      the length of AB.

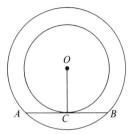

21. AOB is a sector of a circle centre O, radius
    8 cm with $\angle AOB = 135°$.
    Find, leaving your answers in terms of π,

    1 the length of the arc AB,
    2 the area of the sector AOB.

    If the sector is cut out and bent round with OA
    and OB joined, what shape will be made?

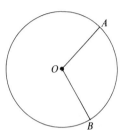

22. 6 cylindrical tins with radius 5 cm and height 10 cm are packed in a rectangular
    box with measurements 30 cm by 20 cm by 10 cm. The space around the tins is
    filled with sawdust for packing. What is the volume of the space to be filled with
    sawdust? Take π as 3.14

23. A child's sandpit is rectangular in shape, 2 m long and $1\frac{1}{2}$ m wide. What weight
    of sand is needed to fill it to a depth of 50 cm? (Assume 1 m^3 of sand weighs
    1500 kg.)

24. A cylinder, diameter 60 cm, contains water to a depth of 70 cm. This water is
    then poured into a rectangular tank 1.1 m long and 0.9 m wide. What will be the
    depth of water in this tank? Take π as $\frac{22}{7}$

25. A new road 4 km long and 25 m wide is to be constructed.

    1 How many square metres of land will be required?
    2 If the soil has to be removed to a depth of 30 cm, how many cubic metres of
      soil will have to be removed?

26. The internal dimensions of the base of a rectangular tank are 2 m by 1 m and it
    can contain water to a depth of 80 cm. How long will it take to fill the tank by
    means of an inlet pipe delivering water at the rate of 50 litres per minute?

27. Ice 10 cm thick covered a circular pond whose surface area is 300 m^2. Find the
    weight of the ice, if 1 m^3 of ice weighs 920 kg.

28. A square sheet of cardboard has sides length 17 cm.
    Out of each corner a square of side 4 cm is cut, and
    the flaps remaining are turned up to form an open
    box of depth 4 cm. Find the volume of the box.

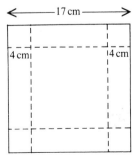

13 | *Further Algebra*

Rules for removing brackets

$$a + (b + c) = a + b + c$$
$$a + (b - c) = a + b - c$$
$$a - (b + c) = a - b - c$$
$$a - (b - c) = a - b + c$$

Note that the minus sign immediately in front of the bracket changes any signs inside the bracket when the bracket is removed.

Examples

$$5(x + 2y) + 2(x - 8y) = 5x + 10y + 2x - 16y = 7x - 6y$$
$$4(x + y) - (3x + 5y) = 4x + 4y - 3x - 5y = x - y$$
$$3(2x + y) - 2(3x - y) = 6x + 3y - 6x + 2y = 5y$$

Fractions

Reduction

Example 1

Simplify $\dfrac{3x^2}{9x}$

$$\frac{3x^2}{9x} = \frac{\cancel{3} \times \cancel{x} \times x}{\cancel{9} \times \cancel{x}}_{3}$$

Cancel by 3 and by x

$$= \frac{x}{3}$$

Addition and subtraction

Examples

2 $\dfrac{a}{6} + \dfrac{2a}{3}$

The lowest number into which 6 and 3 both divide is 6, so change $\dfrac{2a}{3}$ into $\dfrac{4a}{6}$

$$= \frac{a + 4a}{6} = \frac{5a}{6}$$

3 $\dfrac{2b}{5} - \dfrac{b}{4}$

The lowest number into which 5 and 4 both divide is 20, so change $\dfrac{2b}{5}$ into $\dfrac{8b}{20}$ and $\dfrac{b}{4}$ into $\dfrac{5b}{20}$

$$= \frac{8b - 5b}{20} = \frac{3b}{20}$$

Multiplication

Example 4

$$\frac{3a}{5c} \times \frac{10c^2}{a}$$

$$= \frac{3 \times \cancel{a}}{\cancel{5} \times \cancel{c}} \times \frac{\overset{2}{\cancel{10}} \times \cancel{c} \times c}{\cancel{a}} \qquad \text{Cancel by 5, } a \text{ and } c$$

$$= \frac{6c}{1} = 6c$$

Division

Example 5

$$\frac{3x^2}{y^2} \div \frac{x}{y} \qquad \text{Instead of dividing by } \frac{x}{y}, \text{ multiply by } \frac{y}{x}$$

$$= \frac{3 \times x \times \cancel{x}}{y \times \cancel{y}} \times \frac{\cancel{y}}{\cancel{x}} \qquad \text{Cancel by } x \text{ and } y$$

$$= \frac{3x}{y}$$

Equations involving fractions

Examples

6     $\dfrac{3x}{4} = 10$ Multiply both sides by 4

      $3x = 40$ Divide both sides by 3

      $x = 13\frac{1}{3}$

As a check, LHS $= \frac{3}{4} \times 13\frac{1}{3} = \frac{3}{4} \times \frac{40}{3} = 10$. The two sides are both 10, so the equation checks.

7     $\dfrac{2x + 3}{5} = 4$ Multiply both sides by 5

      $2x + 3 = 20$ Subtract 3 from both sides

         $2x = 17$ Divide both sides by 2

           $x = 8\frac{1}{2}$

As a check, LHS $= \dfrac{2x + 3}{5} = \dfrac{(2 \times 8\frac{1}{2}) + 3}{5} = \dfrac{17 + 3}{5} = \dfrac{20}{5} = 4$

The two sides are both 4, so the equation checks.

8     $\dfrac{x}{4} + \dfrac{x}{6} = 15$ Multiply both sides by 12, because 12 is the lowest number into which 4 and 6 both divide.

$$3x + 2x = 180 \qquad \dfrac{x}{4} \text{ multipled by 12 is } 3x, \ \dfrac{x}{6} \text{ multiplied by 12 is } 2x.$$

$$5x = 180$$

$$x = 36$$

As a check, LHS $= \dfrac{x}{4} + \dfrac{x}{6} = \dfrac{36}{4} + \dfrac{36}{6} = 9 + 6 = 15$. The two sides are both 15, so the equation checks.

Exercise 13.1

1. Simplify

    1 $2(a + 2b) + (a - b)$ **6** $5(p - 2q - r) + 3(p - q + 2r)$

    2 $4(c - d) - 3(c + 2d)$ **7** $3(s + 8) - 4(2s - 5)$

    3 $3(2e + f) + 2(e - 2f)$ **8** $x(x - 4) + 3(x - 2)$

    4 $(g - h) - 4(g + 2h)$ **9** $x(2x + 3) - 4(3x - 1)$

    5 $2j + 3k - (j - 3k)$ **10** $x(x^2 + 1) - x^2(x + 1)$

2. Solve the equations

    1 $3(2x - 5) - 4(x + 7) = 13$ **6** $4(x - 4) - 2(x + 7) = 0$

    2 $5(x + 3) + (x - 5) = 9$ **7** $22 - 5x - (x + 10) = 0$

    3 $2(5 + x) - 3(6 - x) = 42$ **8** $2(3x - 4) + (x + 8) = 2(x - 4)$

    4 $5(x - 1) + 3(x - 4) = -11$ **9** $3(x + 2) + 2(x - 4) = x - 3(x + 3)$

    5 $4(x + 3) - 2(x - 9) = 24$ **10** $x(2x + 5) - (x - 2) = 2x(x + 5)$

3. Simplify

    1 $\dfrac{12a^2}{3a}$ **2** $\dfrac{6c^2}{54c}$ **3** $\dfrac{25e^3}{15e}$

4. Simplify

    1 $\dfrac{3a}{8} + \dfrac{a}{6}$ **4** $\dfrac{d}{14} + \dfrac{3d}{7}$

    2 $\dfrac{10b}{3} - \dfrac{2b}{9}$ **5** $\dfrac{3e}{2} - \dfrac{4e}{3}$

    3 $\dfrac{4c}{15} + \dfrac{5c}{6}$

5. Simplify

1 $\dfrac{8a}{15b} \times \dfrac{5b}{4}$ **4** $\dfrac{2g^2}{5} \div \dfrac{4g}{15}$

2 $\dfrac{3}{8b} \div \dfrac{15}{16b^2}$ **5** $\dfrac{6pq}{5} \times \dfrac{25q}{18p}$

3 $\dfrac{3c}{10e} \times \dfrac{2e^2}{9}$

6. Solve the equations

1 $\dfrac{2x}{3} = 20$ **5** $\dfrac{4}{5}x - \dfrac{1}{10}x = 21$ **8** $\dfrac{2x}{9} - \dfrac{x}{6} = -\dfrac{1}{3}$

2 $\dfrac{3x - 4}{7} = 8$ **6** $\dfrac{3x}{4} = -15$ **9** $\dfrac{2(x + 1)}{3} = 1$

3 $\dfrac{5x + 1}{6} = 11$ **7** $\dfrac{5x - 7}{3} = -1$ **10** $\dfrac{x + 1}{8} = \dfrac{2x - 3}{4}$

4 $\dfrac{x}{2} + \dfrac{2x}{3} = 14$

Transformation of formulae

Examples

9 If $ax + b = c$, find x in terms of a, b, c.

$$ax = c - b \qquad \text{Subtract } b \text{ from both sides}$$
$$\qquad\qquad\qquad\quad \text{Divide both sides by } a$$
$$x = \dfrac{c - b}{a}$$

10 If $y = \dfrac{x^2}{2}$, find x in terms of y, if x is a positive number.

Multiply both sides by 2

$$2y = x^2$$
$$x^2 = 2y \qquad \text{Take the square root of both sides}$$
$$x = \sqrt{2y}$$

11   If $I = \dfrac{PRT}{100}$, find T in terms of I, P, R.

$$100I = PRT$$

Multiply both sides by 100
Divide both sides by PR

$$\frac{100I}{PR} = T$$

i.e. $T = \dfrac{100I}{PR}$

12   If $F = \frac{9}{5}C + 32$, find C in terms of F.

Take 32 from both sides

$$F - 32 = \tfrac{9}{5}C$$

Multiply both sides by 5

$$5(F - 32) = 9C$$

Divide both sides by 9

$$\tfrac{5}{9}(F - 32) = C$$

i.e. $C = \tfrac{5}{9}(F - 32)$

Common factors

Examples

13 $6xy + 9xz = 3x(2y + 3z)$ Both terms divide by 3 and by x so $3x$ is a common factor.
Dividing $6xy$ by $3x$ leaves $2y$ and dividing $9xz$ by $3x$ leaves $3z$.

14 $x^2 - x = x(x - 1)$ Both terms divide by x so x is a common factor.
Dividing x^2 by x leaves x and dividing x by x leaves 1.

15 $6x^3 + 4x^2 + 2x = 2x(3x^2 + 2x + 1)$ All terms divide by 2 and by x so $2x$ is a common factor

16   Use factors to find the value of $(2.1 \times 6.9) + (2.1 \times 3.1)$.

(2.1 is a common factor.)

$$(2.1 \times 6.9) + (2.1 \times 3.1) = 2.1 \times (6.9 + 3.1)$$
$$= 2.1 \times 10 = 21$$

Exercise 13.2

1.   **1**   If $ax - b = c$, find x in terms of a, b, c.

     2   If $E = 3v^2$, find v in terms of E, if v is a positive number.

     3   If $v = u + at$, find t in terms of u, v, a.

     4   If $s = 5t^2$, find t in terms of s, if t is a positive number.

     5   If $area = length \times breadth$, find $length$ in terms of $area$ and $breadth$.

     6   If $A = P + RP$, find R in terms of A and P.

     7   If $t = 180n - 360$, find n in terms of t.

     8   If $speed = \dfrac{distance}{time}$, find $distance$ in terms of $speed$ and $time$.

     9   If $3y = 2x - 4$, find x in terms of y.

     10   If $P = \dfrac{V^2}{R}$, find V in terms of P and R, if V is a positive number.

2. Factorise the following:

   1 $14x - 21y$ **5** $15x^2 - 25x$ **8** $9 + 3x^3$

   2 $3xy + 9yz$ **6** $t^2 + t$ **9** $2x^2 + 2xy$

   3 $2\pi a - 2\pi b$ **7** $a^2 + ab - 2ac$ **10** $4b - 2$

   4 $6a - 3b + 9c$

3. Use factors to find the value of

   1 $(3.5 \times 1.3) + (3.5 \times 8.7)$

   2 $(96 \times 2.04) + (4 \times 2.04)$

   3 $(12.9 \times 3.1) - (2.9 \times 3.1)$

   4 $(15.3 \times 5.6) - (15.3 \times 4.6)$

   5 $3.7^2 + (3.7 \times 6.3)$

Curves

Exercise 13.3

1. **To draw the graph of $y = x^2$**
This is not a straight line and several points must be plotted.
Copy and complete this table showing the connection between x and y.

x	-4	-3	-2	-1	0	1	2	3	4
$y\ (=x^2)$	16	9				1			

Draw the x-axis from -4 to 4 and the y-axis from 0 to 16.
Plot these 9 points and join them with a smooth curve.
This shape is called a parabola.

2. The graph of $y = 4x^2$.
    Copy and complete this table of values.

x	-4	-3	-2	-1	0	1	2	3	4
x^2	16								
$y(=4x^2)$	64								

Draw axes with x from -4 to 4 and y from 0 to 70.
Plot the points of the table on the graph, e.g. $(-4, 64)$, etc.
Two extra points to plot are $(3.5, 49)$ and $(-3.5, 49)$.
Join the points with a smooth curve.
This curve is also a parabola. The y-axis is an axis of symmetry of the curve. What are the coordinates of the minimum point on the curve?
By drawing dotted lines on your graph, find the values of x when $y = 40$, correct to 1 decimal place.
This solves the equation $40 = 4x^2$, i.e. $x^2 = 10$. The two solutions are the values of $\sqrt{10}$ and $-\sqrt{10}$, so you can check them by using your calculator.

Other graphs

3. The graph of $y = \dfrac{18}{x}$.

Copy and complete this table of values.

x	-4	-3	-2	-1	1	2	3	4
$y\left(=\dfrac{18}{x}\right)$	$-4\frac{1}{2}$	-6						

$x = 0$ has been omitted from the table because y does not exist when $x = 0$.
Draw axes with x from -4 to 4 and y from -30 to 30.
Plot the points on your graph. Find y when $x = 0.6$ and when $x = -0.6$ and add these two points.
The positive values of x give one part of the graph and the negative values give another part. Draw the graph.
This curve (which is in two parts) is called a rectangular hyperbola.

4. The positive part of $y = \dfrac{1}{x}$.

Draw the x and y axes from 0 to 10, using the same scale on both axes.
Copy and complete this table of values, using your calculator where necessary, and giving values correct to 1 decimal place.

x	0.1	0.2	0.3	0.4	0.5	0.6	0.8	1	2	3	4	5	6	8	10
$y\left(=\dfrac{1}{x}\right)$	10	5													

Plot the points on your graph. Two extra points to help you are (0.15, 6.7) and (0.125, 8).
Join the points with a smooth curve.

Exercise 13.4

1. Simplify

    1 $4(x - 4) - 3(x - 5)$ 4 $8(1 + x) + 12(1 - x)$

    2 $x - 2(x + y) + 3(x - y)$ 5 $4(3x - 1) - 3(x + 2)$

    3 $2(1 + 3x) - 3(5 - x)$

2. Simplify 1 $\dfrac{3xy \times 4xy}{xy}$ 2 $\dfrac{2xy}{3} + \dfrac{xy}{4}$ 3 $\dfrac{1}{3xy} \div \dfrac{1}{4xy}$

3. Simplify 1 $5a^7 \times 4a^6$ 2 $27b^5 \div 9b$

4. Solve the equations:

    1 $\dfrac{3x}{2} + 3 = x$ 4 $\dfrac{5x + 7}{9} = 3$

    2 $3(4x + 2) = 2(2x - 1)$ 5 $\dfrac{5(x - 4)}{9} = 10$

    3 $\tfrac{5}{6}x - \tfrac{3}{4}x = \tfrac{1}{8}$

5. If $y = 7x - 4$ and $z = 5 - 2x$, for what value of x is $2y - z = 0$?

6. 1 I think of a number, divide it by 3 and then add 5. The result is 12. What was the original number?

    2 I think of a number. Two-thirds of this number is 15 more than one-quarter of the number. What is the number?

7. Eric spends half his pocket money on the day he gets it, and one-third on the following day. This leaves him with 50 p. How much pocket money does he get?

8. 1 If $a = 180n + 360$, find n in terms of a.

    2 If $s = a + ar$, find r in terms of s and a.

    3 If $b = 2\sqrt{x}$, find x in terms of b.

    4 If $C = \frac{5}{9}(F - 32)$, find F in terms of C.

    5 If $s = \frac{n}{2}(a + l)$, find n in terms of s, a and l.

9. Factorise the following:

    1 $5x + 15y$ 4 $6x^3 + 12$

    2 $3x^2 - 6x$ 5 $x^3 + xy$

    3 $4ab - 12bc$

10. If $V = \frac{1}{6}x^2h$,   1 find the value of h when $V = 50$ and $x = 4$,   2 find x in terms of V and h, where x is positive.

11. If $\frac{a}{b} = \frac{b}{c}$, where a, b and c are positive, find   1 c in terms of a and b,

    2 b in terms of a and c.

12. Here is a table of values connecting x and y which satisfy the equation $y = ax^2$. Find the value of a.

x	-1	$\frac{1}{2}$	2
y	2	$\frac{1}{2}$	8

13. Factorise $n^2 + n$ and explain why the value of this expression is always even, if n is any positive integer.

14. Factorise, and hence find the value of the following.

    1 $(24.3 \times 12.1) - (24.3 \times 11.1)$

    2 $(8.67 \times 16.9) + (1.33 \times 16.9)$

    3 $97^2 + (3 \times 97)$

    4 $(2 \times 3.142 \times 12.1) - (2 \times 3.142 \times 7.1)$

    5 $68^2 - (24 \times 68) + (56 \times 68)$

15. A paddock is rectangular in shape with width x metres and it is three times as long as it is wide. Find an equation connecting y with x, where y square metres is its area.
    Draw axes for x from 0 to 50 and for y from 0 to 8000.
    Make a table of values of x and y for $x = 0, 10, 20, 30, 40, 50$, and draw the curve representing the equation.
    Use the graph to find the measurements of the paddock when its area is 6000 m², giving them to the nearest metre.

16.   Rectangular plots of land of area $600\,m^2$ are to be sold.
      If the length of a plot is x m and the width is y m, express y in terms of x.
      Draw axes for x and y from 0 to 60. Plot the corresponding values of x and y
      for $x = 10, 15, 20, 30, 40, 50, 60$.   Join the points with a curve.
      If the perimeter of a plot is 120 m, find another equation connecting y and x, and
      by drawing a straight line on the graph find the measurements of the plot.

PUZZLES

36.   How many times in 12 hours do the hands of a clock point in the same direction?

37.   A ship in the harbour has a ladder with 12 rungs, each 30 cm apart, hanging over the side.
      At low tide 4 rungs are covered by the sea. If the tide rises at 40 cm per hour, how many
      rungs will be covered 3 hours later?

38.   Draw 7 regular hexagons of the same size on cardboard and cut them out.
      Join the 3 pairs of opposite points on each hexagon to divide the hexagon into 6 equal
      triangles.
      Colour these triangles as follows, going in clockwise order round the hexagon.
      1st hexagon: Red, orange, yellow, green, blue, purple.
      2nd hexagon: Red, orange, yellow, green, purple, blue.
      3rd hexagon: Red, orange, purple, yellow, green, blue.
      4th hexagon: Red, green, purple, orange, yellow, blue.
      5th hexagon: Red, green, orange, yellow, blue, purple.
      6th hexagon: Red, green, orange, blue, purple, yellow.
      7th hexagon: Red, blue, green, orange, purple, yellow.
      Now arrange the hexagons with one in the centre and the other six around it, so that all
      hexagons meet each other edge to edge. Where two edges meet, their triangles should
      have the same colour.

39.   A shop sells one brand of chocolate bars which are priced at, small, 16p; medium,
      23p and large 39p; and a second brand where the prices are, small, 17p; medium, 24p and
      large 40p. A customer buys some of these bars of chocolate and they cost him exactly
      £1. What does he buy?

40.   In this sentence, each letter of the alphabet has been substituted by another letter chosen
      at random (the same one each time that letter occurs). Can you decode the sentence, and
      say whether it is a true statement?
      XWN   DJKSUN   RV   XWN   WQORXNVKDN   RL   S   UCIWX-SVIZNF
      XUCSVIZN   CD   NJKSZ   XR   XWN   DKP   RL   XWN   DJKSUND   RV
      XWN   XER   SFMSTNVX   DCFND.

14 Grouped statistical data

If the range of data is wide we can put it into convenient groups, called class intervals.

Example 1

The distribution of examination marks of 120 students.

Mark	0–9	10–19	20–29	30–39	40–49	50–59	60–69
f (number of students)	5	14	22	29	27	19	4

The data can be represented by a histogram.

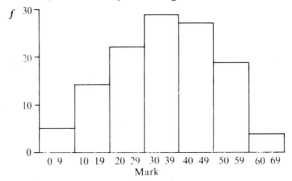

The **modal class** is the class interval which includes most students, here it is the class 30–39 marks.

To find the mean mark we assume that each student has the mark corresponding to the centre of the class interval in which it lies, e.g. the centre of the marks 0–9 is 4.5, of 10–19 is 14.5, and so on. Of the 14 students who got between 10 and 19 marks, some probably got less than 14.5 marks and some more, so 14.5 is the best estimate we can make.

Use the formula $\bar{x} = \dfrac{\Sigma\, fx}{\Sigma\, f}$, taking x as the value at the centre of the interval.

marks	f	x centre of interval	fx
0–9	5	4.5	22.5
10–19	14	14.5	203.0
20–29	22	24.5	539.0
30–39	29	34.5	1000.5
40–49	27	44.5	1201.5
50–59	19	54.5	1035.5
60–69	4	64.5	258.0
	120		4260.0

$$\bar{x} = \frac{\Sigma\, fx}{\Sigma\, f}$$

$$= \frac{4260}{120}$$

$$= 35.5$$

If you are using your calculator to find the numbers in the *fx* column, add them into the memory as you go along, then to get the total you only have to press the 'recall memory' key. For some calculators you may be able to add them up directly. But it is advisable to do a check in case you have missed out some. Does the answer **look** right? Anything above 69 is bound to be wrong. Looking at the distribution we would make a rough estimate that the average mark is between 30 and 39 marks.

Example 2

The lengths of leaves from a bush, using a sample of 60 leaves.

length in cm	5.0–5.4	5.5–5.9	6.0–6.4	6.5–6.9	7.0–7.4	7.5–7.9
f	2	12	20	15	8	3

Measurements in the 1st class will include lengths from 4.95 to 5.45 cm, in the 2nd class from 5.45 to 5.95 cm, and so on.
The centre of the 1st class interval is 5.2 cm, of the 2nd one is 5.7 cm, and so on. In the histogram, since the measurements are continuous, we can label the edges of the intervals, or we can label the centres of the intervals, or we can label the actual intervals as in example **1**.

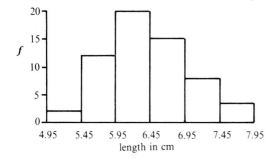
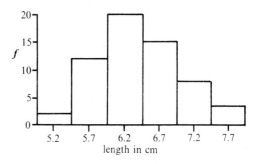

The modal class is the class interval from 6.0 to 6.4 cm. (Actually from 5.95 to 6.45 cm.)

To find the mean length of leaf, copy and complete this table.

x centre of interval	f	fx
5.2	2	10.4
5.7	12	
6.2		
6.7		
7.2		
7.7		
	60	

$$\bar{x} = \frac{\Sigma\,fx}{\Sigma\,f}$$

$$= \frac{\cdots}{60}\ \text{cm}$$

$$= \ldots \text{cm}$$

Give your answer to 1 decimal place. (The correct answer is 6.4 cm.)

Age distributions

Ages are usually given in completed years so in a table such as this a child who has not quite reached the age of 10 years will be included in the 5–9 class interval. Thus the class interval is actually from 5 years to 10 years. A child is included in the 2nd class if he has had his 10th birthday but not his 15th, and the class interval is from 10 years to 15 years.

age in years	f
5–9	2
10–14	3
15–19	5

Compare this with a table for weight.
Weights are usually measured to the nearest kg so a weight of 9.7 kg will go in the 2nd class. But the 1st class can also include weights over 4.5 kg. So the class intervals are 4.5–9.5 kg, 9.5–14.5 kg, 14.5–19.5 kg.

weight in kg	f
5–9	2
10–14	3
15–19	5

Histograms

Ages

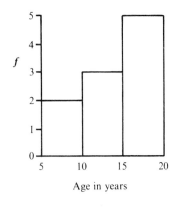

Age in years

Weights

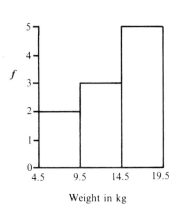

Weight in kg

Exercise 14.1

Draw histograms of the following frequency distributions.

1. Heights of 60 men.

Height in cm	168–170	171–173	174–176	177–179	180–182	183–185
Number of men	2	4	8	13	14	9

Height in cm	186–188	189–191
Number of men	7	3

2. Ages of children in a club.

Age (in completed years)	11	12	13	14	15
Number of children	8	10	6	4	2

3.   Lengths of 30 leaves.

Length in cm	6.0	6.5	7.0	7.5	8.0	8.5
Number of leaves	1	5	7	11	4	2

4.   Times taken by 100 children to travel to school.

Time in minutes	0–5	5–10	10–15	15–20	20–25	25–30
Number of children	3	15	27	34	19	2

5.   Find the mean of the heights given in question 1, using the centres of intervals of the classes, which are
169, 172, 175, 178, 181, 184, 187 and 190 cm respectively.

6.   Find the mean of the ages given in question 2, using the centres of intervals of the ages, which are
11.5, 12.5, 13.5, 14.5 and 15.5 years respectively.
By multiplying the decimal part of your answer by 12, change the answer into years and months, giving it to the nearest month.

7.   Find the mean length of leaf for the data given in question 3. The lengths given are the centres of intervals for the classes.

8.   Find the mean time taken by the children to travel to school for the times given in question 4. Use the centres of intervals of the times, which are
2.5, 7.5, 12.5, 17.5, 22.5 and 27.5 minutes respectively.

9.   State the modal classes of the frequency distributions of questions 1 to 4.

10. The weights of a group of children are given in this frequency distribution.

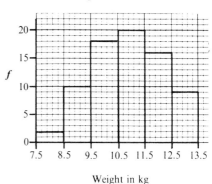

Weight in kg

  1 How many children are there altogether?
  2 What is the modal class?
  3 Find the mean weight, using the centres of intervals, which are 8, 9, 10, 11, 12 and 13 kg respectively.
  4 What fraction of the children weigh less than 9.5 kg?

Exercise 14.2

1.   The heights of 40 plants, given to the nearest cm, are as follows:

Height in cm	3	4	5	6	7	8
Number of plants	1	7	10	12	8	2

  1 Draw a histogram of this distribution.
  2 Find the mean of the distribution.

2. The heights of 80 students are as follows:

Height in cm	150–154	155–159	160–164	165–169	170–174	175–179
Number of students	3	4	9	16	18	17

Height in cm	180–184	185–189
Number of students	7	6

  1 What is the modal class of the distribution?
  2 Draw a histogram of the distribution.
  3 Find the mean height of the students, using the centres of intervals for the heights. These are 152, 157, 162, 167, 172, 177, 182 and 187 cm respectively.

3. The marks of 40 children in a test were as follows:

Mark	0–2	3–5	6–8	9–11	12–14	15–17	18–20
Number of children	4	3	5	7	10	6	5

  1 What is the modal class of this distribution?
  2 Draw a histogram of the distribution.
  3 Find the mean mark, using the centres of intervals for the marks. These are 1, 4, 7, 10, 13, 16 and 19 respectively.

4. The weights of 120 men are as follows:

Weight in kg	60–	65–	70–	75–	80–	85–90
Number of men	4	18	36	50	10	2

(The 1st class includes weights between 60 and 65 kg, and the centre of interval is 62.5 kg, and so on.)

  1 What is the modal class of the distribution?
  2 What is the centre of interval of this class?
  3 Draw a histogram of the distribution.
  4 Find the mean weight.

5. The ages of 100 cars in a survey are as follows:

Age in years	0–2	2–4	4–6	6–8	8–10	10–12	12–14
Number of cars	16	23	24	17	12	7	1

(The 1st class includes cars up to just under 2 years old, the centre of interval is 1 year. The 2nd class includes cars from 2 years to just under 4 years old, the centre of interval is 3 years; and so on.)

  1 What is the modal class?
  2 Draw a histogram of the distribution.
  3 Find the mean age of the cars in the survey.

6. The lengths of 60 leaves on a plant.

Length in cm	7–9	10–12	13–15	16–18	19–21
Number of leaves	4	16	24	13	3

  1 Find the mean length of the leaves, using the centres of intervals for the lengths. These are 8, 11, 14, 17 and 20 cm respectively.
  2 Draw a histogram of the distribution

7. The weekly wages of 30 women.

    Wage (to nearest £20)   60   80   100   120
    Number of women   3   7   15   5

    (The 1st class includes women whose wages are between £50 and £70, and so on.)

    1   Draw a histogram of the distribution.
    2   Find the mean wage. The amounts given are at the centres of intervals for the classes.

8. A machine is set to cut metal into 40 cm lengths. 60 bars cut by the machine had lengths as follows:

    Length in cm   39.7   39.8   39.9   40.0   40.1   40.2   40.3
    Number of bars   1   6   15   17   14   5   2

    Find the mean length of the bars.

9. 30 students were asked in a survey to say how many hours they spent watching television in the previous week. Their answers, in hours to the nearest hour, are as follows:

    12   20   13   15   22   3   6   24   20   15   9   12   5   6   8
    30   7   12   14   25   2   6   12   20   20   18   3   18   8   9

    Tally these data in classes 1–5, 6–10, 11–15, etc.
    Draw a histogram of the distribution.

10. The marks of 25 children in an examination were as follows:

    68   78   64   67   73   94   69   86   62   67   82   79   61
    87   71   81   79   82   77   73   81   84   74   76   66

    Tally these data in classes 60–64, 65–69, 70–74, etc.
    Draw a histogram of the grouped distribution.

11. The histogram shows the times taken by a group of boys to run a race.

    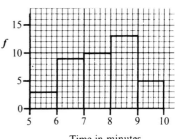

    1   How many boys were there altogether?
    2   What fraction of boys took less than 7 minutes?
    3   What is the modal class of the distribution?
    4   Find the mean time taken by the boys, using the centres of intervals 5.5, 6.5, 7.5, 8.5 and 9.5 minutes for the times.

12. **Collect other data** suitable for grouping, finding means and drawing histograms. Some suggestions are:

The heights of students in your year-group.

The times students spend on their homework.

The ages of cars in a car park. (Estimates based on the registration letter.)

The weekly amounts spent by students on snacks, sweets, drinks, etc.

The distances people travel to work.

The length of time of phone calls.

Guesses from people of the length of a line, the weight of an object or the number of sweets in a jar.

PUZZLES

41. **The 3, 4, 5 problem**

See how many whole numbers you can represent using the figures 3, 4 and 5 once each. Make further rules, such as:

In every number 3 and 4 and 5 must all be used.

Signs such as $+$ $\times$ $-$ $\div$ $\sqrt{}$ and brackets can be used.

Are you going to allow the sign ! It is called 'factorial'.

5! means $5 \times 4 \times 3 \times 2 \times 1$ which equals 120. $4! = 4 \times 3 \times 2 \times 1 = 24$ and $3! = 3 \times 2 \times 1 = 6$.

Are you going to allow decimals such as .5, and recurring decimals such as .3̇ which equals $\frac{1}{3}$?

Examples: $23 = (5 \times 4) + 3$,

$\qquad\qquad 90 = 5! - 4! - 3!$

$$10 = \frac{\sqrt{4} + 3}{.5}$$

Perhaps you had better begin with numbers up to 100, but you will not be able to represent all of them.

42. A weighty problem. Which would you rather have, half a tonne of 10 pence coins or a tonne of 5 pence coins?

43. How many squares are there on a chessboard?

44. Decode this bill. Each capital letter stands for a figure and each figure stands for the corresponding letter.

R	6480	at	LI pence each	UI
I	6489520	at	BI pence each	UI
L	372430	at	BN pence each	RP
L	3711430	at	C pence each	BN
				£L.SE

15 *Percentages*

Percentages

'Per cent' means 'per hundred', so 17% means $\dfrac{17}{100}$ or 0.17.

Example 1

Express $87\frac{1}{2}\%$ as a fraction.

$$87\tfrac{1}{2}\% = \frac{87\frac{1}{2}}{100} = \frac{175}{200} = \frac{7}{8}$$

Example 2

Express $63\frac{1}{4}\%$ as a decimal.

$$63\tfrac{1}{4}\% = \frac{63\frac{1}{4}}{100} = \frac{63.25}{100} = 0.6325$$

To change a fraction or decimal to a percentage, multiply by 100 and write the % sign.

Example 3

$$\frac{5}{6} = \frac{5}{6} \times 100\% = \frac{250}{3}\% = 83\tfrac{1}{3}\%$$

$$0.575 = 0.575 \times 100\% = 57.5\%$$

Example 4

Find 24% of 60 cm, and find $37\frac{1}{2}\%$ of 4 litres.

$$24\% \text{ of } 60\,\text{cm} = \frac{24}{100} \times 60\,\text{cm} = \frac{144}{10}\,\text{cm} = 14.4\,\text{cm}$$

$$37\tfrac{1}{2}\% \text{ of } 4 \text{ litres} = \frac{37\frac{1}{2}}{100} \times 4\,l = \frac{75}{200} \times 4\,l = 1.5 \text{ litres}$$

Example 5

What percentage is 34 g of 2 kg?

(First find what fraction 34 g is of 2 kg, then change this fraction to a percentage.)

$$\frac{34\,g}{2\,kg} = \frac{34\,g}{2000\,g} = \frac{34}{2000} \times 100\% = 1.7\%$$

Example 6

Increase £50 by 15%.

The new amount will be $(100 + 15)\%$, i.e. 115% of £50.

$$115\% \text{ of } £50 = £\frac{115}{100} \times 50 = £57\tfrac{1}{2} = £57.50$$

(If using a calculator, find 1.15×50.)
(Alternatively, you could find 15% of £50, i.e. £7.50, and then add this to the original £50, making £57.50.)

Example 7

Decrease £900 by 12%.

The new amount will be $(100 - 12)\%$, i.e. 88% of £900.

$$88\% \text{ of } £900 = £\frac{88}{100} \times 900 = £792$$

(If using a calculator, find 0.88×900.)
(Alternatively, you could find 12% of £900, i.e. £108, and then subtract this from the original £900, leaving £792.)

Profit and Loss

Example 8

A dealer buys an article for £75 and sells it for £90. What is his percentage profit?

Percentage profit is always based on the cost price, unless otherwise stated. Here the profit is £15 on a cost price of £75.

$$\% \text{ profit} = \frac{15}{75} \times 100\% = 20\%$$

Example 9

A dealer buys an article, adds 30% to the cost price for his profit, and marks the selling price at £6.50. What did the article cost him?

The selling price is $(100 + 30)\%$, i.e. 130% of the cost price.
130% of the cost price is £6.50
10% of the cost price is 50 p
100% of the cost price is £5.00
The article cost him £5.00.

You can find this answer using your calculator by dividing £6.50 by 1.3 since this is the same as $(6.50 \div 13) \times 10$.

Simple Interest

Example 10

If £600 is invested at 8% per annum for 4 years, what is the Simple Interest?

Every £100 invested gains £8 interest per year.
So £600 invested gains £48 interest per year.
£600 invested for 4 years gains $£48 \times 4 = £192$.
The Simple Interest is £192.

This can also be worked out using the formula

$$I = \frac{PRT}{100}$$ where I is the Simple Interest
                                    P is the Principal, (the money invested)
                                    R is the rate per cent (per annum)
                                    T is the time (in years)

In this example, $P = £600$, $R = 8$, $T = 4$

$$I = \frac{PRT}{100} = £\frac{600 \times 8 \times 4}{100} = £192$$

Compound Interest

If the interest earned on money invested is added to the investment, then that money earns interest in future years. This is called Compound Interest. If money is invested at 8% per annum interest, and interest is added to the capital annually, then after 1 year the investment is increased by 8%, becoming 108% of the previous amount. So to find the new amount, multiply by 1.08.
Thus if £600 is invested at 8% per annum for 4 years,
After the 1st year the amount invested becomes £600 × 1.08   = £648
After the 2nd year the amount invested becomes £648 × 1.08   = £699.84
After the 3rd year the amount invested becomes £699.84 × 1.08 = £755.83
(to the nearest penny).
After the 4th year the amount invested becomes £755.83 × 1.08 = £816.30
(to the nearest penny).
Subtracting the original amount of £600 will give the Interest.
The Compound Interest is £216.30 (compared with the Simple Interest of £192.)

If the rate of interest is $R\%$, the multiplying factor is $1 + 0.01R$.

Loans

If you borrow money then you probably have to pay interest on the loan. Usually you agree to make repayments at so much per month or per week and these amounts include the interest, so that you pay back more than you borrowed. The sooner you repay a loan the less the interest will be. The bank, finance company or other lender must tell you the true rate of interest. In advertisements look for the letters APR (Annual Percentage Rate), for instance APR 24.6% means that you will pay at that rate of interest over the period of the loan. It might be possible to find another source from which you could borrow money at a cheaper rate of interest.

Appreciation

Objects such as pictures, antiques and jewellery can gain in value in the same way as money invested increases. This is called appreciation. For instance, if someone owns a picture worth £600 and hopes it will appreciate at the rate of 8% over the next few years then at the end of 4 years the picture would be worth approximately £820. (The figures are the same as in the working for the Compound Interest question on the previous page, but the value here has been given to the nearest £10 as that seems a sensible approximation for an estimated value.)

Depreciation

Example 11

A machine was originally worth £4000. It depreciates in value by 10% each year. What will it be worth at the end of 3 years?

This is similar to Compound Interest in reverse. Every year the machine loses 10% of its value, so it is worth 90% of its previous value. To find its new value, multiply by 0.9.

After 1 year the machine is worth   £4000 × 0.9 = £3600
After 2 years the machine is worth £3600 × 0.9 = £3240
After 3 years the machine is worth £3240 × 0.9 = £2916

If the rate of depreciation is $R\%$, the multiplying factor is $1 - 0.01R$.

VAT. Value Added Tax

This tax is added to the cost of many things you buy. In most shops the price marked includes the tax so you do not have to calculate it.
Occasionally, however, the prices are given without VAT and it has to be added to the bill.
The present rate of this tax is 15% so the final price is 115% of the original price. To find the final price, multiply the original price by 1.15.

Example 12

> A builder says he will charge £80 for doing a small job. To this, VAT at 15% is added. What is the total cost?
>
> The total cost is £80 × 1.15 = £92.

If a price includes VAT, to find the original price divide by 1.15.

Example 13

> A video recorder costs £350. How much of this cost is tax?
>
> The original price was £$\dfrac{350}{1.15}$ = £304.35
>
> The VAT is £350 – £304.35 = £45.65

The rate of tax might be changed. If it has, work out these examples using the up-to-date rate.

Income Tax

This is tax taken as a proportion of any money you earn. Most employees pay tax as PAYE which means 'Pay as you earn', so the tax is deducted from the pay by the employer, and the amount depends on how much is earned.

You are allowed a Personal Allowance, and maybe other Allowances. These give an amount you can earn without paying tax on it, then any income above that is taxed at a Basic Rate. There is also a Higher Rate tax so that people with high incomes pay more.

Example 14

> Mr Taylor earns £12 000 a year. How much income tax will he pay?
>
> (We will imagine that the Personal Allowance is £3000 and the Basic rate of tax is 25%. The questions in this book use imaginary rates, since every year, on Budget Day, the tax rates can be altered and we cannot forsee what they will be when you are reading this book. Also, Allowances vary according to whether you are single or married, or if you have children.)

Income	£12 000
Personal Allowance	£3 000
Taxable Income	£9 000

Tax. 25% of £9000 = £2 250

Mr Taylor pays £2250 income tax in that year. That leaves him with £9750. (The tax will be deducted in equal amounts each week, if he is paid weekly, or each month if he is paid monthly. In addition to having tax deducted from his earnings he will also have National Insurance contributions deducted.)

If you know the up-to-date tax rates, work out this example using them.

Exercise 15.1

1. Express these percentages as fractions in their simplest forms.

   1 36%   **2** 45%   **3** $17\frac{1}{2}$%   **4** $3\frac{1}{3}$%   **5** $66\frac{2}{3}$%

2. Express as decimals.

   1 47%   **2** 95%   **3** $22\frac{1}{2}$%   **4** $6\frac{1}{4}$%   **5** 99.9%

3. Change these fractions or decimals to percentages.

   1 $\frac{3}{4}$ **2** $\frac{5}{8}$ **3** 0.15   **4** $\frac{1}{3}$ **5** 0.875

4. Find

   1 48% of 3 m   **4** $62\frac{1}{2}$% of 2.4 cm

   2 30% of 2 kg   **5** 115% of £4

   3 $16\frac{2}{3}$% of $\frac{1}{2}$ hour

5. Find what percentage the 1st quantity is of the 2nd.

   1 £3.60, £5.00   **4** 750 g, 2 kg

   2 16 cm, 2 m   **5** 50 p, 75 p

   3 36 minutes, 1 hour

6. **1** Increase £6 by 4%   **4** Decrease £75 by 20%

   2 Increase £2.60 by 15%   **5** Increase £300 by 12%

   3 Decrease £120 by 10%

7. **1** Find the percentage profit if an article costing £2.50 to make is sold for £3.

   2 Find the percentage loss if an article costing £3 is sold for £2.50.

   3 Find the percentage profit if a car is bought for £800 and sold for £980.

   4 Find the percentage loss if furniture which costs £600 is sold for £480.

   5 A restaurant bill for £15 became £16.80 after a service charge was added. What was the percentage rate of the service charge?

8. **1** By selling a car for £980 a dealer made 40% profit on what he had paid for it. How much had he paid for it?

    2 To clear goods during a sale a shopkeeper reduced the price by 10% and sold them for £3.60. What was the original price?

    3 This bottle of shampoo contained 330 ml of liquid. What quantity should an ordinary bottle hold?

    4 The duty, £36, on a camera is 24% of its value. What is the value of the camera?

    5 After an 8% pay-rise Miss Scott earned £9720 per year. What was she earning before the rise?

9. Find the Simple Interest if

    1 £250 is invested for 3 years at 8% per annum,

    2 £600 is invested for 4 years at 11% p.a.,

    3 £840 is invested for 2 years at 10% p.a.,

    4 £360 is invested for 5 years at 4% p.a.,

    5 £1000 is invested for 4 years at $7\frac{1}{2}$% p.a.

10. Using your calculator find the Compound Interest for the data of question 9, parts **1**, **2**, **3**.

11. Mr Parmar buys some DIY materials marked £24. VAT at 15% is added to this price. What is the total cost, including the tax?

12. Mr Kent employed a firm to do some repairs and the bill, including VAT at 15%, came to £184. How much of this was the price for the work, and how much was the tax?

13. Assuming that the income tax rates were: Personal Allowance £2200, Basic rate of tax 30%; find how much tax Miriam Kirby paid in the year if her salary was £9000. If this tax was paid in equal monthly instalments, how much tax did she pay per month?

14. A firm owns machinery which is judged to depreciate in value by 5% each year. If it was valued at £2000 three years ago, what is it worth today, to the nearest £?

Exercise 15.2

1. Write down the percentages equivalent to these fractions.

   $\frac{1}{2}$, $\frac{1}{4}$, $\frac{1}{5}$, $\frac{1}{10}$, $\frac{1}{20}$, $\frac{1}{100}$

2. Write down the fractions equivalent to these percentages.

   30%, $33\frac{1}{3}$%,   40%, $66\frac{2}{3}$%,   75%

3. What is 48 minutes as a percentage of $1\frac{1}{2}$ hours?

4. A grocer bought 10 cases of tinned fruit at £7.50 per case, each case containing 24 tins. He sold 200 tins at 42 p each but the remainder were damaged and unfit for sale. Find his percentage profit.

5. The price of a camera is increased by 30%. Later, in a sale, the price is reduced by 20% of its new value. This final price is £78. What was the original price?

6. Debbie knits a jumper from 12 balls of wool costing 40 p per ball. In addition the pattern costs 20 p. She sells the jumper for £8.00. What is the percentage profit on her outlay?

7. A car insurance premium is £195 but there is a deduction of 60% of this for 'no claims discount'. How much is deducted, and how much remains to be paid?

8. One firm will lend £800 at 10% per annum Simple Interest while another will lend it at $9\frac{1}{2}$% per annum Simple Interest. If the money is needed for 2 years, how much cheaper would it be to borrow from the second firm?

9. £100 was invested for a child and left for 5 years, to gain Compound Interest, until the child was older.
   During the 1st 2 years the rate of interest was 6% per annum, then the rates for the next 3 years were 7%, 8% and 9% respectively.
   Use your calculator to find how much money was in the account at the end of the 5 years, to the nearest 10 p.

10. Machinery which cost £5600 when new is judged to depreciate in value by 20% in its first year and by 10% each year in future years. What is its estimated value after the first 3 years?

11. Jenny started work and earned £60 per week. Income tax during that year was based on a Personal Allowance of £2000 and income tax on income over that amount taxed at 30%. Jenny worked for only 30 weeks in that tax-year. How much did she earn? How much tax did she pay? In the following tax-year her wages were raised to £65 per week and she worked for the full year of 52 weeks. The income tax Personal Allowance was £2200 and the basic rate of tax remained at 30%. How much tax did she pay over the year, and how much was this per week, to the nearest penny?

12. A firm prints photographs on paper of size 10 cm square. If they decide to make larger prints, size 11.2 cm square,

    1   what is the new area?
    2   The firm have advertised their prints as being 25% larger. Is this correct?

13. Instead of using a more accurate value for π, the value 3 was used in calculating the area of a circle of radius 10 cm. Use your calculator to find the percentage error in the result.
(Use either 3.1416 or the value given by the π key on your calculator as the more accurate value of π.)

$$\text{Percentage error} = \frac{\text{difference between true and wrong value}}{\text{true value}} \times 100\%$$

14. Copy and complete this phone bill. (The rates are not up-to-date.)

Quarterly rate	£17.35
Previous reading Present reading	
001501 001622	
___ units at 5.0 p	___
Total (exclusive of VAT)	___
Add VAT at 15%	___
Total payable	___

(If you know the up-to-date rates you may prefer to use them.)

15. A house was valued at £25 000. During the next year, due to a rise in house prices, its value appreciated by 10%. In the second year its value appreciated by 8% and in the 3rd year also by 8%. What was the house worth at the end of the 3 years?

16. Here is an advertisement for a loan.

Secured Loans Weekly Equivalent Payments				e.g. £8250 over 5 yrs = £227.98 per month
LOAN	10 yrs	$7\frac{1}{2}$ yrs	5 yrs	Total cost of repayment
£2250	£10.52	£11.69	£14.34	= £13 678.80
£3200	£14.96	£16.63	£20.40	APR 22.4% variable. Total cost greatly reduced on early settlement
£5500	£25.71	£28.58	£34.89	

1 What does the advertisement quote for the annual percentage rate of interest?

Mr Parker wishes to borrow £3200 to buy a car and he decides he can afford to repay about £15 per week.

2 For how long will he take out the loan?
3 What will the total payment be?
4 Instead of this, he thinks he ought to pay more weekly, so as to repay the loan in 5 years. How much extra per week will this cost him, and what will the total payment be in this case?

17. The diagram is a pie chart showing the expenses of a catering firm. The total expenses were £54 000. If the angles at the centre of each sector were Wages, 150°; Food, 120°; Fuel, 40°; Extras, 50°; find the cost of each item.
In the following year the cost of food rose by 6%, fuel increased by 10% and wages increased by 8%. The cost of the extras decreased by 10%. Find the new total cost.

PUZZLES

45. What is this? On graph paper label the x and y axes from 0 to 55, using the same scale on both axes. Mark these points. Join each point to the next one (working downwards in columns) except where there is a cross after the point. Add a circle, centre (17, 42), radius 1 unit. Also add shading or any other lines you think necessary.

(6, 41)	(15, 33)	(16, 6)	(20, 8)	(30, 8)	(30, 31)	(16, 45)
(7, 42)	(13, 30)	(17, 6)	(21, 8)	(26, 7)	(26, 34)	(14, 46)
(7, 43)	(12, 27)	(17, 7)	(21, 9)	(26, 5)	(15, 33) ×	(15, 45)
(6, 43)	(11, 25)	(18, 7)	(22, 12)	(48, 5)	(15, 35)	(14, 44)
(5, 42)	(10, 20)	(18, 8)	(23, 10)	(51, 7)	(26, 36)	(7, 43) ×
(6, 41)	(12, 23)	(19, 10)	(24, 11)	(55, 14)	(26, 34) ×	(21, 47)
(6, 39)	(11, 19)	(20, 11)	(24, 9)	(55, 17)	(26, 36)	(22, 55)
(7, 35)	(12, 21)	(21, 11)	(26, 11)	(52, 21)	(27, 39)	(23, 51) ×
(7, 33)	(13, 16)	(25, 15)	(26, 9)	(52, 16)	(27, 43)	(16, 42)
(8, 36)	(14, 19)	(24, 18)	(28, 11)	(51, 12)	(25, 46)	(16, 44)
(8, 34)	(15, 15)	(25, 20) ×	(29, 9)	(47, 8)	(24, 55)	(17, 43)
(9, 36)	(15, 18)	(16, 5)	(31, 10)	(46, 10)	(22, 47)	(17, 44)
(10, 34)	(16, 13)	(18, 5)	(30, 13)	(46, 13)	(20, 47)	(18, 43).
(11, 37)	(14, 8)	(18, 6)	(30, 16)	(45, 16)	(18, 46)	
(12, 35)	(11, 7)	(19, 6)	(32, 20) ×	(42, 20)	(17, 47)	
(13, 36)	(11, 5)	(19, 7)	(31, 10)	(39, 22)	(17, 45)	
(15, 35)	(16, 5)	(20, 7)	(33, 8)	(35, 27)	(15, 47)	

46. What is the next symbol in this sequence?

47. Yesterday a trader bought a number of vases for £63. Today he bought 28 similar vases at the same price, and he paid the same number of £'s for them as the number of vases he bought yesterday. How many vases has he altogether?

Miscellaneous section C

Exercise C1   Aural Practice

If possible find someone to read these questions to you.
You should do all of them within 10 minutes.
Do not use your calculator.
Write down the answers only.

1.   What change shall I have from £1 after buying 2 magazines, one for 35 pence and the other for 50 pence?
2.   When 15% tax is added to £100, what is the new price?
3.   A rectangle 8 cm by 5 cm is cut out of a square piece of paper of side 9 cm. What area is left?
4.   Give an approximate value for the square root of 6 × 20.
5.   How many minutes are there in $\frac{3}{4}$ of an hour?
6.   If a car costing £500 is sold for £600, what is the percentage profit?
7.   What is the cost of 99 articles at 5 pence each?
8.   How many pieces of ribbon of length 20 cm can be cut from a piece 3 metres long?
9.   Write down the prime numbers between 20 and 30.
10.   If 42 out of 50 boys passed an exam, what percentage failed?
11.   A rectangular lawn is 10 metres long and 7 metres wide. What is its perimeter?
12.   One angle of a triangle is 70° and the other two angles are equal. What size are they?
13.   If 20 equal packages weigh 50 kg, what is the weight of 1?
14.   The product of two girls' ages is 77. How old is the younger girl?
15.   A water tank is 4 m long, 3 m wide and 2 m deep. How many cubic metres of water does it hold?

Exercise C2   Multi-choice Exercise

Select the correct answer to each question.

1.   A length of 9060 mm is equal to

   A   9.06 m   **B**   9.06 km   **C**   90.6 cm   **D**   90 600 cm

   E   0.0906 km

2.   What is the solution of the equation $5x - 6 = 10 - x$?

   A $x = \frac{3}{8}$ **B** $x = \frac{2}{3}$ **C** $x = 1$ **D** $x = 2\frac{2}{3}$

   E $x = 4$

3. Four goats are tethered to posts at A, B, C and
    D and the boundaries of the regions they can
    graze are shown. The regions which can be
    grazed by more than two goats are

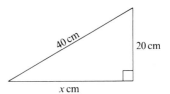

    A   1, 2, 3, 5, 6, 7   B   1, 2, 3, 4, 5, 6, 7

    C   1, 3, 5, 7   D   2, 4, 6

    E   2, 6

4. The value of x is

    A   30   B $\sqrt{120}$ C $\sqrt{200}$

    D $\sqrt{1200}$ E $\sqrt{2000}$

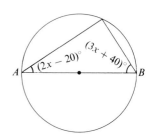

5. Which one of these statements is **not** correct, if $d = \frac{1}{2}$, $e = \frac{1}{5}$, $f = \frac{3}{10}$?

    A $d - e = f$ B $d - 2e = de$ C $2d^2 = 1$ D $d + f = 4e$

    E $\dfrac{de}{f} = \dfrac{1}{3}$

6. AB is a diameter of the circle. The value of x
    is

    A   4   B   12   C   14

    D   32   E $32\frac{1}{2}$

    [Circle diagram with A, angles $(2x - 20)°$ and $(3x + 40)°$, and B]

7. Given that $m = \dfrac{a + b + c}{3}$, the expression for c in terms of m, a and b is

    A $\dfrac{m - a - b}{3}$ B $3(m - a - b)$ C $3m - a - b$

    D $\dfrac{m}{3} - a - b$ E $3m - ab$

8. If $OX = 9$ cm and $PX = 6$ cm, what is the
    length of PT? O is the centre of the circle.

    A   6 cm   B   9 cm   C   12 cm

    D   15 cm   E $\sqrt{306}$ cm

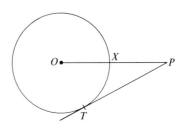

9. A salesman is paid a commission of 8% on the value of goods he sells. If his commission is £60, what value of goods has he sold?

    A £420   **B** £480   **C** £600   **D** £690

    E £750

10. Simplify $4(3e + f - g) + 5(2e - f + 2g)$

    A $22e - f - 14g$ **B** $22e - f + 6g$ **C** $22e + f + 6g$

    D $22e + 9f + 6g$ **E** $22e + 9f + 14g$

11. The area of this parallelogram is

    A $0.3\,\text{cm}^2$ **B** $0.37\,\text{cm}^2$ **C** $1.5\,\text{cm}^2$

    D $3\,\text{cm}^2$ **E** $3.7\,\text{cm}^2$

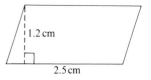

12. These circles with the same centre have radii 11 cm and 9 cm. The area of the ring between the circles is

    A $2\pi\,\text{cm}^2$ **B** $4\pi\,\text{cm}^2$

    C $10\pi\,\text{cm}^2$ **D** $20\pi\,\text{cm}^2$

    E $40\pi\,\text{cm}^2$

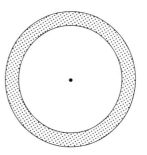

13. A bicycle wheel is 70 cm in diameter. How far has the bicycle travelled when the wheel has made 500 complete turns? (Take π as $\frac{22}{7}$)

    A 110 m   **B** 220 m   **C** 350 m   **D** 1100 m

    E 2200 m

14. Which of these triangles are congruent to each other?

    A I and II only
    B I and III only
    C II and III only
    D I, II and III
    E no two of them

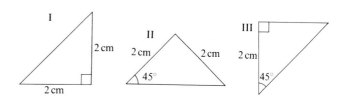

15. A courtyard is 10 m long and 6 m wide. It is paved with flagstones which are $\frac{1}{2}$ m square. How many are needed?

    A 32   **B** 60   **C** 64   **D** 120   **E** 240

16. Simplify $(h^2)^3 \times (h^4)^2$

    A h^{13} **B** h^{14} **C** h^{24} **D** h^{40} **E** h^{48}

17. The volume of this rectangular box, in m³, is

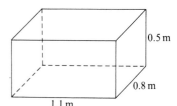

   A   0.0044   **B**   0.044   **C**   0.44

   D   4.4   **E**   44

18. A card is drawn from a pack of 52 cards. After it is replaced, another card is drawn. What is the probability that the 1st card is a heart and the 2nd card is a club?

   A $\frac{1}{169}$ **B** $\frac{1}{16}$ **C** $\frac{1}{8}$ **D** $\frac{1}{4}$ **E** $\frac{1}{2}$

19. O is the centre of the circle and the radius is 7 cm. The chord AB is of length 6 cm. What is the length of OX, in cm?

   A   4   **B**   5   **C** $\sqrt{13}$

   D $\sqrt{40}$ **E** $\sqrt{58}$

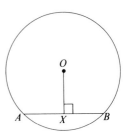

20. A woman buys 5 packets of biscuits at x pence each, and 3 packets of biscuits at y pence each. What is the average cost per packet?

   A $\dfrac{x+y}{2}$ pence   **B** $\dfrac{x+y}{8}$ pence   **C** $\dfrac{5x+3y}{2}$ pence

   D $\dfrac{5x+3y}{8}$ pence   **E** $\dfrac{5x+3y}{x+y}$ pence

21. The gradient of the line PQ is

   A -3 **B** $-\frac{3}{4}$ **C** $\frac{3}{4}$

   D $-\frac{4}{3}$ **E** $\frac{4}{3}$

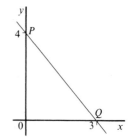

22. The value of 5.9247×10^{-2} when written correct to 3 significant figures is

   A   0.0592   **B**   0.059247   **C**   0.0593   **D**   0.00592

   E   0.00593

23. Which diagram represents the locus of points inside the triangle PQR which are equidistant from P and R?

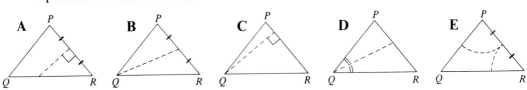

24. A dealer buys a picture for £840 and sells it for £700. What is his percentage loss on the deal?

 A $16\frac{2}{3}\%$ **B** 20%   **C** 80%   **D** $83\frac{1}{3}\%$ **E** 120%

25. What is the value of $4x^3 - 3x^2$ when $x = -1$?

 A -7 **B** -1 **C** 1   **D** 7   **E** 55

26. The area of this trapezium is

 A $42\,cm^2$ **B** $48\,cm^2$

 C $54\,cm^2$ **D** $96\,cm^2$

 E $240\,cm^2$

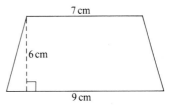

27. $ABCD$ is a square with diagonal BD, $\triangle CDE$ is isosceles with $CD = DE$. What is the size of $\angle BDE$?

 A $80°$ **B** $85°$ **C** $90°$

 D $95°$ **E** $100°$

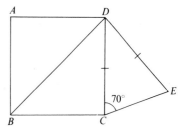

28. $\dfrac{19.5 \times 0.21}{5.1}$ is approximately equal to

 A 0.0008   **B** 0.008   **C** 0.08   **D** 0.8   **E** 8

29. The volume of this prism is

 A $80\,cm^3$ **B** $96\,cm^3$

 C $160\,cm^3$ **D** $240\,cm^3$

 E $480\,cm^3$

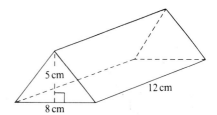

30. The histogram shows the distances from
    home to school of a group of children.
    The probability that a child chosen at
    random from this group lives within 1
    mile of the school is

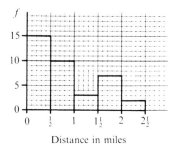

Distance in miles

A $\frac{10}{37}$ B $\frac{12}{37}$ C $\frac{13}{37}$

D $\frac{15}{37}$ E $\frac{25}{37}$

Exercise C3   Revision

1. Write correct to 2 significant figures

   1 639
   2 263
   3 0.0847
   4 5256
   5 0.517

2. Copy the diagram and

   1 reflect in the line AB,

   2 reflect ▐ in the line CD,

   3 rotate ▐ through 90° clockwise
      about the point E,

   4 rotate ▐ through 180° about
      the point G.

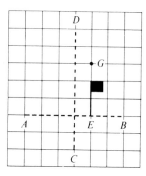

3. Find the total cost of the ingredients used in making a cake from 150 g of butter,
   150 g of sugar, 3 eggs and 200 g of flour, when flour costs 40 p for a 2 kg bag,
   butter 50 p for 250 g, sugar 60 p for a kg bag and eggs 80 p per dozen.

4. How many square tiles of length 50 cm are needed to cover the floor of a
   rectangular room 5 m by 4 m?

5. $C = \dfrac{1000P}{V}$, where P is power in kilowatts, V is voltage in volts, C is current in

   amps. If the local voltage is 240 volts, what is the current for a 2 kW fire, to the
   nearest amp?

6. Simplify

   1 5.32×100 **4** $55 \div 0.11$
   2 0.07×0.5 **5** $\dfrac{6.3 \times 0.8}{0.56}$
   3 $2.8 \div 70$

7. *O* is the centre of the circle and
TP is a tangent touching the circle
at *P*. Find the sizes of the angles
a, *b* and *c*.

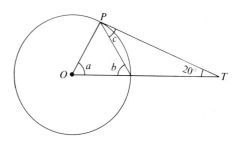

8. **1** Multiply 3.8×10^4 by 5×10^{-2}, giving the answer in standard index form.
   2 Divide 3.8×10^4 by 5×10^{-2}, giving the answer in standard index form.

9. *ABCD* is a rectangle. Find
   1 the length of *DE*,
   2 the area of $\triangle ADE$,
   3 the length of *AB*.

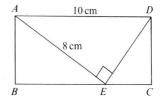

10. A cylinder has a radius of 14 cm. Find the area of one end. If its volume is
    9240 cm³, find its height. Take π as $\frac{22}{7}$.

11. A rectangular water tank is 120 cm long, 60 cm wide and 50 cm high. How many
    litres of water will it hold?

12. This table gives the times of 80 phone calls.

Time (in minutes)	0–2	2–4	4–6	6–8	8–10	10–12
Number of calls	18	22	16	14	8	2

    Draw a histogram of this distribution.
    Using the centres of intervals which are 1, 3, 5, 7, 9 and 11 minutes, find the mean
    time per call (to the nearest 0.5 minute).

13. Construct a triangle with sides 10 cm, 9 cm and 7 cm. Measure the largest angle.
    Draw a line from this angle perpendicular to the opposite side. Measure this line,
    to the nearest mm. Hence find the area of the triangle.

14. Solve the equations

    1 $7x + 1 = x - 14$

    2 $4(x - 5) - (x + 1) = 3$

    3 $5 - 8x = 9 - 3x$

    4 $3(x - 4) - 2(2x - 3) + 16 = 0$

    5 $3(x^2 + x - 2) - 2(x^2 + 3x - 5) = x^2 - 2$

15. A woman has a salary of £12 000. If for income tax she has a personal allowance
    of £2200 and tax is paid on the remainder of her income at 27%, find how much
    tax she pays in the year. If her salary is raised by £1000, how much extra tax will
    she pay?

Exercise C4   Revision

1. **1** The marks on a harbour wall show the water level at -2 (feet). Where will it be when the water has risen 5 feet?

    2 At its highest point the water level was at 10 (feet), and several hours later it was at -6 (feet). What was the fall in the tide?

2. Factorise

    1 $2x^2 + 8xy$ **2** $x^2 - 12x$ **3** $12x^2 + 4$

3. In a certain quarter the quarterly rental charge for a telephone was £14.20, and each unit used cost 4.30 pence. To the total amount, VAT was added at 15%. What was the telephone bill in that quarter if 600 units had been used?

4. **1** If a circle has a circumference of 100 m, what is its radius?

    2 If a circle has an area of 100 m², what is its radius?

    Take π as 3.142 and give answers to the nearest 0.1 m.

5. Find the Simple Interest on £125 for $4\frac{1}{2}$ years at 8% per annum.

6. A soil sample is found to have the following composition.

Air	25%
Water	25%
Mineral material	45%
Organic material	5%

    Draw a pie chart showing this information.

7. $\triangle ABC$ is isosceles with $AB = AC$ and $BC = 6$ cm. O is the centre of the circle and the radius is 5 cm. Find BD, OD, AD and the area of $\triangle ABC$.

    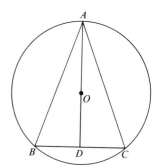

8. Identify whether the quadrilateral $ABCD$ is necessarily a parallelogram, trapezium, rectangle, square or rhombus, if it has the following properties.

    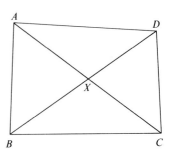

    1 $AX = BX = CX = DX$ and angles at X are all 90°.

    2 $AX = BX = CX = DX$

    3 $AX = CX$ and $BX = DX$

    4 $AX = CX$, $BX = DX$ and angles at X are all 90°.

    5 $\angle ADX = \angle CBX$

9. Which of these triangles are right-angled?

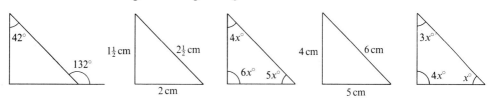

10. The diagram represents an octagon formed by cutting equal isosceles triangles from the corners of a square of side 12 cm.

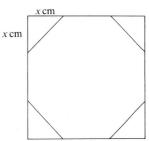

Find, in terms of x, the total area of the four corners.

If the area of the octagon is $\frac{7}{8}$ of the area of the original square, find the value of x.

Find the perimeter of the octagon, correct to the nearest mm.

11. **1** If $v^2 = u^2 + 2as$, find a in terms of u, v, s.

2 If $V = \frac{1}{3}\pi r^2 h$, find h in terms of V, r and π.

3 If $S = 4\pi r^2$, and r is positive, find r in terms of S and π.

12. The diagram shows the cross-section of a railway cutting, in the form of a trapezium. What is the area of this cross-section?

If the cutting is 200 m long, what volume of earth will have to be removed in constructing the cutting?

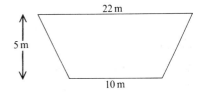

13. A rectangular block has height h cm and a square base of side x cm.

1 If the total surface area is A cm², find an expression for A in terms of x and h.

2 Find the value of A when $x = 5$ and $h = 3$.

3 Find an expression for h in terms of A and x.

4 Find the height when the total surface area is 440 cm² and the length of a side of the base is 10 cm.

14. Draw a rectangle $ABCD$ with $AB = 12$ cm and $BC = 8$ cm. Join BD. Construct the locus of points inside the rectangle which satisfy the following conditions. (Label each locus clearly.)

(1) 2 cm from the side AB,
(2) 5 cm from the corner B,
(3) equidistant from B and D,
(4) equidistant from the lines AD and DB.

Mark a point S which is 2 cm from AB and 5 cm from B.
Mark a point T on AB which is equidistant from B and D.
Mark a point U which is equidistant from AD and DB, and 2 cm from AB.

15. The time spent on homework by 30 students in a certain week was as follows:

(Times in hours, to the nearest hour.)

```
8    3    3    6  9    5  20    7  12  14  25    2    6  12  20
20  18  18  12  9  20  15  24    5    3  22  15  13  16  20
```

Tally the information and make a frequency distribution of the data using class intervals 1–5, 6–10, 11–15, 16–20, 21–25.
Draw a histogram of the distribution.
What is the modal class?
Find the mean of the grouped distribution, to the nearest 0.1 hour, using the centres of intervals, which are 3, 8, 13, 18 and 23 hours.

Exercise C5   Practical work and Investigations

1. **Ways of paying for goods and services**

   e.g. Cash, cheque, credit card, hire-purchase, bank loan, payments by instalments, tokens such as TV licence stamps, having an account at a shop.
   Find out details about each method. Consider the advantages and disadvantages of each.

2. **Planning for a Wedding**

   This is a most important occasion in a couple's life and deserves proper planning. You can imagine it is your own wedding in a few years' time or the wedding of imaginary friends.
   Decide what type of wedding. Church, other place of worship, Registry Office? It can be a very simple wedding with just two witnesses or a very grand one. Plan all the details of the wedding, and make a list of costs involved, with a separate note of who pays for each. Traditionally the bride's father paid for most things but that is not always the case nowadays. There are many small details to include, for instance, transport to the wedding, legal costs, wedding ring or rings. Plan the timetable for the day, so that the ceremony begins on time, and the couple leave for their honeymoon on time, especially if they have a train or plane to catch.
   Illustrate your booklet with pictures, e.g. of the bride's dress.
   (Magazines often have articles about weddings just before Easter, so that is a good time to find information for this topic.)

3. **Models of the main solid figures**

   Make a set of models of the cube, cuboid, prism, etc., and display them.
   As well as making models you could make a collection of tins and boxes of different shapes, arrange them in a display and take a photograph of them.

Plaited cubes

It is interesting to make a plaited cube. It has a different pattern to an ordinary net since faces have to overlap.

Copy the pattern. (It is useful to use the 2 cm squares on graph paper.)

Cut it out and crease all the lines, bending the paper away from the numbers so that the numbers stay on the outside. Now cover up number 1, by putting the square above number 5 sideways on top of it. Next cover up number 2, then 3 and so on. 5 is covered by 6, 7 is covered by 8. Finally there is one square left. Cut the corners off this one and tuck it in.

If you make several such cubes you can use them to investigate volumes and surface areas of different rectangular shapes. You can also use them as dice, but they may not give fair results. (You could investigate to see if the results were biased.)

Here also is a pattern for a plaited tetrahedron. The triangles are equilateral. Perhaps you can find out how to make other solid figures by plaiting.

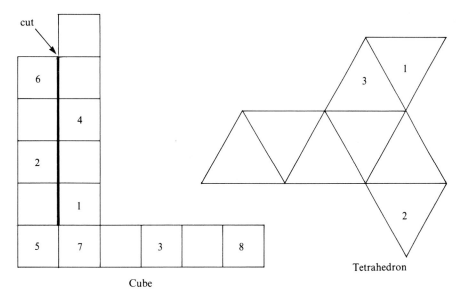

Cube   Tetrahedron

4. **Pythagoras' theorem**

Write down the theorem as a beginning.
Can you find any ways of proving the theorem?

Dissections

1   Find the centre X of the square $BCRS$. Draw lines through X parallel to AC and to CT. This divides the square into 4 sections which you can cut out. Also cut out square $ABPQ$. Rearrange these 5 pieces to make the square $ACTU$.

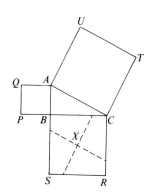

2   Tangrams. Use thin cardboard to make this. Start with two equal squares and cut into 7 pieces as shown.

Rearrange these 7 pieces to make one large square.

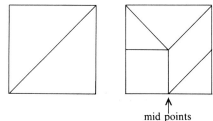

This is an ancient puzzle. The pieces make many more shapes, using all 7 pieces each time. The pieces can be turned over.

Make a parallelogram, an isosceles trapezium, a rectangle, an isosceles right-angled triangle and a trapezium with 2 adjacent right angles. Here are some other designs to make, and you can invent others.

Problem

If you had a long piece of rope, divided by knots into 12 equal parts, how could you use it to make a right angle on the ground, e.g. to mark out a rectangular playing-area?

Sets of numbers

The ones you probably know are $3:4:5$, $5:12:13$ and $8:15:17$.
Investigate these and similar patterns to find others.

hypotenuse	1 other side	sum	difference	3rd side
5	4	9	1	3
13	12	25	1	5
··	··	··	1	7
5	3	8	2	4
17	15	32	2	8
··	··	72	2	12

Pythagoras

Consult library books and try to find out something about him. When did he live? Where? Like you, he tried to investigate patterns in numbers.

A square root spiral

It is interesting to draw, and good practice in drawing accurately. See how far you can get. Start near the centre of a large piece of paper.
ABC is a right-angled triangle with sides $AB = BC = 1\,$cm, so $AC = \sqrt{2}\,$cm. Draw CD perpendicular to AC, with D on the opposite side of AC to B, and with $CD = 1\,$cm. Join AD. ACD is a right-angled triangle with $AC = \sqrt{2}\,$cm and $CD = 1\,$cm, so AD is $\sqrt{3}\,$cm.
Now draw DE perpendicular to AD, 1 cm long, and join AE.
Carry on in a similar way.

5. **π**

Here are some ideas:
Measure the circumference C and diameter D of circles of different sizes from a penny to a large wheel and find the value of π from $\dfrac{C}{D}$.

Show that the area of a circle is πr^2 by cutting a circle into small sectors and rearranging them into the shape of an approximate parallelogram with length πr and height r.

Write π to as many decimal places as are shown on your calculator. See if you can find a list giving more decimal places. People have invented phrases to help them to remember the first few decimal places of π. One of these is 'Sir, I have a number.' The number of letters in each word gives π as 3.1416. Can you invent a phrase of your own, or even a rhyme?

There are various infinite series which give π, such as

$$\pi = 4 - \frac{4}{3} + \frac{4}{5} - \frac{4}{7} + \frac{4}{9} - \frac{4}{11} + \frac{4}{13} - \frac{4}{15} + \cdots$$

Use your calculator to work out several terms of this.
Archimedes, who lived about 200 B.C., found a value for π by considering a pattern for the perimeters of regular polygons with 6, 12, 24, 48 and 96 sides inscribed in a circle, and then polygons outside and touching a circle. (The circumference is greater than the perimeter of polygons inside, and less than the perimeter of polygons outside the circle.) He gave π as a number between $3\frac{1}{7}$ and $3\frac{10}{71}$. Write these numbers as decimals to see how close he was.

Make a list of all the formulae you know which involve π.

Find π using probability and by tossing sticks. If you toss sticks over a set of parallel lines then the sticks may either land touching or across a line, or land completely between the lines. The probability that a stick will touch a line is $\dfrac{2s}{\pi d}$, where the sticks are $s\,$cm long and the lines are $d\,$cm apart.
Use the floorboards of the room if they form parallel lines, otherwise draw lines on the floor. Find 10 thin sticks with length about $\frac{3}{4}$ of the distance between the lines. Toss the sticks randomly 50 times, and find the total number n, out of 500, which land touching or across a line. Then $\dfrac{n}{500}$ is an estimate of the probability.
Put $\dfrac{n}{500} = \dfrac{2s}{\pi d}$ and rearrange this equation to find an experimental value for π.
Find the percentage error.

Find π using probability and random numbers.

If you choose 2 numbers at random they can either have a common factor, e.g. 40 and 75 have a common factor 5, or they can be prime to each other, i.e. have no factor in common, e.g. 40 and 63 have no common factor although they both have factors.

The probability that 2 numbers are prime to each other is $\dfrac{6}{\pi^2}$.

Get 500 pairs of random numbers from random number tables, a computer, or using the numbers from a phone directory. Numbers less than 100 will do. Find how many pairs are prime to each other. If there are n pairs, then $\dfrac{n}{500}$ is an estimate of the probability. Put $\dfrac{n}{500} = \dfrac{6}{\pi^2}$, and rearrange this equation to find an experimental value for π. Find the percentage error.

6. **The parabola**

Make a topic booklet about the parabola, which is the curve of the graph of $y = x^2$, or the graph of any other quadratic function.
Draw the graph of $y = x^2$.

By slicing a cone in a certain way, a parabola will be obtained in the sliced surface. Make a cone from modelling clay and find out how to slice it. (Other types of slices will give circles, ellipses and hyperbolas.)

The parabola as a locus.
With the same centre A, draw circles with radii 1 cm, 2 cm, 3 cm, etc.
Draw a series of parallel lines as tangents to these circles, all on the same side of A.
Mark the points where each tangent cuts the circle one size larger.
Join all these points, including the point A, with a smooth curve.

The parabola as an envelope.
(An envelope is an outline of a curve produced by straight lines, which form tangents to the curve.)
Use a piece of tracing paper approximately 18 cm by 12 cm.
Draw a line 1.5 cm away from a long edge and mark dots 0.4 cm apart all along this line.
Mark a dot for point P 4 cm from the line and halfway between the shorter edges of the paper.
Now fold the paper so that the 1st dot on the line lies on top of P. Make a firm crease. Now make the next dot lie on P. Make another firm crease.
Repeat until all the dots in turn have covered P. You should get a clear outline of a parabola. Hold your paper up to the light to see more clearly.
(The curve-stitching design explained in the next question also gives the envelope of a parabola.)
The parabola occurs naturally when an object is thrown at an angle into the air. Notice the water from a fountain. The parabola is also used in design, e.g. in bridges. The 3-dimensional versions are used in searchlights, and in modern architecture. Find out more about these and other uses.

7. **Curve stitching and String Art**

Curve stitching is done with embroidery thread onto cardboard. Here is a basic pattern to get you started. Draw any lines and mark points on the wrong side of the cardboard so that only the thread shows on the right side.

Draw 2 lines AB, AC 9 cm long, meeting at A at an angle of about 50°.

Mark 8 points along AB 1 cm apart and number them from 1 to 8 starting 1 cm from A. Mark 8 points along CA 1 cm apart and number them from 1′ to 8′ starting 1 cm from C.

3-strand embroidery thread is suitable to use. Choose a colour which shows up against the background of the cardboard.

Begin by making a knot then go through point 1 from the wrong side to the right side. Prick the hole at 1′ so that you can find it from the right side and go through hole 1′ from right side to wrong side. Go on the wrong side to 2′ (because that is nearer than 2), go through 2′ and then through 2. Then go through 3 and 3′, and so on until you have used all the numbers. Fasten off the thread by looping under some on the wrong side, and tying it. On the right side the threads will make the outline of a parabola.

Now you can invent your own patterns. Perhaps start with two sides of a square, then the opposite two sides, then the other pairs of sides in another colour.

String Art is based on the same idea but it is done on a board with nails and thread. Paint the board or cover it with cloth, to contrast with the colour of the thread. Use nails $\frac{3}{4}$ inch long, with large heads so that the thread will not slip off. Draw the pattern above on paper, put it over the board and then knock nails in positions 1 to 8 and 1′ to 8′. Remember which is which and then tear off the paper.

Start by knotting the thread round nail 1, leaving a small end to tuck in later. Take the thread to 1′ and go round the nail, then go to 2′ and round the nail, then to 2, 3, 3′, 4′ and so on. Fasten off round nail 8 and try to tuck the end out of sight.

Now invent your own patterns using this basic design.

You may get further ideas from the next question.

8. **Cardioids and other designs from circles**

Draw a circle and divide the circumference into 72 equal parts. (If you choose a radius just larger than that of your protractor you can mark off points every 5° along the protractor edge.)

Number the points from 1 to 72 in order.

Join 1 to 2, 2 to 4, 3 to 6, 4 to 8, and so on, with straight lines. After joining 36 to 72 imagine the numbering continues past 72, or continue numbering, so that the point numbered 2 is also number 74. Continue joining 37 to 74, 38 to 76, etc. Number 72 will join to 144, which is the same point, so just make a dot there. You can investigate similar ideas by joining 1 to 3, 2 to 6, 3 to 9 etc., then 1 to 4, and so on. You can also number points in a positive direction and a negative direction and join 1 to −2, 2 to −4, etc.

For extended patterns, don't draw the circle, only mark the points, and manage without numbering them. Draw another concentric circle with a radius 2 or 3 cm larger. When you join 2 points, extend the line in both directions until it meets the outer circle.

These patterns could be done as curve stitching. Remember to do the drawing on the wrong side of the work in this case.

A mystic rose pattern.
Divide the circumference into 20 equal parts. Join every point to every other one. Try a mystic rose extended pattern, or try using different colours.

The mystic rose makes a good pattern for string art, but use a number of points which is a prime number, such as 23. Get a large board and 1 inch nails. Start by joining points which are nearly opposite so go 1 to 12, 12 to 23, and continue going round missing out 10 nails each time. When you get back to 1 go 1 to 11, 11 to 21, 21 to 8, etc. missing out 9 nails each time. Eventually you go 1 to 2, 2 to 3, 3 to 4, etc., when you should wind the string firmly round each nail.

Patterns in squares.
Draw a square side 12 cm. Mark points round the perimeter every 2 cm, starting at a corner. Join every point to every other point.

To make an extended design, don't mark the square, only put dots for the points. Draw another square to surround them, with 2 cm of space in-between. Extend all lines in both directions to meet the outer square.

Experiment with other designs.

You could also experiment with designs based on equilateral triangles or other regular polygons.

9. **Introduction to Trigonometry**

Draw several right-angled triangles with $\angle A = 20°$, and AB of different lengths such as 4 cm, 5 cm, 8 cm, 10 cm, 12 cm. On large paper you can make AB larger still.

Measure BC in each triangle and find the ratio $\dfrac{BC}{AB}$ as a decimal, to 2 decimal places.

Set down the results in a table.

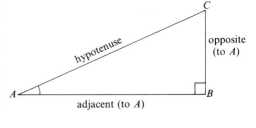

Angle $A = 20°$			
side BC	side AB	$\dfrac{BC}{AB}$ as a fraction	$\dfrac{BC}{AB}$ as a decimal
. . .	4 cm	$\dfrac{...}{4}$	. . .
	5 cm		
	. . .		

What do you notice? If the results in the 4th column are nearly the same, find the average of these results, and call this number 'tan 20°'. If the results are quite different, perhaps you should check your work again.

The side AC is the hypotenuse of the triangle. (This is the name given to the side opposite to the right angle.) In relation to $\angle A$, side BC is the opposite side. AB is the side which is next to $\angle A$, but is not the hypotenuse, and we call that the adjacent side (to $\angle A$). You have found the value of $\dfrac{\text{opposite side}}{\text{adjacent side}}$. This ratio is referred to as the **tangent** of $\angle A$, tan A for short.

So tan 20° $= 0.364$ means that if the right-angled triangle has an angle of 20° and you find $\dfrac{\text{opposite side}}{\text{adjacent side}}$ you will always get 0.364, whatever size the triangle is.

Since this ratio is always the same, it can be printed in a book of tables, in the table headed 'tangents', and it is stored in your calculator under the key $\boxed{\text{tan}}$. Make sure your calculator is set to work in degrees then press 20 $\boxed{\text{tan}}$ and it will show 0.36397 . . . which is a more accurate value.

You will get different ratios if you change the angle A from 20° to other sizes. Repeat your work with different triangles with $\angle A = 30°$, and then with $\angle A = 40°$, 50°, 60° or other values. Set down the results in a table.

angle	tangent of angle
20°	0.36
30°	
40°	
. . .	

You will notice that the value for tangent gets larger as the angle gets larger. What would its value be if $\angle A = 45°$?

You can do similar investigations with the ratio $\dfrac{BC}{AC}$. This is $\dfrac{\text{opposite}}{\text{hypotenuse}}$ and this is referred to as the **sine** of $\angle A$, sin A (pronounced sine A) for short, and you can check the ratios on your calculator using the $\boxed{\text{sin}}$ key. As $\angle A$ gets big and approaches 90°, what value does sin A approach?

The third set of ratios is $\dfrac{AB}{AC}$, or $\dfrac{\text{adjacent}}{\text{hypotenuse}}$, and this is called the **cosine** of $\angle A$, or cos A for short.

These three sets of ratios, tan, sin and cos, are used for calculations in Chapter 20.

10. **For the Computer Programmer**

More suggestions for programs:

1 To calculate areas and volumes of various figures.
2 To find the 3rd side of a right-angled triangle.
3 To draw graphs of quadratic functions.
4 To work out Simple Interest, Compound Interest, VAT, Income Tax, etc.

To the student:

4   Making plans for revision

As the time of the examination draws nearer you should look back over your progress and see if you are satisfied with it, and make a plan of action for the future. If you have been working steadily from the beginning of the course, you may not need to make any extra effort. If you enjoy the challenge of Maths you are probably working well and learning everything as you go along. But if you find some of the work difficult and are feeling discouraged, perhaps a little extra effort at this stage, and perhaps a change in the way you approach your work, will help to improve your standard, and you will feel more confident.

In addition to lessons and set homework you should spend some time each week on individual study. Make a plan for this depending on how much time you have available and what you need to learn or practise. In addition to Maths, you will have work to do in all your other subjects, so take these into consideration. If you have to do a 'Project' in any subject, then start it in good time or you will find yourself at the last minute spending all your time on it, and your other work is neglected.

There is a revision checklist on page 404. You could copy this, and use it to decide what you are going to do. You could work through this book again in order, spending so much time on each chapter. Choose a suitable selection of questions to do, either straightforward ones if you need practice in these, or the more challenging questions if you are more confident with the topic. Alternatively, you could use the revision exercises in the miscellaneous sections A to E of the book. You might prefer to revise all the arithmetic, then the algebra, then the geometry, and so on. The important thing is that **you** should decide for yourself what **you** need to do, and then plan how you are going to do it.

Sort out your difficulties as you go along. Try to think things out for yourself as far as possible, rather than having to be shown how to do everything. But if you need extra help, then **ask** someone to help you, either your teacher, someone in your class or a higher class, a parent or a friend.

Keep a list of what you are doing. At first there will be a lot to do and not much done, but you will find it encouraging when after a few weeks you can see that you are making real progress.

About Chapters 16 to 20

More Arithmetic comes in Chapter 16, including some real-life applications which you will find useful to know later. There is more Geometry in Chapter 17, dealing with Similarity and Enlargements, and this leads on to Scale Drawing in Chapter 18. The transformations of translation, reflection, rotation and enlargement are summarised and given further practice in Chapter 19. In Chapter 20 you can learn how to use trigonometry for calculating lengths and angles instead of measuring them. (If you do not have a calculator with trig. functions on, that is keys labelled sin, cos, tan; then now is the time to get one.)

16 *Ratio and rate*

Ratio and Proportion

Examples

1. Express $25\,\text{cm} : 1\frac{1}{2}\,\text{m}$ as a ratio in its simplest form.

    $\dfrac{25\,\text{cm}}{1\frac{1}{2}\,\text{m}} = \dfrac{25\,\text{cm}}{150\,\text{cm}} = \dfrac{25}{150} = \dfrac{1}{6}$. Ratio is $1:6$

2. Divide £24 in the ratio $3:5$

    $3:5$ gives 8 parts. 1 part is $\dfrac{\text{£}24}{8} = \text{£}3$

    Shares are $3 \times \text{£}3$ and $5 \times \text{£}3$, i.e. £9 and £15.

3. The angles of a triangle are in the ratio $4:5:6$. Find their sizes.
    $4:5:6$ gives 15 parts.   The sum of the angles is $180°$.

    1 part is $\dfrac{180°}{15} = 12°$

    The angles are $4 \times 12°$, $5 \times 12°$, $6 \times 12°$, i.e. $48°$, $60°$ and $72°$.

4. Children aged 12 years, 9 years and 4 years share £1 in proportion to their ages. How much does the youngest child get?

    Shares are in the ratio $12:9:4$, i.e. 25 parts.

    1 part is $\dfrac{\text{£}1}{25} = 4\,\text{p}$

    The youngest child gets $4 \times 4\,\text{p}$, i.e. 16p.

5. Increase $12\,\text{kg}$ in the ratio $5:3$

    New weight is $\dfrac{5}{3}$ of $12\,\text{kg} = \dfrac{5}{3} \times 12\,\text{kg} = 20\,\text{kg}$

6. Decrease £120 in the ratio $9:10$

    New amount is $\dfrac{9}{10}$ of $\text{£}120 = \text{£}\dfrac{9}{10} \times 120 = \text{£}108$

Exercise 16.1

1. Express as ratios in their simplest forms

    1 13.2 cm : 16.5 cm

    2 75 p : £1.80

    3 3 hours 20 minutes : 5 hours 20 minutes

    4 750 g : 3.6 kg

    5 600 ml : 2 litres

2. 1 Divide £2.25 in the ratio 2 : 3

    2 Divide £1.54 in the ratio 4 : 7

    3 Divide 60 p in the ratio 7 : 3

    4 Divide £1.75 in the ratio 6 : 1

    5 Divide £4 in the ratio 7 : 3

3. 1 Increase £270 in the ratio 5 : 3

    2 Increase £37.50 in the ratio 9 : 5

    3 Decrease £280 in the ratio 4 : 7

    4 Decrease £12 in the ratio 5 : 8

    5 Increase £25 in the ratio 11 : 10

4. The edges of two cubes are 4 cm and 6 cm. Find the ratio of their volumes.

5. The angles of a quadrilateral are in the ratio 2 : 3 : 5 : 8. Find their sizes.

6. A line AB of length 9 cm is divided at P so that $AP : PB = 3 : 7$. Find the length of AP.

7. The costs of manufacture of an article are divided among labour, materials and overheads in the ratio 8 : 4 : 3. If the materials for 1000 articles cost £650, what is the total cost of these articles?

8. Three men invest £2000, £3500 and £4500 respectively into a business and agree to share the profits in the ratio of their investments. The profits in the first year were £8000. How much did they each receive?

9. A shade of paint is made up of 3 parts blue and 4 parts purple. How many litres of blue are needed to make up 10.5 litres of this paint?

10. To make gunmetal, copper, tin and zinc are used in the ratio 43 : 5 : 2. What quantities of tin and zinc are used with 21.5 kg of copper?

11. Two boys share some apples in the ratio 4 : 3. The boy with the larger share took 56 apples. How many did the other boy take?

12. What is the ratio of $75\,g : 2\,kg$ in its simplest form?

13. A concrete mixture is made by mixing cement, sand and gravel by volume in the ratio $1 : 2 : 4$. How much sand and gravel must be added to $0.5\,m^3$ of cement?

14. For these cylinders, find the ratio of

   1 their base-radii,

   2 their heights,

   3 the areas of their bases,

   4 their volumes.
      (Do not substitute a numerical value
      for π as it will cancel out.)

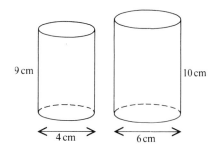

9 cm   10 cm   4 cm   6 cm

Direct and Inverse Proportion.   (Arithmetical methods)

Quantities which increase in the same ratio are in **direct proportion**.

Example 7

   If 21 notebooks cost £7.56, what do 28 similar notebooks cost?

   The price is in direct proportion to the quantities.
   Ratio of quantities, new : old $= 28 : 21 = 4 : 3$
   Ratio of prices $= 4 : 3$

   New price $= \dfrac{4}{3}$ of £7.56 $= £\,\dfrac{4}{3} \times 7.56 = £10.08$.

Quantities which vary so that one increases in the same ratio as the other decreases are in **inverse proportion**.

Example 8

   If there is enough food in an emergency pack to last 12 men for 10 days, how long would the food last if there were 15 men?

   As the number of men increases, the time the food will last decreases.
   Ratio of number of men, new : old $= 15 : 12 = 5 : 4$
   Ratio of times, new : old $= 4 : 5$

   New time the food lasts for $= \dfrac{4}{5}$ of 10 days $= 8$ days.

These questions were solved using the unitary method, in Chapter 1. Repeat the questions of Exercise 1.4, numbers 25 to 30, using this method. Then you can decide which method you prefer to use.

Variation.   (Algebraic methods)

Direct variation

If y is directly proportional to x, i.e. y varies directly as x, then $y = mx$, where m is a positive constant number.

(The word 'directly' need not be included as it is assumed that the variation is direct variation if the word 'inverse' is not included.)

If we know some corresponding values of x and y we can find the value of m.

Example 9

If y varies as x and $y = 40$ when $x = 2$, find the equation connecting x and y, and find the value of y when $x = 3$.

$y = mx$
When $x = 2$, $y = 40$ so $40 = m \times 2$, $m = 20$
The equation is $y = 20x$
When $x = 3$, $y = 20 \times 3 = 60$

Inverse variation

If y is inversely proportional to x, i.e. y varies inversely as x, then y varies as $\dfrac{1}{x}$, so $y = \dfrac{m}{x}$ where m is a positive constant.

Example 10

If y varies inversely as x and $y = 5$ when $x = 3$, find the equation connecting x and y, and find the value of y when $x = 6$.

$y = \dfrac{m}{x}$

When $x = 3$, $y = 5$ so $5 = \dfrac{m}{3}$, $m = 15$

The equation is $y = \dfrac{15}{x}$

When $x = 6$, $y = \frac{15}{6} = 2\frac{1}{2}$.

Exercise 16.2

1. If y varies directly as x and $y = \frac{1}{2}$ when $x = 5$, find y when $x = 20$.

2. If y varies as x and $y = 4$ when $x = 4$, find the equation connecting y with x and find the value of y when $x = 5$.

3. If y varies inversely as x and $y = 15$ when $x = 3$, find the value of y when $x = 5$.

4. If y varies inversely as x and $y = 18$ when $x = 2$, find the value of y when $x = 3$.

5. If y varies as x and $y = 1000$ when $x = 5$, find the equation connecting y with x. What is the value of y when $x = 10$?

6. If y is inversely proportional to x and $y = \frac{1}{2}$ when $x = 3$, what is the value of y when $x = 6$?

7. A variable A is proportional to r. If $A = 20$ when $r = 2$, find the value of A when $r = 5$.

8. If w is directly proportional to d and $w = 24$ when $d = 6$, find the value of w when $d = 7$.

9. If y is inversely proportional to x and $x = 3$ when $y = 4$, find the equation connecting y with x, and find the value of y when $x = 4$.

Rate

The word **rate** is used in many real-life situations.

For example:
A man is paid for doing a job at the rate of £6.75 per hour.

Grass seed is sown to make a lawn at the rate of 2 oz per square yard.

Income tax is paid at the standard rate of 25 p in the £ (or whatever the current rate is).

A car uses petrol at the rate of 40 miles to the gallon.

Wallpaper paste powder is added to water at the rate of 1 packet to 6 pints of water.

Exercise 16.3

Use the data above in questions 1 to 5.

1. How much will the man be paid if the job takes 6 hours?

2. How many lbs of grass seed will be needed to make a rectangular lawn, 8 yards by 7 yards? (16 oz = 1 lb.)

3. In addition to his normal work, a man did a part-time job and earned £120. How much tax at the standard rate had to be paid out of this?

4. If I use half the packet of wallpaper paste, how much water must I mix it with?

5. How much petrol will the car use on a journey of 100 miles, approximately?

6. A plumber charges £143 for a job taking 22 hours. What rate does he charge per hour?

7. A car used 12 litres of petrol on a journey of 150 km. What is the petrol consumption in km/litre?

8. Two bottles of detergent are shown. What is the cost per litre of the two brands? Which one is the better value for money if the two brands are equally effective in use?

9. Water flows from a tap at the rate of 20 litres/minute. How long will it take to fill a tank holding 240 litres?

10. A firm offers a discount of 5 p in the £. What will you actually pay for goods which are priced at £7.20?

Rateable Value

The local council needs money to run its own services such as Education, Health, Leisure, Police.

It assesses the value of each property and gives it a **rateable value**. Thus the rateable value of a particular house could be £245. A bigger or better house would have a greater rateable value.

The council then decides how much money it will need to collect for the next year, and it sets a **rate** such as 84 p in the £.

This means that for every £1 of rateable value the householder or property owner would pay 84 p in rates.

For the house with a rateable value of £245 the annual rates bill would be

245 × 84 p = £205.80.

Exercise 16.4

1. How much would the rates bill be on a house with rateable value £320 if the rate was 92 p in the £?

2. How much would the rates bill be on a house with rateable value £465 if the rate was £1.32 in the £?

3. If the rateable value of a house is £360 and the annual rates are £324, what rate in the £ has been set?

4. If the rate was £1.20 in the £ and a householder paid £420 in rates, what was the rateable value of the house?

5. If the rates rise by 12 p in the £, how much extra would be paid by a householder whose house had a rateable value of £260?

Rate of Exchange

At Banks and a few other places you can change money into different currencies. The Banks make a small charge (commission) for changing the money. The rate of exchange varies slightly from day to day and may change considerably at times, depending on the financial situations in the countries concerned. In order to attract customers, some banks may offer slightly better rates than others.

Here are some of the rates quoted on one particular day. These amounts are equivalent to £1.

Australia	2.18 dollars
Austria	19.70 schillings
Belgium	58.60 francs
Canada	1.95 dollars
Denmark	10.67 kroner
France	9.24 francs
Germany	2.81 marks
Greece	189 drachmae
Holland	3.18 guilders
Ireland	$1.04\frac{1}{2}$ punts
Israel	2.30 shekels
Italy	1955 lire
Japan	221 yen
Malta	0.5180 lire
New Zealand	2.70 dollars
Norway	10.34 kroner
Portugal	209 escudos
Spain	188.25 pesetas
Switzerland	2.31 francs
United States	1.41 dollars
Yugoslavia	648 dinars

For example,

£10 will be worth 10×9.24 French francs

$$= 92.4 \text{ francs}$$

£15 will be worth 15×1.95 Canadian dollars

$$= 29.25 \text{ dollars}$$

1500 Spanish pesetas will be worth

$$£\frac{1500}{188.25} = £7.97$$

10 Irish punts will be worth $£\dfrac{10}{1.04\frac{1}{2}}$

$$= £\frac{10}{1.045} = £9.57$$

Exercise 16.5

Using the rates of exchange given in the list, say how much you get if you change these amounts.

1. £100 into Greek money.
2. £150 into Swiss francs.
3. £12 into U.S. dollars.
4. £3000 into Japanese money.
5. £200 into Yugoslavian money.

Using the rates of exchange given in the list, change this money into British currency, to the nearest penny.

6. 5000 Australian dollars.
7. 2000 Belgian francs.
8. 4000 German marks.
9. 1000 Portuguese escudos.
10. 200 Norwegian kroner.

If you know the up-to-date exchange rates, repeat these questions using them.

Speed

The rate at which distance is travelled is called **speed** and it is found from the formula

$$\text{speed} = \frac{\text{distance}}{\text{time}}$$

It is measured in units such as miles per hour, km per hour, metres per second. The abbreviation for metres per second is m/s or ms^{-1}.

The formula rearranged gives time $= \dfrac{\text{distance}}{\text{speed}}$, distance $=$ speed $\times$ time.

The units have to correspond, e.g. metres, seconds, metres per second or km, hours, km per hour.

If the speed is variable, these formulae will give or use the **average speed**.

Velocity is a word used instead of speed when the direction of motion is included, so that if the direction from point A to point B is being regarded as positive, a speed in the opposite direction will have a negative velocity.

Average speed

Example 11

A car travels 45 km at an average speed of 30 km/hour and then travels 175 km at 70 km/hour. What is the average speed for the whole journey?

(Do **not** just average the two speeds 30 and 70, getting 50, since this is wrong.)

$$\text{Average speed} = \frac{\text{total distance}}{\text{total time}}$$

The total distance is 220 km.
The time for the first part of the journey is $1\frac{1}{2}$ hours.
The time for the second part of the journey is $2\frac{1}{2}$ hours.
The total time is 4 hours.

$$\text{Average speed} = \frac{220}{4} \text{ km/hour} = 55 \text{ km/hour}.$$

Exercise 16.6

1. Find the time taken to travel 81 km at an average speed of 45 km/hour.

2. Find the distance travelled by a train going for 3 hours 20 minutes at an average speed of 66 miles/hour.

3. Mrs Owen travels 21 miles to work and the journey normally takes 35 minutes. What is her average speed?

4. On a journey to work, Mr Davies travelled 5 miles through town in 30 minutes and then 16 miles along the motorway in 15 minutes. What was his average speed over the whole journey?

5. A train travels 70 km at a speed of 100 km/hour and then another 52 km at a speed of 65 km/hour.

    1   What is the total time taken?
    2   What is the average speed, to the nearest km/hour?

6. A boat travels for $1\frac{1}{2}$ hours at 10 km/hour and for the next $3\frac{1}{2}$ hours at 15 km/hour.

    1   What is the total distance travelled?
    2   What is the average speed?

7. A train travels for 2 hours at 100 km/hour and then for 1 hour at 85 km/hour. Find its average speed for the whole journey.

8. Two motorists, Mr Bowen and Mr Crane, set off at 9 a.m. to travel to a town 120 km away. Mr Bowen arrives there at 11.30 a.m. and Mr Crane arrives there at noon.

    1   What is the ratio of their times taken?

    2   What is the ratio of their average speeds?

Exercise 16.7

1. £900 is raised and is divided among 3 charities, *A*, *B* and *C* in the proportion 4 : 5 : 6. Find the amount each charity receives.
    If these amounts are represented on a pie chart, calculate the angle of each sector.

2. The measurements of two rectangles are (a) length 12 cm and width 9 cm. (b) length 24 cm and width 7 cm.
    Find

    1   the ratio of their perimeters,

    2   the ratio of their areas,

    3   the ratio of the lengths of their diagonals.

    4   If all the sides are increased by 3 cm, find the new ratio of their areas.

3. The insurance for the contents of a house are charged at £6.50 per £1000 of value. How much will the insurance cost for contents valued at £8500?

4. 1   Find the value of the number *x* if the ratio of *x* : 3 is the same as the ratio 4 : 5.

    2   Find the value of the positive number *x* if the ratio of 4 : *x* is the same as the ratio *x* : 25.

5. The radius of the circle in the diagram is 4 cm. Find the ratio of the areas of the small square, the circle and the large square, leaving your answer in terms of π.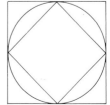

6. Whilst on holiday, Mr Wood bought a carton containing 10 packets of cigarettes for 1260 pesetas. On returning home he sold these packets to his friends for £1 each. How much profit (in £'s) did he make?
    The rate of exchange at the time was 210 pesetas = £1.

7. A firm buys petrol and diesel oil in the ratio 5:7, spending £2700 altogether per week. If the price of petrol is increased by 5% and the diesel oil by 3%, find the percentage increase in the total cost, correct to 1 decimal place.

8. A man gave some money to his four children in the ratio 2:4:5:9. If the difference between the largest and the smallest share was £175, how much did he give altogether?

9. A firm allows a discount of 5 p in the £ for prompt payment of a bill. If the bill is for £480, how much should be paid, if it is paid quickly?

10. A tin of paint holding 2.5 litres will cover an area of 45 m². What is the rate in square metres per litre?

11. Mrs Modi wants to buy some toothpaste. Which size is the best value for money?

12. On a holiday journey the car mileage indicator readings and times were as follows:

Time	9.05 a.m.	11.45 a.m.	12.15 p.m.	2.00 p.m.
Mileage indicator reading	16335	16463	16463	16526

    (I had stopped to visit a place of interest from 11.45 a.m. to 12.15 p.m.)

    1 What was the average speed for the part of the journey up to 11.45 a.m.?

    2 What was the average speed for the part of the journey from 12.15 p.m.?

    3 I estimate that my car used 5 gallons of petrol on the journey.
       What is the approximate fuel consumption in miles per gallon?

13. Two tourists, Alan and Bill, returned to England, each with 300 francs to change back into British money. When Alan changed his the rate was 12.0 francs to the £, and a week later when Bill changed his the rate was 12.5 francs to the £. Who got more British money, and how much more?

14. If the rates of exchange are £1 = 1.75 dollars and £1 = 11.9 francs, how much is 14 dollars worth

    1 in British currency,
    2 in francs?

15. The weight of liquid contained in a cylindrical tin of fixed radius varies as the height of the tin. When the height was 20 cm the liquid weighed 8 kg. Find the weight of similar liquid in a tin of the same radius with height 15 cm.

16. The time taken to travel a given distance varies inversely as the average speed. When the average speed is 25 miles/hour the time taken is 3 hours. What is the time taken when the average speed is 30 miles/hour?

17. The weight W kg of a bar varies directly as ld^2, where l cm is its length and d cm its diameter. If $W = 5.6$ when $d = 3.5$ and $l = 48$, find the equation for W in terms of l and d. Hence find the weight of a bar of this type of length 42 cm and diameter 5 cm.

18. The load which can just be carried by a metal girder of a certain type varies inversely as its length. A load of 10 tonnes can just be carried by a girder 2 m long. What load can just be carried by a girder of the same type which is 1.6 m long?

19. A main road through a village has a speed limit of 40 miles per hour. A motorist covers the $1\frac{1}{2}$ mile section in 2 minutes. Did he break the speed limit?

20. A car passes a point A at 3.58 p.m. and reaches a point B $3\frac{1}{2}$ km distant at 4.03 p.m. What is the average speed of the car?

PUZZLES

48. There are two discs; one is red on both sides, the other is red on one side and green on the other, but they are otherwise identical. Without looking, one is picked at random and placed flat on the table. If the top side of this disc is red, what is the probability that the hidden side is also red? Is it $\frac{1}{4}$, $\frac{1}{3}$, $\frac{1}{2}$, $\frac{2}{3}$ or $\frac{3}{4}$?

49. S H A R O N   Each figure is represented by a different letter.
   + S A R A H   Find which figure each letter represents.
   ─────────   There are three different solutions, so begin with the one where
     S A N D R A $A = 9$.

50. Jill has lost her timetable. She remembers that tomorrow's lessons end with Games, but she cannot remember the order of the first 5 lessons. She asks her friends, who decide to tease her.
   Alison says, 'Science is 3rd, History is 1st'.
   Brenda says, 'English is 2nd, Maths is 4th'.
   Claire says, 'History is 5th, Science is 4th'.
   Denise says 'French is 5th, English is 2nd'.
   Emma says 'French is 3rd, Maths is 4th'.
   Naturally, Jill is very confused by all this. Then her friends admit that they have each made one true statement and one untrue one.
   When is Maths?

17 *Similarity*

Similar figures

Similar figures have the same shape.
All corresponding lengths are in proportion.
All corresponding angles are equal.

Transformations: Enlargement

A figure and its enlargement are similar figures.
The ratio $\dfrac{\text{length of line on enlargement}}{\text{length of line on original}}$ is called the **scale factor** of the enlargement.
So length of line on enlargement = scale factor × length of line on original.
Corresponding lines on the two figures are parallel.

Examples

1 Enlargement with scale factor 2

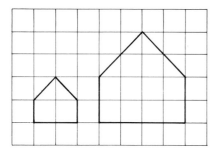

2 Enlargement with scale factor 3

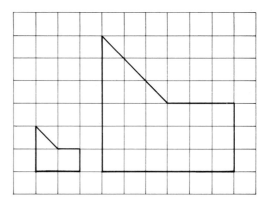

3 The lengths of these rectangles are in the
ratio $4:10 = 2:5$
The breadths of these rectangles are
in the ratio $3:7.5 = 6:15 = 2:5$
(All angles are 90°)
The rectangles are similar.

Note that the **areas** are not in the same proportion as the lengths.
Ratio of areas $= 3 \times 4 : 7.5 \times 10 = 12:75 = 4:25$

4   Two similar cylinders have heights of 6 cm and 10 cm. If the smaller one has a
radius of 4.2 cm, what is the radius of the larger one?

Ratio of heights $= 6:10 = 3:5$
Because the cylinders are similar, the radii are in the same ratio as the heights.
The larger radius is $\frac{5}{3}$ of the smaller radius $= \frac{5}{3} \times 4.2$ cm $= 7$ cm.

Exercise 17.1

1.   Copy these figures and for each one draw an enlargement with scale factor 2.

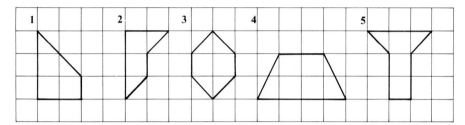

2.   What is the scale factor
     of the enlargement which
     transforms figure *A* into
     figure *B*?

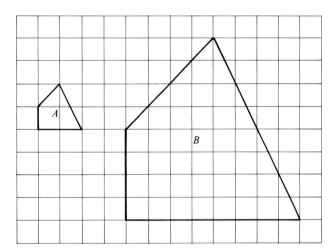

3.   **1** In what ratio, in its simplest form, are
         the lengths of these rectangles?
     2 In what ratio, in its simplest form, are
         the breadths of these rectangles?
     3 Are these rectangles similar?
     4 What is the ratio of the lengths
         of their diagonals?

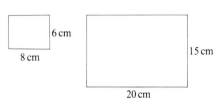

4.   **1** What is the ratio of the heights of these
         cylinders?
     2 What is the ratio of the radii of these
         cylinders?
     3 Are these cylinders similar?

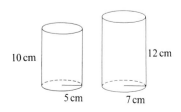

5.   Two circles have diameters 8 cm and 10 cm. What is the ratio of their radii?

6.   These pyramids have square bases with edges
     4 cm and 6 cm. Their heights are 6 cm and
     9 cm.

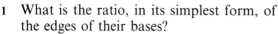

   1   What is the ratio, in its simplest form, of
       the edges of their bases?
   2   What is the ratio, in its simplest form, of
       their heights?
   3   Are the pyramids similar?

7.   Two spheres have radii 15 cm and 20 cm. What is the ratio of their diameters?

8.   These circles, with the same centre, have radii 3 cm
     and 4 cm.
     Without substituting any numerical value for π,
     find

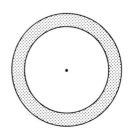

   1   the ratio of the lengths of their circumferences,
   2   the ratio of their areas.
   3   What fraction of the whole area is shaded?

9.   Two similar cones have heights in the ratio $3:7$. If the base radius of the larger
     one is 14 cm, what is the base radius of the smaller one?

Similar triangles

Similar triangles have the same shape.
(If they have the same size also, they are called congruent triangles.)

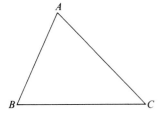
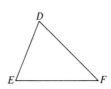

If the triangles ABC, DEF are similar then they have the same shape, so
$\angle A = \angle D$
$\angle B = \angle E$
$\angle C = \angle F$

Their sides are in proportion, so the ratios $\dfrac{AB}{DE}$, $\dfrac{AC}{DF}$ and $\dfrac{BC}{EF}$ are equal.

Examples

(1)   (2)   (3)

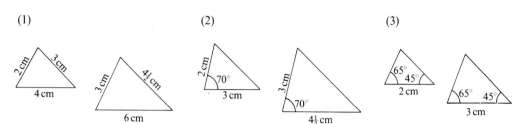

We recognise that the triangles are similar because:

In (1), the three sides of the first triangle are proportional to the three sides of the second triangle. The ratio in each case is $2:3$.

In (2), two sides of the first triangle are proportional to two of the sides of the second triangle, and the angles included between the two sides are equal.

In (3), the three angles of the first triangle are equal to the three angles of the second triangle, (i.e. the triangles are equiangular).
(The 3rd angle in each triangle is $180° - (65° + 45°) = 70°$.)

Example 5

Name a pair of similar triangles.
Find the lengths of DE and BD.

$\triangle ABD$ is similar to $\triangle ACE$ because the 3 angles of $\triangle ABD$ are equal in turn to the 3 angles of $\triangle ACE$ (because of the parallel lines).
So the sides are in the same ratio.

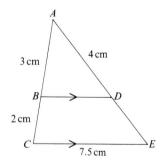

$\dfrac{EA}{DA}$ is in the same ratio as $\dfrac{CA}{BA}$ which is $\frac{5}{3}$.

So EA is $\frac{5}{3}$ of $DA = \frac{5}{3} \times 4\,\text{cm} = \frac{20}{3}\,\text{cm} = 6\frac{2}{3}\,\text{cm}$.
Then $DE = (6\frac{2}{3} - 4)\,\text{cm} = 2\frac{2}{3}\,\text{cm}$.
$DE = 2.7\,\text{cm}$ to the nearest mm.

$\dfrac{BD}{CE}$ is in the same ratio as $\dfrac{BA}{CA}$, which is $\frac{3}{5}$.

So BD is $\frac{3}{5}$ of $CE = \frac{3}{5} \times 7.5\,\text{cm} = 4.5\,\text{cm}$.

Centre of Enlargement

If there is a centre of enlargement O and a scale factor k, then each point A is mapped to a position A_1 on the line OA such that distance $OA_1 = k \times$ distance OA.

Examples

When the scale factor is 2   When the scale factor is 3

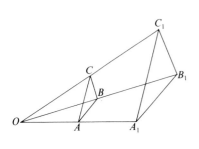

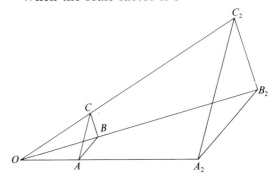

$$OA_1 = 2 \times OA$$
$$OB_1 = 2 \times OB$$
$$OC_1 = 2 \times OC$$

$$OA_2 = 3 \times OA$$
$$OB_2 = 3 \times OB$$
$$OC_2 = 3 \times OC$$

Since lines are altered in the same ratio the mapped figure is similar to the original figure with lengths in the ratio $k : 1$.

In the 1st diagram:
$\Delta A_1 B_1 C_1$ is similar to ΔABC and $A_1 B_1 = 2AB$, $B_1 C_1 = 2BC$, $A_1 C_1 = 2AC$

In the 2nd diagram:
$\Delta A_2 B_2 C_2$ is similar to ΔABC and $A_2 B_2 = 3AB$, $B_2 C_2 = 3BC$, $A_2 C_2 = 3AC$.

Exercise 17.2

1. 1 Explain why these triangles are similar.
    2 What is the ratio $BC : EF$?
    3 Which angle is equal to $\angle C$?

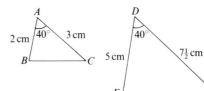

2. 1 Explain why these triangles are
        similar.
    2 Name an angle equal to $\angle B$.

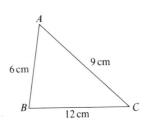

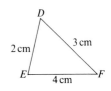

3. **1** Explain why triangles *ABC*, *ADE* are similar.
   2 What is the ratio *AD* : *AB*?
   3 What is the ratio *ED* : *CB*?
   4 If *DE* = $4\frac{1}{2}$ cm, what is the length of *BC*?

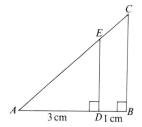

4. **1** What is the ratio $\dfrac{AC}{DC}$ in its simplest form?

   2 What is the ratio $\dfrac{BC}{EC}$ in its simplest form?

   3 Are the triangles *ABC* and *DEC* similar?

   4 What is the ratio $\dfrac{AB}{DE}$?

   5 Which angle is equal to ∠*A*?
   6 Which angle is equal to ∠*B*?

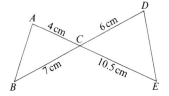

5. Copy these diagrams onto squared paper.
   Using *O* as the centre of enlargement and a scale factor 2, transform the line *AB* into a line *A′B′*.

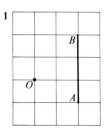
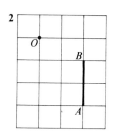
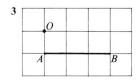
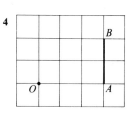

6. Copy these diagrams onto squared paper.
   Using *O* as the centre of enlargement and a scale factor of 3, transform triangle *T* into a triangle *T′*.

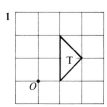
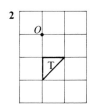
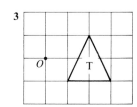

Exercise 17.3

1. Squared paper has been used to draw a
   figure representing a cuboid.
   Copy the figure onto squared paper and
   then draw an enlargement with scale
   factor 2.

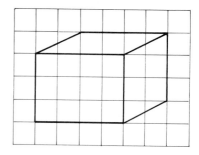

2. Two model boats are similar in shape. Their lengths are in the ratio 2:5. The
   smaller one is 10 cm wide. How wide is the larger one?

3. Two rectangular boxes are similar in shape. The smaller one has length 20 cm,
   width 16 cm and height 10 cm.

   1 The larger one has height 15 cm. What are its other measurements?
   2 Find the volumes of these boxes and hence find the ratio of the volumes, in
   its simplest form.

4. **1** Name two similar triangles.
   2 Find the ratio $AX : XC$.

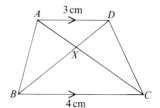

5. A stick 2 m long is placed vertically so
   that its top is in line with the top of a cliff,
   from a point A on the ground 3 m from
   the stick and 120 m from the cliff.
   How high is the cliff?

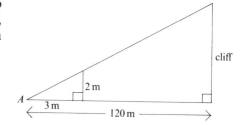

6. The diagram shows a regular pentagon
   with all diagonals drawn.

   1 Name a triangle similar to $\triangle ABE$, with AB
   as one of its sides.
   2 Name two triangles, of different sizes,
   similar to $\triangle ASR$, each with AB as one of its
   sides.

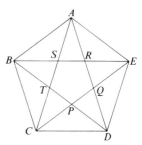

7. 1 Name 3 similar triangles.
   2 In what ratio are $BC:DE:GF$?
   3 Which point is the mid-point of AG?

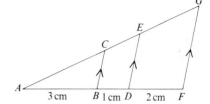

8. A triangle is transformed by enlargement with scale factor 3 into a similar triangle.

   1 One side of the new triangle has length 4.5 cm. What is the length of the corresponding side of the original triangle?
   2 One angle of the new triangle has size 66°. What is the size of the corresponding angle of the original triangle?

9. Copy this diagram onto squared paper. Triangle ABC has been enlarged into triangle $A'B'C'$. What is the scale factor of the enlargement?
   By joining $A'A$, $B'B$, $C'C$ and continuing these lines, find on your diagram the position of the centre O of the enlargement.

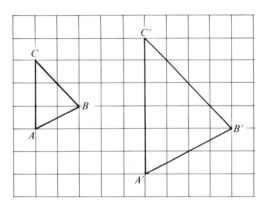

PUZZLES

51. A friend offered £100 to provide prizes for a Charity Tombola on condition that exactly 100 prizes were bought. The committee running the Tombola wanted to buy prizes costing £10, £2 and 50 pence, with more than one at each price. How could they fulfil the conditions of the gift?

52. Mark, the racing driver, did his first practice lap at 40 miles per hour. What speed would he have to average on his second lap if he wanted to produce an average for the two laps of 80 miles per hour?

53. A practical test. You are given 27 packages and told that 26 of them are of equal weight but 1 is slightly lighter. You are also given a balance-type weighing scale so that you can weigh some on one side against some on the other. However, you are only allowed to make 3 weighings. How can you find the lighter one?

54. Arrange (a) three 1's, (b) three 2's, (c) three 4's, without using any mathematical signs, so that you represent the highest possible number in each case.

18 *Scale drawing*

Horizontal and vertical lines

A spirit level shows whether lines are horizontal.
A plumb line (a heavy weight on a thin string) shows whether lines are vertical.

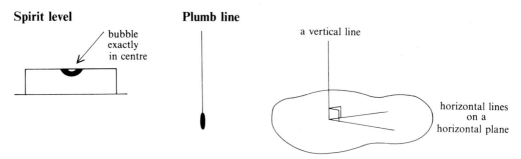

Spirit level

bubble
exactly
in centre

Plumb line

a vertical line

horizontal lines
on a
horizontal plane

Compass Directions

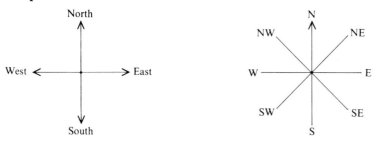

North

West ← → East

South

NW N NE

W E

SW S SE

Bearings. 3-figure bearings

Bearings (directions) are measured from the North, in a clockwise direction. They are given in degrees, as 3-figure numbers.

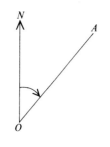

Angles of elevation and depression

Both of these are measured from the horizontal direction.

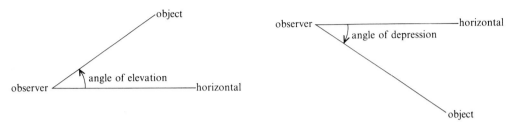

Scale Drawing

Scales can be given in various ways, such as
      1 cm represents $\frac{1}{2}$ m
or 2 cm represents 1 m
or Scale 1 : 50

or $\frac{1}{50}$ scale.

The symbol ≡ can be used for 'represents', e.g. 2 cm ≡ 1 m.

In any scale drawing, the scale should be stated.

The scale of a map

Some possible scales are 1 : 1250, 1 : 2500, 1 : 10 000, 1 : 25 000, etc.

The scale 1 : 100 000 means that
1 unit represents 100 000 units, so
1 cm represents 100 000 cm, which is 1 km.

The scale 1 : 250 000 means that
1 unit represents 250 000 units, so
1 cm represents 250 000 cm, which is 2.5 km.

Examples

1   Show the directions given by the bearings 060°, 300°.

Direction OA has a bearing of 060°   Direction OB has a bearing of 300°

To find the bearing of a reverse direction, add 180°. If this comes to 360° or more, subtract 180° instead.

2   Find the bearings of *AO* and *BO* from example 1.

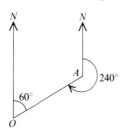

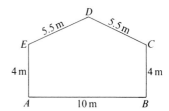

Bearing *OA* was 060°.   Bearing *OB* was 300°.
Bearing *AO* is 060° + 180° = 240°   Bearing *BO* is 300° − 180° = 120°

3   This diagram shows a sketch of one end of a building. Draw an accurate scale drawing, using a scale of 1 : 100.
By measurement, find how high the highest point is from ground level.

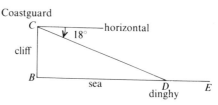

1 : 100 means that 1 cm will represent 1 m.
Begin by drawing the line *AB*, 10 cm long. Make accurate right angles at *A* and *B*, and draw the lines *AE* and *BC*, both 4 cm long.
To find point *D*, use compasses. With centre *E*, radius 5.5 cm, draw an arc, and with centre *C*, same radius, draw an arc which will cut the first arc at *D*. Join *CD* and *ED*.
To find the height of *D* above *AB*, construct a perpendicular line from *D* to *AB*. (By symmetry, this will be the line from *D* to the mid-point of *AB*.) This distance is 6.3 cm on the scale drawing.
So the highest point is 6.3 m above ground level.

4   A coastguard on a cliff 80 m high sees a dinghy out to sea at an angle of depression of 18°. How far is the dinghy from the foot of the cliff?

Sketch diagram

A suitable scale would be 1 cm to represent 20 m.
Begin by drawing a horizontal line *BE* for the sea, make an accurate right angle at *B*, and draw the cliff *BC*, making this line 4 cm long. The angle of depression is 18° so the angle in the triangle at the top of the cliff is 72°.
Measure an angle of 72° giving the direction of the line *CD*.
Draw this line and extend it to meet *BE* at *D*. Measure *BD*.
BD is 12.3 cm, so the actual distance is 12.3 × 20 m.
The dinghy is 246 m from the foot of the cliff.
(It would be sensible to give this distance as approximately 250 m.)

Exercise 18.1

1. Find the bearings given by *OA*, *OB*, *OC*, *OD* and *OE*.

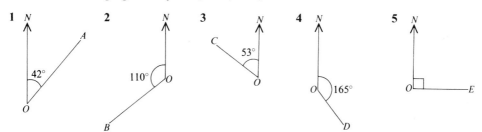

2. Draw sketches to show the directions given by the bearings

   1 200°   **2** 020°   **3** 290°   **4** 135°   **5** 002°

3. Find the bearings of the directions *AO*, *BO*, *CO*, *DO* and *EO* in question 1.

4. **1** The bearing of *OA* is 033°.
   The bearing of *OB* is 123°.
   Fine the size of ∠*AOB*.

   2 The bearing of *OA* is 160°.
   The bearing of *OB* is 240°.
   Find the size of ∠*AOB*.

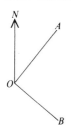

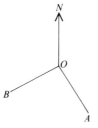

   3 The bearing of *OA* is 040°.
   The bearing of *OB* is 310°.
   Find the size of ∠*AOB*.

   4 The bearing of *OA* is 035°.
   The angle *OAB* is 95°.
   Find the bearing of *BA*.

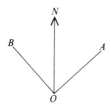

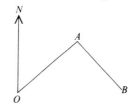

   5 The bearing of *OA* is 240°.
   The angle *OAB* is 80°.
   OA = *AB*.
   Find the bearing of *OB*.

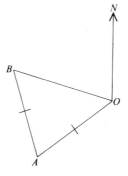

5. A map has a scale of 2 cm to represent 1 km. What is this scale in ratio form? If two villages are 8.4 cm apart on the map, what is the actual distance between them?

6. A hall is 20 m long and 13.5 m wide. What measurements should be used on a plan to a scale of 1 : 250?

7. The scale of a map is 1 : 25 000. What is the actual distance in km between two points which are 8 cm apart on the map?

8. Draw an accurate scale drawing of this garden which is 25 m long and 15 m wide, using a scale of 1 cm to represent 2 m.
    The lawn is 17 m long and 11 m wide and the path round three sides of it is 1 m wide.
    In the centre of the lawn, draw in a circular pond of diameter 5 m.
    Find the area of the vegetable plot.

9. There are four towns A, B, C, D. B is 100 km North of A, C is 90 km on a bearing of 140° from A, D is 120 km on a bearing 260° from A.
    Draw an accurate scale drawing and find the distances between the towns B and C, C and D, B and D.

10. From a point A on top of a cliff 70 m high two boats B and C have angles of depression of 33° and 42°, and both boats are due East of A.
    Draw an accurate scale drawing, and find how far apart the boats are.

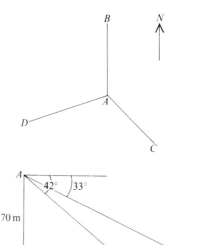

11. Draw an accurate scale drawing of a rectangular field, 80 m long and 50 m wide. By measurement on your drawing, find the actual distance from a corner of the field to the opposite corner, to the nearest metre.

12. A boy stands 60 m from the base of a tower and on the same level as the base. He finds that the angle of elevation of the top of the tower is 14°. Draw an accurate scale drawing and use it to find the height of the tower to the nearest metre. (Ignore the height of the boy.)

13. An explorer walks 1000 m on a bearing of 070° and he then walks 2000 m on a bearing of 160°. Draw an accurate scale drawing of his route.
By measurement, find the bearing he must follow to return directly to his starting point, and find how far he has to go.

14. The map shows the positions of 4 towns *A*, *B*, *C*, *D*.

This table shows the distances by road between the towns, in km.

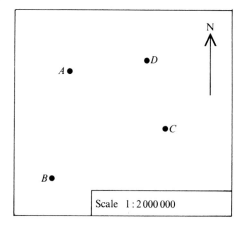

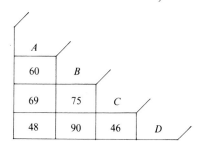

1   A helicopter must fly directly from *B* to *D*. On what bearing must it fly?

2   How much further is it for a motorist to travel from *B* to *D* than for the helicopter?

Bearings, Alternative Notation

In this notation, bearings are measured from North or South, whichever is the nearer direction, and they are measured towards the East or towards the West.

Examples:

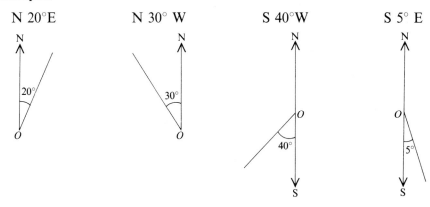

Exercise 18.2

1. Using this notation, find the bearings given by OA, OB, OC, OD, OF.

1

W—————E, N up, S down, with A at 20° from N in NW region.

2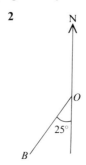

3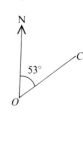

4

N up, from O angle 110° to D (going down-right).

5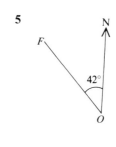

2. Draw sketches to show the directions given by the bearings

   1 N 40° E   **2** S 15° W   **3** N 80° W   **4** N 4° E   **5** S 10° E

Exercise 18.3

1. A model of a hall of rectangular shape is made to a scale of 2 cm to 1 m. The height of the model is 16 cm and its floor measurements are 25 cm by 32 cm. Find the height and floor measurements of the hall and hence calculate its volume.

2. The angle of elevation of a balloon due West of an observer A and 600 m high is 42°. How far is the observer from a point on level ground vertically below the balloon?

3. A fishing boat is 20 km due North of its harbour. It sails on a bearing of 110° at an average speed of 12 km/hour. Show this information on a scale drawing. After 2 hours there is a gale warning on the radio. In what direction should the boat be headed to get straight back to the harbour, and how far has it to go? If it increases its speed to 16 km/hour, how long will it take?

4. The diagram shows a rectangular field. Treasure is hidden in the field (1) 60 m from A, (2) equidistant from B and D. Draw a scale drawing of the field and draw loci for conditions (1) and (2). Mark with T the position of the treasure. How far is the treasure from corner B?

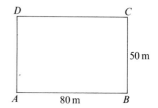

5. A boat is just off the cape at *A* and it wants to reach the harbour at *B*. On what
    bearing must the boat sail?
    The distance *AB* is actually 10.8 km. What is the scale of the map?
    After reaching *B*, the boat then sails to a bay at *C*. What is the actual distance
    from *B* to *C*?
    From *C*, on what bearing must the boat sail to return round the cape at *A*?

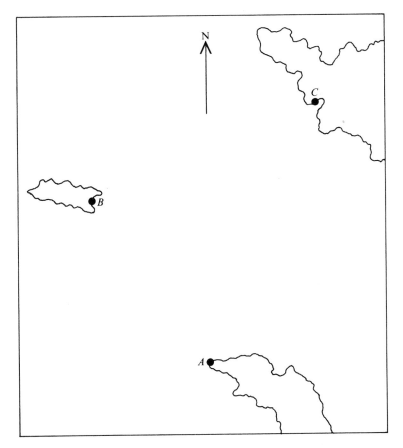

6. There are radio stations at 3 places *A*, *B*,
    C. Broadcasts from *A* can be heard within
    a distance of 30 km, those from *B* within
    a distance of 40 km, and those from *C*
    within a distance of 45 km.
    Draw an accurate scale drawing and mark
    the loci of the boundaries of the three
    broadcast receiving areas. Shade in the
    region where all three stations can be
    heard.

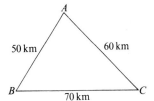

7. Treasure is hidden in the triangular field
    ABC (1) equidistant from *AB* and *BC*,
    (2) 10 m from *AC*.
    Draw a scale drawing of the field and draw
    loci for conditions (1) and (2). Mark with
    T the position of the treasure.
    How far is it from corner *A*?

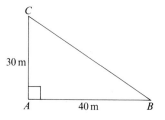

8. A camper pitches his tent equidistant
    from the farm, the shop and the cafe.
    Show on an accurate scale drawing
    where this is. How far is he from any of
    the three places?

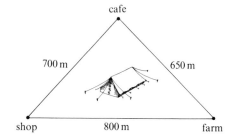

9. A camper pitches his tent equidistant from
    the beach, the river and the road. Show on
    an accurate scale drawing where this is.
    How far from the beach is it?

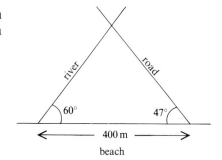

10. In a sailing race the boats go round a triangular
    course *ABC*, with *AB* = 4 km, *BC* = 5 km and
    CA = 6 km. If the direction of *AB* is due
    North, on what bearing do the boats head
    from *B* to *C*?

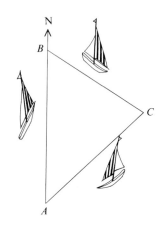

11. This plan of the ground floor of a house is drawn to a scale of 1 cm represents 1 m.
What are the measurements of

  1 the lounge,   **2** the dining-room,   **3** the kitchen?
  4 What is the area of the lounge? A carpet for this room costs £18 per m². What is the cost of the carpet?

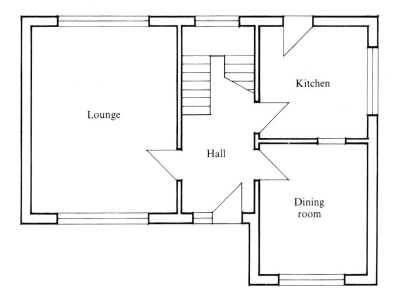

PUZZLES

55 A group of six children have to send a team of four of them to take part in a quiz. But they all have their own views on whether they will take part or not.
Laura won't be in the team unless Michelle is also in it.
Michelle won't be in the team if Oliver is.
Naomi won't be in the team if both Laura and Michelle are in it.
Oliver won't be in the team if Patrick is.
Patrick will be in the team with any of the others.
Robert won't be in the team if Laura is, unless Oliver is in it too.
Which 4 took part in the quiz.?

56. See how many of the numbers from 1 to 100 you can represent using three 9's, and the usual signs.
e.g. $78 = (9 \times 9) - \sqrt{9}$
(You will not be able to represent them all.)

19 *Transformations. Vectors*

Transformations have been introduced in Chapters 3 and 17. They are summarised here.

In these examples the line AB where A is (2, 1) and B is (3, 2) is transformed into the line $A'B'$. A' is called the **image** of A, B' is the image of B and the line $A'B'$ is the image of the line AB.

Translation

e.g. the translation 4 units in the x-direction, 1 unit in the y-direction.

A (2, 1) is transformed into A' (6, 2)
B (3, 2) is transformed into B' (7, 3)
The line AB is translated into the line $A'B'$.

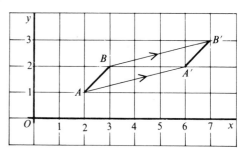

Enlargement with scale factor 2, and centre of enlargement O (0, 0).

A (2, 1) is transformed into A' (2×2, 2×1), i.e. (4, 2)
B (3, 2) is transformed into B' (6, 4)
The line AB is transformed into the line $A'B'$.
AB and $A'B'$ are parallel and
length $A'B' = 2 \times$ length AB.
Triangles $OA'B'$ and OAB are similar with lengths in the ratio $2:1$.

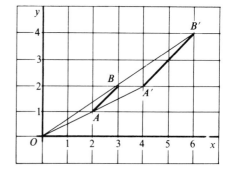

If the scale factor is 3 then
A (2, 1) is transformed into A' (3×2, 3×1), i.e. (6, 3)
B (3, 2) is transformed into B' (9, 6)
The line AB is transformed into the line $A'B'$.
AB and $A'B'$ are parallel and length $A'B' = 3 \times$ length AB.
Triangles $OA'B'$ and OAB are similar with lengths in the ratio $3:1$.

Reflection in the *x*-axis

A (2, 1) is transformed into *A'* (2, − 1)
B (3, 2) is transformed into *B'* (3, − 2)
The line *AB* is reflected into the line *A'B'*.
AB and *A'B'* are equal in length and the *x*-axis
is a line of symmetry between *AB* and *A'B'*.

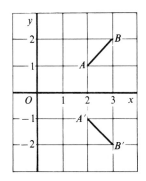

Reflection in the *y*-axis

A (2, 1) is transformed into *A'* (− 2, 1)
B (3, 2) is transformed into *B'* (− 3, 2)
The line *AB* is reflected into the line *A'B'*.
AB and *A'B'* are equal in length and the *y*-axis
is a line of symmetry between *AB* and *A'B'*.

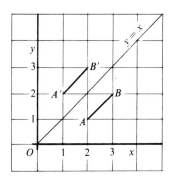

Reflection in the line *y* = *x*

A (2, 1) is transformed into *A'* (1, 2)
B (3, 2) is transformed into *B'* (2, 3)
The line *AB* is reflected into the line *A'B'*.
AB and *A'B'* are equal in length and the line
y = *x* is an axis of symmetry between *AB* and
A'B'.

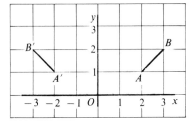

Reflection in the line *y* = − *x*

A (2, 1) is transformed into *A'* (− 1, − 2)
B (3, 2) is transformed into *B'* (− 2, − 3)
The line *AB* is reflected into the line *A'B'*.
AB and *A'B'* are equal in length and the line
y = − *x* is an axis of symmetry between *AB*
and *A'B'*.

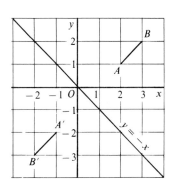

Rotation about the origin through 90° anticlockwise ($\frac{1}{4}$ turn)

A (2, 1) is transformed into A' (−1, 2)
B (3, 2) is transformed into B' (−2, 3)
The line AB is rotated into the line $A'B'$.
AB and $A'B'$ are equal in length.

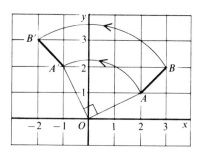

Rotation about the origin through 180° ($\frac{1}{2}$ turn)

A (2, 1) is transformed into A' (−2, −1)
B (3, 2) is transformed into B' (−3, −2)
The line AB is rotated into the line $A'B'$.
AB and $A'B'$ are equal in length.
O is a point of symmetry between AB and
$A'B'$.

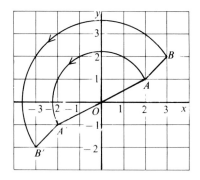

Rotation about the origin through 90° clockwise ($\frac{1}{4}$ turn)

(or 270° anticlockwise, $\frac{3}{4}$ turn)

A (2, 1) is transformed into A' (1, −2)
B (3, 2) is transformed into B' (2, −3)
The line AB is rotated into the line $A'B'$.
AB and $A'B'$ are equal in length.

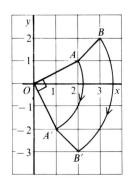

Rotations can be made about other points.

e.g. AB rotated through 90° anticlockwise about point A.

A is unaltered.
B is transformed into B' (1, 2).

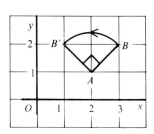

Enlargements can have centres of enlargement other than the origin.

e.g. Enlargement with scale factor 2 and centre of enlargement C (3, 0)

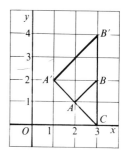

A is transformed into A' (1, 2)
B is transformed into B' (3, 4)
AB and $A'B'$ are parallel and length $A'B' = 2 \times$ length AB.
Triangles $CA'B'$ and CAB are similar with lengths in the ratio $2:1$.

Reflections in other lines

e.g. Reflection in the line $y = 3$.

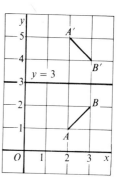

A is transformed into A' (2, 5)
B is transformed into B' (3, 4)
AB and $A'B'$ are equal in length and $y = 3$ is an axis of symmetry between AB and $A'B'$.

Exercise 19.1

1. State which single transformation will map

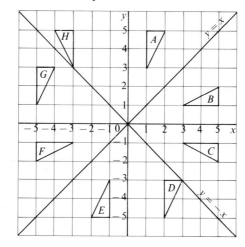

    1 A into B

    2 A into C

    3 A into D

    4 A into E

    5 A into F

    6 A into G

    7 A into H

    8 B into C

    9 C into F

    10 D into G.

2. On graph paper draw x and y axes from 0 to 6.
   Plot the points $A(3, 1)$, $B(3, 2)$, $C(6, 1)$, $D(6, 5)$. Join AB and CD.
   What is the scale factor of the enlargement which maps AB onto CD?
   Let E be the centre of this enlargement. What are the coordinates of E?

3. Describe the transformations which map the
   triangles

   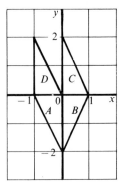

   1   A onto B

   2   A onto C

   3   A onto D

   4   B onto C

   5   C onto D.

4. Draw the x-axis from 0 to 6 and the y-axis from 0 to 9. Take the origin as centre
   of enlargement.
   A is (1, 1), B is (2, 1) and C is (2, 3). Enlarge triangle ABC with scale factor 3
   mapping it into triangle $A_1B_1C_1$.
   State the coordinates of A_1, B_1, C_1.
   What is the ratio of length of B_1C_1 : length of BC?

5. In the diagram triangle OAB is
   rotated clockwise about the
   origin through $90°$ onto position
   OA_1B_1.
   Triangle OA_1B_1 is reflected in the
   x-axis onto triangle OA_2B_2.
   Draw the 3 triangles on your
   own diagram.
   What single transformation
   would map triangle OAB onto
   triangle OA_2B_2?

   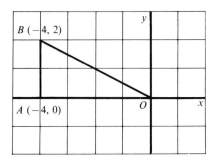

6. An operation is described as 'Translate 4 units parallel to the x-axis then reflect
   the image point in the line $y = x$'.

   1   What is the final position of the point (3, 4)?
   2   What is the point whose final position is (3, 4)?

7. Draw the x-axis from 0 to 7 and the y-axis from -4 to 5. Taking C (1, 2) as
   centre of enlargement, A (3, 0) is mapped into A_1 (7, -4). What is the scale
   factor of the enlargement?
   Using this same transformation B (2, 3) is mapped into B_1. What are the
   coordinates of B_1?
   What is the ratio length A_1B_1 : length AB?

In questions 8 to 11 draw x and y axes from -8 to 8 using equal scales on both axes.
Draw the triangle ABC where A is (1, 1), B is (4, 2) and C is (3, 7).

8. Reflect triangle ABC about the y-axis. What are the coordinates of the image
    points A_1, B_1, C_1?
    Rotate triangle $A_1 B_1 C_1$ about the origin through 180°. What are the coordinates
    of the image points A_2, B_2, C_2?
    What single transformation would map triangle ABC onto triangle $A_2 B_2 C_2$?

9. Rotate triangle ABC anticlockwise about the origin through 90°. What are the
    coordinates of the image points A_1, B_1, C_1?
    Reflect triangle $A_1 B_1 C_1$ about the x-axis. What are the coordinates of the image
    points A_2, B_2, C_2?
    What single transformation would map triangle ABC onto triangle $A_2 B_2 C_2$?

10. Reflect triangle ABC about the line $y = 1$. What are the coordinates of the image
    points A_1, B_1, C_1?
    Reflect triangle $A_1 B_1 C_1$ about the line $y = x$. What are the coordinates of the
    image points A_2, B_2, C_2?
    What single transformation would map triangle ABC onto triangle $A_2 B_2 C_2$?

11. Translate triangle ABC to triangle $A_1 B_1 C_1$ by moving each point 3 units in the
    x direction and then -2 units in the y direction. What are the coordinates of the
    image points A_1, B_1, C_1?
    Transform triangle $A_1 B_1 C_1$ to triangle $A_2 B_2 C_2$ by translating each point -8
    units in the x direction and then 3 units in the y direction.
    What are the coordinates of the image points A_2, B_2, C_2?
    What single transformation would map triangle ABC onto triangle $A_2 B_2 C_2$?

Vectors

A vector quantity has a size and a direction.

Examples:
Velocity. A plane overhead is travelling towards London at a speed of 600 mph.
Displacement. A boy is 400 m from home, and due South of it.
Force. Kick the ball as hard as you can in the direction of the goal.

The line AB can represent the vector of a displacement from A to B.

If A is (1, 2) and B is (5, 3) then the displacement is
4 units in the x direction and 1 unit in the y direction.

This vector can be represented by the matrix $\begin{pmatrix} 4 \\ 1 \end{pmatrix}$.

This also represents the **translation** of A to B.

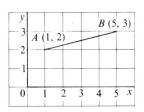

Any other line parallel to AB with the same length also represents the vector $\begin{pmatrix} 4 \\ 1 \end{pmatrix}$.

Notation

If the vector is represented by a line AB this is written as $\overline{AB}$, $\overrightarrow{AB}$ or **AB**.

The lines on diagrams can be marked with arrows to show the directions of the vectors. In this diagram, $\overrightarrow{AB}$ is $\begin{pmatrix} 3 \\ 2 \end{pmatrix}$ and $\overrightarrow{CD}$ is $\begin{pmatrix} -3 \\ -2 \end{pmatrix}$.

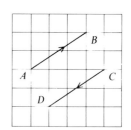

Equal vectors have the same size and the same direction. In this diagram $\overrightarrow{AB}$ and $\overrightarrow{DC}$ are equal vectors.

Addition of vectors

1   The rule for addition is $\overrightarrow{AB} + \overrightarrow{BC} = \overrightarrow{AC}$.
This is shown in the diagram.

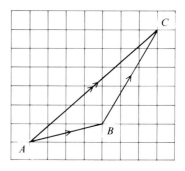

2   To add $\overrightarrow{AB} + \overrightarrow{AD}$ draw $\overrightarrow{AB}$ and $\overrightarrow{AD}$.
Make a parallelogram with BC equal to AD.
Then $\overrightarrow{AB} + \overrightarrow{AD} = \overrightarrow{AB} + \overrightarrow{BC} = \overrightarrow{AC}$.
This is shown in the diagram.

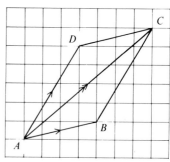

Subtraction of vectors

1   To subtract $\overrightarrow{AB} - \overrightarrow{BC}$, draw $\overrightarrow{AB}$, and draw
$\overrightarrow{BE}$ equal and in the opposite direction to $\overrightarrow{BC}$.
Then $\overrightarrow{AB} - \overrightarrow{BC} = \overrightarrow{AB} + \overrightarrow{BE} = \overrightarrow{AE}$.
This is shown in the diagram.

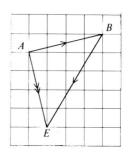

2 To subtract $\overrightarrow{AB} - \overrightarrow{AD}$.

Since $\overrightarrow{AD} + \overrightarrow{DB} = \overrightarrow{AB}$, then $\overrightarrow{AB} - \overrightarrow{AD} = \overrightarrow{DB}$.
This is shown in the diagram.

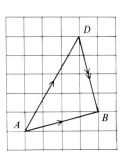

Multiplication by a number

If $\overrightarrow{CD} = 2\,\overrightarrow{AB}$, then $\overrightarrow{CD}$ is a vector twice as long as $\overrightarrow{AB}$ and parallel to $\overrightarrow{AB}$.
If $\overrightarrow{CD} = -3\,\overrightarrow{AB}$, then $\overrightarrow{CD}$ is a vector three times as long as $\overrightarrow{AB}$, parallel to $\overrightarrow{AB}$ but in the opposite direction because of the minus sign.
These are shown in the diagrams.

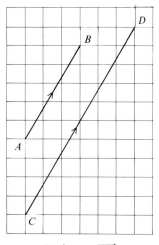

$$\overrightarrow{CD} = 2\,\overrightarrow{AB}$$

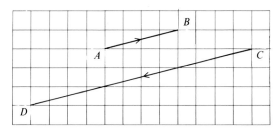

$$\overrightarrow{CD} = -3\,\overrightarrow{AB}$$

Exercise 19.2

1. Copy the diagrams and show a vector representing $\overrightarrow{AB} + \overrightarrow{BC}$.

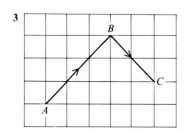

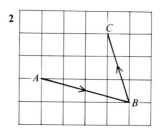

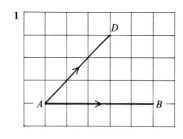

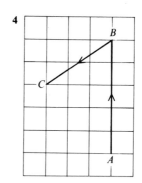

2. Copy the diagrams and show a vector representing $\overrightarrow{AB} + \overrightarrow{AD}$.

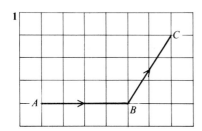

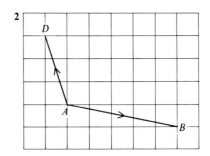

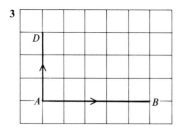

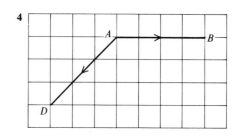

3. Copying the vectors of question 1 again, show a vector representing $\overrightarrow{AB} - \overrightarrow{BC}$.

4. Copying the vectors of question 2 again, show a vector representing $\overrightarrow{AB} - \overrightarrow{AD}$.

5. Copy the vector $\overrightarrow{AB}$ in question 1, part **2** and draw vectors representing $2\overrightarrow{AB}$, $3\overrightarrow{AB}$ and $-\overrightarrow{AB}$.

6. Copy the vector $\overrightarrow{BC}$ in question 1, part **4** and draw vectors representing $2\overrightarrow{BC}$ and $-3\overrightarrow{BC}$.

7. **1** Write down the vectors $\overrightarrow{AB}$, $\overrightarrow{CD}$, $\overrightarrow{EF}$, $\overrightarrow{GH}$, $\overrightarrow{JK}$, $\overrightarrow{LM}$ and $\overrightarrow{NP}$ as column vectors.
    2 Which two vectors are equal?
    3 Which vector is equal to $\overrightarrow{AB}$ in size but not in direction?
    4 Which vector is equal to $2\overrightarrow{CD}$?

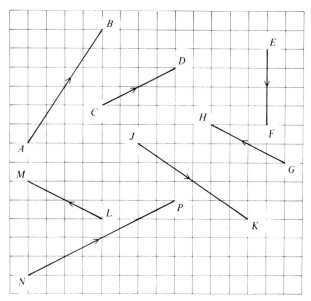

The lines are drawn on a unit grid.

8. On a graph, plot A, B, C, D such that A is (3, 2), B is (5, 6), C is (0, 4) and D is a point such that $\overrightarrow{AD} = \overrightarrow{BC}$.
    What are the coordinates of D?
    What kind of quadrilateral is $ABCD$?

Exercise 19.3

1. In the diagram, describe the transformations which map

    1 ΔA into ΔB
    2 ΔA into ΔC
    3 ΔA into ΔD
    4 ΔD into ΔE
    5 ΔF into ΔG
    6 ΔH into ΔG

    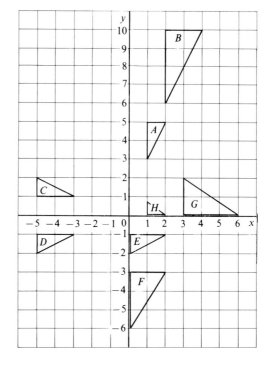

2. Draw x and y axes from -4 to 8. Plot the points A (1, 1) and B (4, 2) and draw the line AB.
    Find the image of the line AB after the following transformations.
    Give the coordinates of the new positions of A and B.

    1   Translate 2 units in the x direction and -3 units in the y direction.
    2   Enlarge, with centre at the origin, scale factor 2.
    3   Reflect in the line $y = -x$.
    4   Rotate about the origin through $\frac{1}{4}$ turn anticlockwise.

3. Draw x and y axes from -8 to 8. Draw the triangle ABC where A is (1, 1), B is (4, 2) and C is (3, 7).

    1 A is translated to A_1 $(-5, -6)$. Describe this translation. Using the same translation, translate B and C and draw the new triangle $A_1 B_1 C_1$.
    2   Triangle ABC is transformed by reflecting it in the y-axis. Draw the new triangle $A_2 B_2 C_2$.
    3   Triangle ABC is transformed by rotating it about the origin through $\frac{1}{4}$ turn clockwise. Draw the new triangle $A_3 B_3 C_3$.
    4   What transformation would map triangle $A_3 B_3 C_3$ into triangle $A_2 B_2 C_2$?

4. A point (x, y) is transformed by enlargement, centre the origin, scale factor 3, and the image point is $(6, -9)$. Find the values of x and y.

5. In the diagram, state the transformations which map

    1   ΔA into ΔB 4   ΔA into ΔE

    2   ΔA into ΔC 5   ΔA into ΔF

    3   ΔA into ΔD 6   ΔH into ΔG.

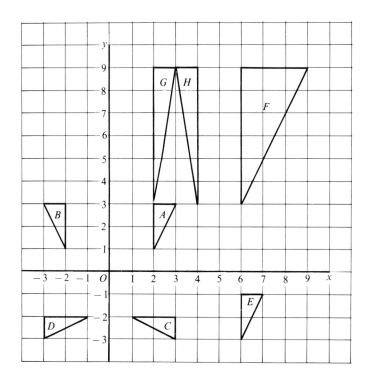

6. In ΔABC, A is (2, 1), B is (4, 3) and C is (7, 0).
   Find the coordinates of the image points A_1, B_1, C_1 when ΔABC is rotated about the origin through 180°. If Δ$A_1 B_1 C_1$ is then reflected in the x-axis, find the coordinates of the image points A_2, B_2, C_2. What single transformation would map ΔABC onto Δ$A_2 B_2 C_2$?

7. P is the point (2, 5). Q is the image of P under the translation T which is 'translate 3 units in the x direction and 1 unit in the y direction'.
   The enlargement, centre at the origin, scale factor 2 is carried out on points P and Q giving points P' and Q'. Say how the point P' can be mapped into Q', expressing this in terms of T.

8. The square $OABC$ where O is the origin, A is (1, 0), B is (1, 1) and C is (0, 1) is transformed into $OA_1 B_1 C_1$ by the enlargement, centre the origin, scale factor 3. Find the area of $OA_1 B_1 C_1$.

9. On your own diagrams show vectors representing

   1 $\overrightarrow{AB} + \overrightarrow{CD}$

   2 $\overrightarrow{AB} - \overrightarrow{CD}$

   3 $2\overrightarrow{AB}$

   4 $2\overrightarrow{AB} + \overrightarrow{CD}$.

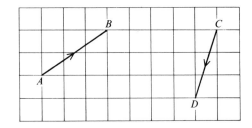

10. In the diagram, which vectors represent

    1 $\overrightarrow{AB} + \overrightarrow{AC}$

    2 $\overrightarrow{AB} - \overrightarrow{AC}$

    3 $2\overrightarrow{AG}$

    4 $\overrightarrow{AG} + \overrightarrow{GC}$

    5 $\overrightarrow{AG} - \overrightarrow{AB}$?

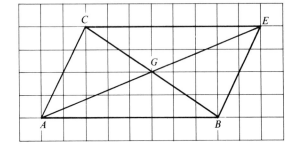

11. Write $\overrightarrow{AB}$ and $\overrightarrow{BC}$ in column form. D is a point

    such that $\overrightarrow{CD} = \begin{pmatrix} -2 \\ 1 \end{pmatrix}$, and E is a point such

    that $\overrightarrow{AE} = \begin{pmatrix} 0 \\ -1 \end{pmatrix}$.

    Find the length of $\overrightarrow{DE}$.

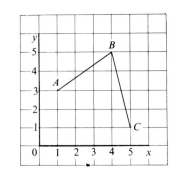

PUZZLE

57. Here is the final table in the local league. Every team has played every other team once. What was the score in the match between the Allsorts and the Dribblers?

	played	won	drawn	lost	goals for	goals against	points
Allsorts	3	3	0	0	4	0	6
Buskers	3	1	1	1	4	4	3
Cobblers	3	0	2	1	3	4	2
Dribblers	3	0	1	2	0	3	1

20 Trigonometry

(There is a practical introduction to this section in Exercise C5.)

There are three main relationships in a right-angled triangle:

$$\text{sine } A = \frac{\text{opposite}}{\text{hypotenuse}} = \frac{a}{c}$$
(sin A)

$$\text{cosine } A = \frac{\text{adjacent}}{\text{hypotenuse}} = \frac{b}{c}$$
(cos A)

$$\text{tangent } A = \frac{\text{opposite}}{\text{adjacent}} = \frac{a}{b}$$
(tan A)

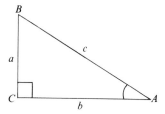

To find a side, given one side and an angle

If the hypotenuse is known, or if it is the side to be found, use the sine or cosine ratio. Otherwise use the tangent ratio, and in this case use the angle opposite the side you are trying to find.

Examples

1   To find AB.

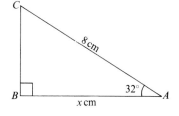

$$\cos 32° = \frac{\text{adj}}{\text{hyp}}$$

$$\cos 32° = \frac{x}{8}$$

$$x = 8 \times \cos 32°$$

$$= 6.784$$

$$AB = 6.78 \text{ cm (to 3 sig. figs.)}$$

(To use your calculator if it has got trig. functions, make sure it is set to work in degrees, then press 32, then cos, getting 0.8480 . . . then multiply this by 8, i.e. 32 $\boxed{\cos}$ $\boxed{\times}$ 8 $\boxed{=}$

If your calculator has not got trig. functions you can find the value of cos 32° from trig. tables.)

(Note that the formula $\cos A = \frac{\text{adj}}{\text{hyp}}$ can be rearranged as adj = hyp $\times \cos A$. This will give $x = 8 \times \cos 32°$ directly.)

2   To find AC.

Use tan ratio. Also use the angle opposite to AC, i.e. angle B, which is $54°$.

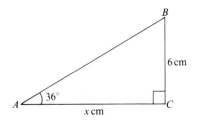

$$\tan 54° = \frac{\text{opp}}{\text{adj}}$$

$$\tan 54° = \frac{x}{6}$$

$$x = 6 \times \tan 54°$$

$$= 8.258$$

$$AC = 8.26 \, \text{cm (to 3 sig. figs.)}$$

(On your calculator, make sure it is set to work in degrees then press
54 $\boxed{\tan}$ $\boxed{\times}$ 6 $\boxed{=}$)

(Note that the formula $\tan B = \dfrac{\text{opp}}{\text{adj}}$ can be rearranged as opp $=$ adj $\times$ tan B. This will give $x = 6 \times \tan 54°$ directly.)

3   To find AC.

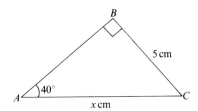

$$\sin 40° = \frac{\text{opp}}{\text{hyp}}$$

$$\sin 40° = \frac{5}{x}$$

$$x = \frac{5}{\sin 40°}$$

$$= 7.779$$

$$AC = 7.78 \, \text{cm (to 3 sig. figs.)}$$

(on your calculator press 5 $\boxed{\div}$ 40 $\boxed{\sin}$ $\boxed{=}$)

To find an angle, given two sides

If one of the sides is the hypotenuse, use the sine or cosine ratio. Otherwise use the tangent ratio.

Examples

4   To find $\angle A$

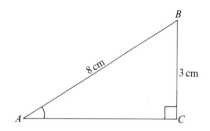

$$\sin A = \frac{\text{opp}}{\text{hyp}}$$

$$= \frac{3}{8} \, (=0.375)$$

$$\angle A = 22.0°$$

(Give the answer in degrees correct to 1 decimal place. On your calculator, make sure it is set to work in degrees. Find the key for the inverse of the sine function. It might be labelled $\sin^{-1}$, or arc sin. You will probably have to press the F key then the sin key to get it. Press 3 $\boxed{\div}$ 8 $\boxed{=}$ $\boxed{\text{inverse sine}}$)

The size of $\angle B$ can now be found by subtraction. The angles of the triangle add up to $180°$. Since $\angle C = 90°$ then $\angle A + \angle B = 90°$.
So $\angle B = 90° - 22.0° = 68.0°$.

5   To find $\angle A$

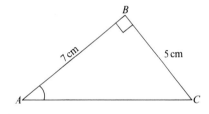

$$\tan A = \frac{\text{opp}}{\text{adj}}$$

$$= \frac{5}{7} \, (=0.7143)$$

$$\angle A = 35.5°$$

(On your calculator press 5 $\boxed{\div}$ 7 $\boxed{=}$ $\boxed{\text{inverse tan}}$)

Also $\angle C = 90° - \angle A = 90° - 35.5° = 54.5°$.

An isosceles triangle can be split into two congruent right-angled triangles.

Example 6

To find BC.

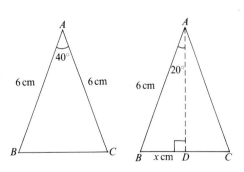

$$\sin 20° = \frac{\text{opp}}{\text{hyp}}$$

$$\sin 20° = \frac{x}{6}$$

$$x = 6 \times \sin 20°$$

$$2x = 12 \times \sin 20°$$

$$= 4.104$$

$$BC = 4.10 \, \text{cm (to 3 sig. figs.)}$$

Exercise 20.1

1. Use the sine ratio to find the length of side AC in these triangles.

1
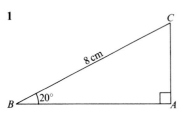

2
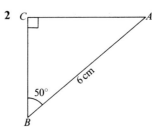

3
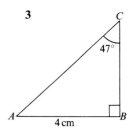

2. Use the cosine ratio to find the length of side BC in these triangles.

1
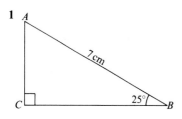

2
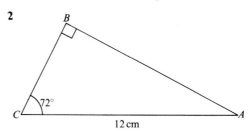

3
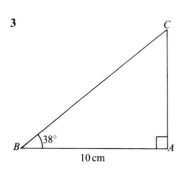

3. Use the tangent ratio to find the length of side AC in these triangles.

1
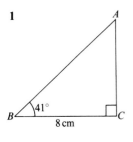

2
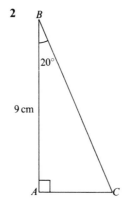

3
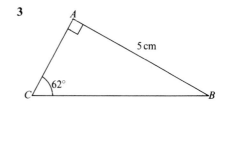

4. Use the sine ratio to find the marked angle in these triangles.

1

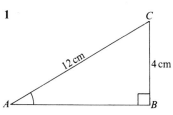

2

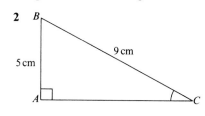

3

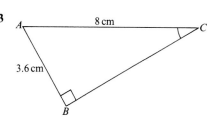

5. Use the cosine ratio to find the marked angle in these triangles.

1

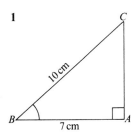

2

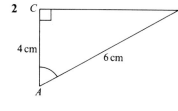

3

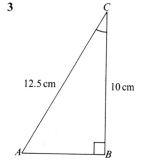

6. Use the tangent ratio to find the marked angle in these triangles. By subtraction find the third angle of each triangle.

1

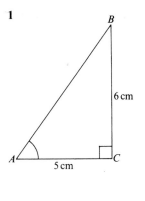

2

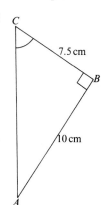

3

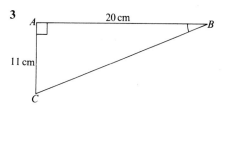

7. **1** Write down, as fractions, the ratios for sin A, cos A, tan A, sin B, cos B, tan B.

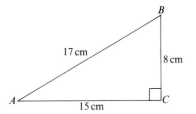

2 Calculate AB, and write down, as fractions, the ratios for sin A, cos A, tan A.

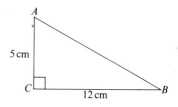

3 Calculate AC, and write down, as fractions in their simplest forms, the ratios for sin B, cos B, tan B.

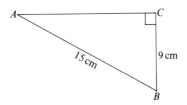

8. Calculate the length of the side AC in these right-angled triangles, giving the answers to 3 significant figures.

1
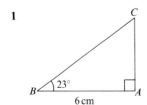

2
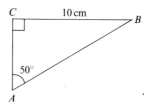

3
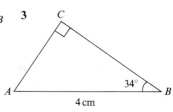

4
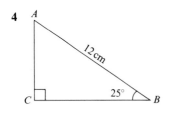

5
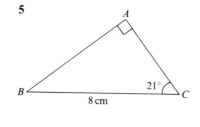

6
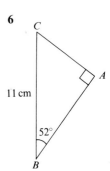

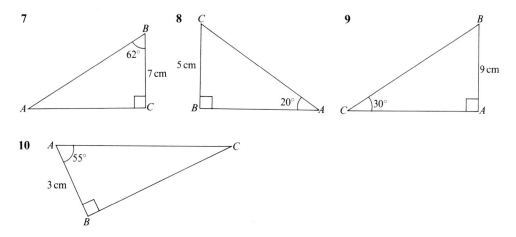

7   8   9

10

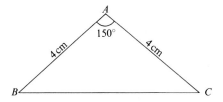

9. Sketch this isosceles triangle and draw the axis of symmetry. Use the right-angled triangles formed to calculate the length of BC, to 3 significant figures.

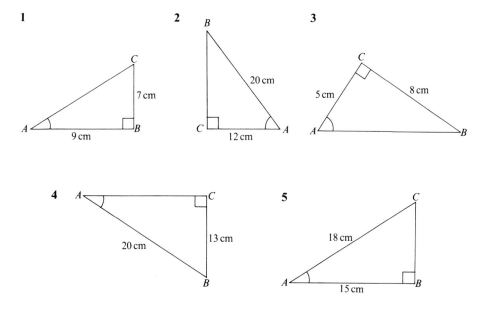

10. Calculate $\angle A$ in these right-angled triangles, in degrees, to 1 decimal place.

1   2   3

4   5

Example 7

A tower 30 m high stands at a point A. At a point B on the ground which is level with the foot of the tower the angle of elevation of the top of the tower is 28°. Find the distance of B from A.

Let T be the top of the tower. $\angle TAB$ is a right angle since TA is vertical and AB is horizontal.
To find AB use $\angle BTA$, which is 62°.

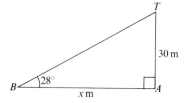

$$\tan 62° = \frac{\text{opp}}{\text{adj}}$$

$$\tan 62° = \frac{x}{30}$$

$$x = 30 \times \tan 62°$$

$$= 56.42$$

B is 56 m from the tower (to the nearest m)

Example 8

There are three landmarks A, B and C. A is due North of B and C is due West of B. From A the distance to B is 56.4 m and the distance to C is 112.0 m. Find the bearing of C from A.

$\angle ABC$ is a right angle since A is North of B and C is West of B.

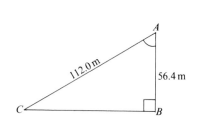

$$\cos \angle CAB = \frac{\text{adj}}{\text{hyp}}$$

$$= \frac{56.4}{112.0} \; (=0.5036)$$

$$\angle CAB = 59.8°$$

$$= 60° \text{ to the nearest degree.}$$

The bearing of C from A is $180° + 60° = 240°$

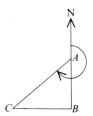

Exercise 20.2

1. When a kite is flying, the string makes an angle of 22° with the horizontal, and the string is 200 m long. How high is the kite?

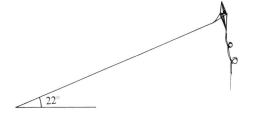

2. The angle of elevation of the top of a church steeple from a point on the ground 120 m away is 32°.
   Find the height of the steeple.

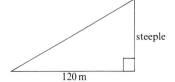

3. A speedboat travels 8 km North and then 3 km East. On what bearing must it be steered to go directly back to the starting point?

4. *P* is a point 30 cm away from the centre *O* of a circle radius 11 cm. *PT* is a tangent touching the circle at *T*. What is the size of ∠*OTP*? Calculate the angle *OPT*.

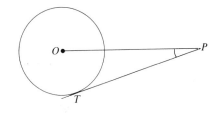

5. A surveyor who wishes to find the width of a river stands on one bank at a point *X* directly opposite a tree *T*. He then walks 80 m along the river bank to a point *C*. The angle *XCT* is found to be 72°. Calculate the width of the river.

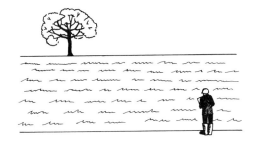

6. From a point at the top of a tower 30 m high, what is the angle of depression of a landmark on the ground 100 m away from the foot of the tower?

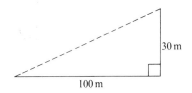

Exercise 20.3

1. A boy is 100 m due East from the
    foot of a tall tower, and on level
    ground. He measures the angle of
    elevation of the top of the tower
    as 38°. Calculate the height of the
    tower.

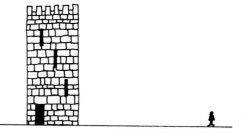

2. A man walks 10 km North-East and then 7 km South-East. How far is he from
    his starting-point, and on what bearing must he walk to go directly back to his
    starting-point?

3. Triangle ABC is isosceles with $AB = AC$.
    $BC = 10$ cm.

    1 Find the height AD.

    2 Find the area of $\triangle ABC$.

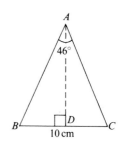

4. AC is a diameter of a circle, centre O,
    radius 3 cm.
    What is the size of $\angle B$?
    Calculate the length of BC.

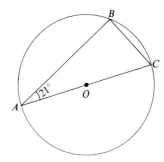

5. A plane flies due East from A to B. C is a town
    80 km from A on a bearing of 038°.

    1 Find the distance of the plane from C when
       it is at D, the nearest point to C.

    2 Find the distance of the plane from C when
       it is at B, where $\angle ACB = 90°$.

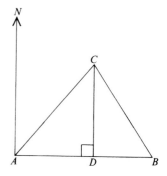

6. *ABCD* is a parallelogram.
   BC = 10 cm, ∠*ABC* = 57° and
   ∠*BAC* = 90°.
   Calculate

   1   *AB*,

   2   *AC*,

   3   the area of Δ*ABC*,

   4   the area of the parallelogram.

7. *P* and *Q* are places 900 m apart on a coastline running East–West.
   A ship *S* is at sea on a bearing of 341°
   from *P*, and on a bearing of 071° from *Q*.

   1   What size is ∠*QSP*?

   Find   2   *SP*,   3   *SQ*,

   4   the distance of *S* from the nearest point
       on the coast.

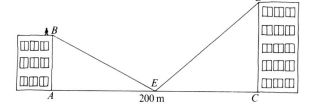

8. *AB* and *CD* are walls of two blocks of flats, which are 200 m apart. From *E*,
   the mid-point of *AC*, the angle of elevation of *B* is 12° and the angle of elevation
   of *D* is 24°.

   Find   1   *AB*,   2   *CD*.

   3   If a person is standing
       on the roof at *B*, what
       is the angle of
       elevation of *D*?

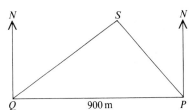

9. 1   Find the height of Δ*AOB*,
       and hence find the area of
       Δ*AOB*.

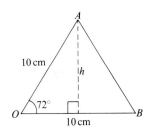

2   *O* is the centre of a circle of radius
    10 cm. What fraction of the whole
    circle is sector *AOB*? Find the area
    of sector *AOB*.
    Hence, using your answer to **1**, find
    the shaded area. Take π as 3.14.

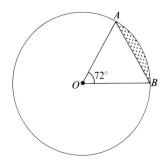

10. *A* and *B* are points on two
    mountain peaks. The distance
    between *A* and *B* on a map is
    12 cm. The scale of the map is
    1 : 50 000. Find the horizontal
    distance *AC*, in km. The
    heights of *A* and *B* are given as
    2900 m and 3650 m respectively.
    Calculate the angle of
    elevation of *B* from *A*.

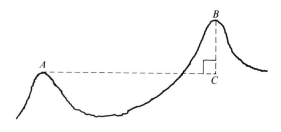

PUZZLES

58. Mary is the eldest of five children and she is responsible for bringing her brothers, Tony
    and James, and her sisters, Patricia and Wendy, home from school. This journey includes
    crossing a river by a small rowing-boat, which only holds two of them at a time, and only
    Mary and Tony can row this. Usually they all get across quite quickly, but one particular
    afternoon the children were quarrelsome and Mary did not want to leave the two boys
    together, or the two girls together, unless she was with them to keep them in order. She
    usually sent Wendy across the river first, with Tony, but on this afternoon Wendy refused
    to go with Tony and insisted she would only go in the boat with Mary. Then James said
    it was his turn to go across before Wendy did.
    How did Mary get them all across the river peacefully?

59. What is the area of a square of side 21 cm?
    Draw a square of side 21 cm on cardboard
    and divide it into 4 pieces as shown. Cut
    the pieces out and rearrange them to form a
    rectangle.
    What are the measurements of the rectangle?
    What is the area of the rectangle?
    Where has the extra 1 cm² come from?

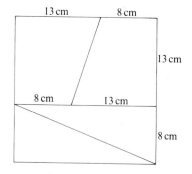

60. Write the numbers from 100 to 200 as the sum of consecutive integers.
    e.g. $100 = 18 + 19 + 20 + 21 + 22$
    $\quad\ 101 = 50 + 51$
    $\quad\ 102 = 33 + 34 + 35$
    $\quad\ 104 = 2 + 3 + 4 + \cdots + 13 + 14$
    It is possible to do this for every number except one of them. Which number is this?

Miscellaneous section D

Exercise D1   Aural Practice

If possible find someone to read these questions to you.
You should do all of them within 10 minutes.
Do not use your calculator.
Write down the answers only.

1.   If 1 gallon of petrol costs £1.60, how much will 2 gallons cost?
2.   Pat's mother is 28, and is four times as old as Pat. How old will Pat be next year?
3.   How many edges has a cuboid?
4.   If £1 is equal to 1.4 dollars, how many dollars will I get from £20?
5.   The base of a triangle is 10 cm and the height is 7 cm. What is its area?
6.   What is the total cost of 8 articles at 99 pence each?
7.   A rectangular piece of paper measuring 40 cm by 20 cm is cut into squares with side 5 cm. How many squares can be made?
8.   There are two parcels with total weight 11 kg. One is 3 kg heavier than the other. What does the heavier one weigh?
9.   Two angles of an isosceles triangle are each 75°. What is the size of the other angle of the triangle?
10. Write in figures the number 'one million, two thousand, three hundred and forty-five'.
11. How many centimetres is 7 cm short of 1 metre?
12. What is $\frac{1}{2} + \frac{1}{3}$?
13. How many minutes are there from 10.35 a.m. to 12 noon?
14. What is 0.3×40?
15. 25% of 80 kg of potatoes were bad, and $\frac{1}{3}$ of the remainder were too small for sale. What weight were fit for sale?

Exercise D2   Multi-choice Exercise

Select the correct answer to each question.

1.   If you face North–West and turn 135° clockwise, you will then be facing

   A   East   **B**   South   **C**   SE   **D**   SW   **E**   NE

2.   Simplify $(-3x) \times (-4x) \div (-2x)$

   A -6 **B**   6   **C** $-6x$ **D** $6x$ **E** $-6x^2$

3. A triangular field has sides 40 m, 50 m and 60 m. Which of these triangles makes a correct scale drawing of the field?

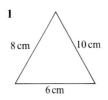

1 8 cm 10 cm 6 cm

2 18 cm 15 cm 12 cm

3 8 cm 6.4 cm 9.6 cm

A 1 and 2 only   **B** 2 only   **C** 2 and 3 only   **D** 3 only

E 1, 2 and 3

4. The area of a rectangle with sides 0.04 m and 0.03 m is

A $0.0012\,m^2$ **B** $0.012\,m^2$ **C** $0.12\,m^2$ **D** $0.14\,m^2$

E $1.2\,m^2$

5. A shortbread recipe uses flour, butter, sugar and nuts in the ratio, by weight, of $9:6:3:2$. How much butter is used in making 1 kg of the mixture?

A 30 g   **B** 100 g   **C** 150 g   **D** 300 g   **E** 450 g

6. sin P is

A $\frac{3}{4}$ **B** $\frac{3}{5}$ **C** $\frac{4}{3}$

D $\frac{4}{5}$ **E** $\frac{5}{4}$

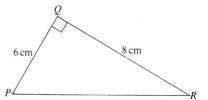

7. TX and TY are tangents 12 cm long and OT is 13 cm. O is the centre of the circle. What is the radius of the circle?

A 1 cm   **B** 5 cm   **C** 6 cm

D 6.5 cm   **E** $\sqrt{313}\,cm$

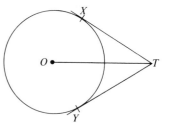

8. $\dfrac{5x}{6} - \dfrac{x}{3} + \dfrac{x}{8}$ is equivalent to

A $\dfrac{5x}{8}$ **B** $\dfrac{5x}{11}$ **C** $2x$ **D** $\dfrac{3x}{8}$ **E** $\dfrac{3x}{11}$

9. The angle of depression of A from B is

A $12°$ **B** $23°$

C $35°$ **D** $47°$

E $67°$

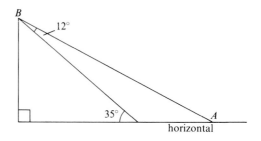

10. What is the circumference of a circle of radius 5 cm? (Take π as 3.14)

   A   15.7 cm   **B**   31.4 cm   **C**   62.8 cm   **D**   78.5 cm

   E   314 cm

11. Raffle tickets are numbered from 1 to 50. What is the probability that the winning ticket is a multiple of 7 or includes a figure 7?

   A $\frac{4}{50}$ **B** $\frac{7}{50}$ **C** $\frac{8}{50}$ **D** $\frac{11}{50}$ **E** $\frac{12}{50}$

12. This figure consists of a square of side 10 cm and an isosceles triangle of height 8 cm. The area of the whole figure is

   A   60 cm^2 **B**   80 cm^2 **C**   90 cm^2

   D   140 cm^2 **E**   180 cm^2

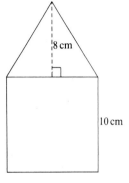

13. A circle has a diameter of 10 cm and a square has a side of 10 cm. The ratio of their areas is

   A   1 : 1   **B**   1 : 2   **C**   1 : 4   **D**   π : 1   **E**   π : 4

14. The mean of 5 numbers is 50 and the mean of 4 of these numbers is 45. What is the 5th number?

   A   5   **B** $8\frac{3}{4}$ **C**   25   **D**   55   **E**   70

15. Which of these lines does **not** pass through the point $(-1, -2)$?

   A $y = -2$ **B** $x = -1$ **C** $x + y = -3$ **D** $y = -2x$

   E $3y = 2x - 4$

16. Which region represents the points inside the triangle which are nearer to P than to Q and nearer to R than to P?

   A   1 and 2   **B**   2 and 3

   C   3 and 4   **D**   1 and 4

   E   3 only

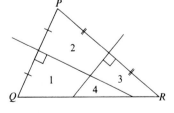

17. The value of 1.207×10^4 when written correct to 3 significant figures is

   A   1207   **B**   1210   **C**   12 000   **D**   12 070

   E   12 100

18. In this semicircle, $AB = 16$ cm, $BC = 12$ cm.
     What is the length of OB?

     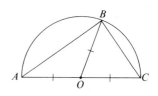

     A   10 cm   **B**   12 cm   **C**   14 cm

     D   20 cm   **E** $\sqrt{200}$ cm

19. Goods selling at £9.60 are being sold at a profit of 20% on the cost price. What
     did they cost?

     A   £7.68   **B**   £8.00   **C**   £9.12   **D**   £11.20

     E   £12.00

20. A car travels for $2\frac{3}{4}$ hours at an average speed of 60 km/hour and then for
     $2\frac{1}{4}$ hours at an average speed of 80 km/hour. What is its average speed for the
     whole journey?

     A   69 km/hour   **B**   70 km/hour   **C**   75 km/hour

     D   80 km/hour   **E**   140 km/hour

21. The average age of 5 boys is 12 years 4 months. A sixth boy of age
     11 years 10 months joins the group. What is the average age of the six boys?

     A   11 years 10 months   **B**   12 years 0 months

     C   12 years 1 month   **D**   12 years 3 months

     E   12 years 4 months

22. The height of this parallogram, in cm, is

     A $7\sin 55°$ **B** $7\cos 55°$

     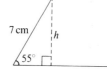

     C $7\tan 55°$ **D** $\dfrac{7}{\sin 55°}$

     E $\dfrac{\sin 55°}{7}$

23. What is the solution of the equation $3 - (5 - x) = 4 + 6x$?

     A $x = -2$ **B** $x = -1\frac{1}{5}$ **C** $x = -\frac{6}{7}$ **D** $x = \frac{6}{7}$

     E $x = 1\frac{1}{5}$

24. $(1 - \frac{1}{2}) \times (1 - \frac{1}{3}) \times (1 - \frac{1}{4})$ is equal to

     A $\frac{1}{12}$ **B** $\frac{1}{4}$ **C** $\frac{2}{3}$ **D** $1\frac{11}{12}$ **E** $\frac{23}{24}$

25. The direction with a bearing of 303° is

     A OA **B** OB **C** OC

     D OD **E** OF

     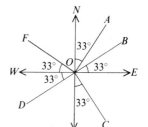

26. A map scale is shown as '1 cm represents 500 m'. This scale is shown in ratio form as

    A   1 : 5   **B**   1 : 50   **C**   1 : 500   **D**   1 : 5000

    E   1 : 50 000

27. If $3b$ girls share $6k$ cakes, the number of cakes each one gets is

    A $6k - 3b$ **B** $2bk$ **C** $18bk$ **D** $\dfrac{b}{2k}$ **E** $\dfrac{2k}{b}$

28. The bearing of R from P is

    A   025°   **B**   065°   **C**   155°

    D   205°   **E**   245°

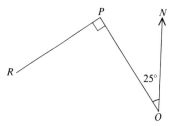

29. $\tan \angle QPR$ is

    A $\frac{1}{2}$ **B** $\frac{2}{3}$ **C** $\frac{3}{2}$

    D $\frac{3}{4}$ **E** $\frac{4}{3}$

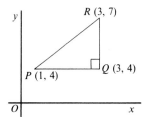

30. In a triangle the sizes of the angles are $(x + 12)°$, $(2x - 40)°$ and $y°$. What is the value of y when $x = 38$?

    A   86   **B**   94   **C**   130   **D**   142   **E**   144

Exercise D3   Revision

1. On a small photograph, a building is 4 cm high and its width is 10 cm. On an enlargement, if the building is 10 cm high, what is its width?

2. State how many axes of symmetry these figures have.

    1   Isosceles triangle   **4**   Circle
    2   Equilateral triangle   **5**   Regular hexagon
    3   Parallelogram

    State the order of rotational symmetry of these figures.

    6   Square   **9**   Regular pentagon
    7   Rectangle   **10**   Outline of a 50 pence coin
    8   Equilateral triangle

3. The end of this solid prism is a
    right-angled triangle.

    1 Find the length of *AB*.
    2 Find the total surface area of the
       prism.
    3 Find the volume of the prism.

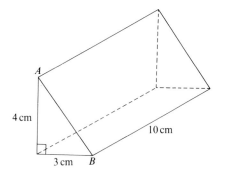

4. From a point on horizontal ground 700 m away from the base of a very tall
    tower, the angle of elevation of the top of the tower is 15°. Use trig. to calculate
    the height of the tower, to the nearest 10 m.

5. A man buys a painting as an investment. He pays £2000 for it and estimates that
    its value should increase by 10% each year. He plans to sell it in 3 years time.
    How much profit does he hope to gain on this investment?

6. A train starts at 2.30 p.m. and reaches the next stop at 3.45 p.m. If its average
    speed is 52 km/hour, what is the distance it has travelled?

7. A lawn-mower has blades 35 cm wide and it is used to cut a lawn 50 metres by
    21 metres. Find, in km, the least distance travelled by the mower in covering the
    ground once over, ignoring the turns made at each end.

8. These windows are similar in
    shape, consisting of a semicircle
    above a rectangle. What is the
    ratio of their perimeters?

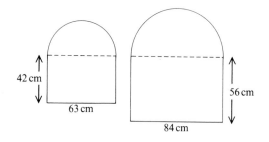

9. The rateable value of a house was £200. The water authority charged for water
    and services as follows:- a standing charge of £15 plus a charge of 30 p in the £
    on the rateable value. How much did it cost the householder in water rates that
    year?

10. With centre of enlargement *A*, *P* is mapped
    into *B* and *Q* is mapped into *C*.

    1 What is the scale factor of the enlargement?
    2 What is the ratio of lengths *BC* : *PQ*?

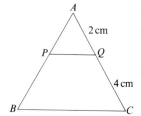

11. The profits on a business were £4800. The three partners divided this amount amongst themselves in the ratio $3:5:7$. How much did each receive?

12. $ABCD$ is a rhombus with $\angle ABC = 60°$. What sort of triangles are

    1 $\triangle ABC$,
    2 $\triangle ABD$,
    3 $\triangle ABX$?

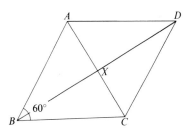

13. One quantity W varies directly as another quantity a. Given that $W = 4$ when $a = 2$, find the value of W when $a = 5$, and find a when $W = 108$.

14. Find the perpendicular height AD of this isosceles triangle ABC, and hence find the area of $\triangle ABC$. Use trig. to calculate the size of $\angle B$.

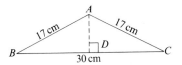

15. 1 What is the bearing of B from A?
    2 What is the bearing of C from B?
    3 What is the bearing of B from C?

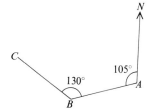

Exercise D4 Revision

1. Three years ago the cost of an article was £24, made up of charges for labour, materials and other expenses in the ratio $9:4:3$. Since then labour costs have increased by one-third, the price of materials has increased by one-fifth and the cost of other expenses has increased by one-tenth. What is the cost of the article now?

2. A spherical wire cage for holding a plant-pot is formed by fastening together 3 circular hoops of diameter 30 cm and one smaller hoop of diameter 20 cm. Find the total length of wire needed. Take π as 3.14 and give the answer to the nearest 0.1 m above.

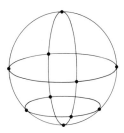

3.   In the sunshine, a stick which is 1 m high has a shadow of length 0.8 m on the horizontal ground. At the same time a flagpole has a shadow which is 4.8 m long. How high is the flagpole?

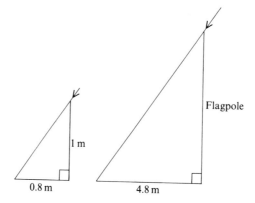

4.   **1**   What is the probability of getting a six when a fair die is thrown? In 120 throws, what is the approximate number of sixes you would expect to get?

   2   What is the probability of getting an ace if a card is dealt to you from a full pack of 52 cards? If a card was dealt in this way 120 times, what is the approximate number of times you would expect to get an ace?

   3   If the probability that the bus to take you to school is late on any one morning is reckoned to be $\frac{1}{10}$, how many times approximately would you expect to be late out of 120 mornings?

5.   The area of a triangle is 90 cm² and the base is 12 cm. What is the perpendicular height?

6.   When travelling abroad a man bought 15 watches for 700 francs. Use your calculator to find the average cost per watch, in £'s to the nearest 10p, if the rate of exchange was 3.4 francs to the £.

7.   *P* is a point on the rim of a bicycle wheel, initially touching the ground at *A*. The bicycle is moved forward until *P* touches the ground at *B*, the wheel having moved through one revolution.

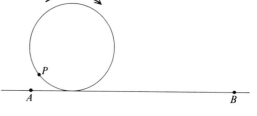

   Copy the drawing and sketch the locus of *P*.
   If the diameter of the wheel is 35 cm, find the length of *AB*.
   How many metres will a cyclist have travelled when the wheel has made 100 revolutions? Take π as 3.14.

8.   A shop allows a discount of 10% on all purchases during a sale. What was the original price of an article which was sold for £35.10?

9. Triangle ABC is equilateral. D is a point on AC such that $AD:DC = 3:1$. Triangle ADE is equilateral. Name a triangle congruent to $\triangle ACE$. Which line is equal to CE?

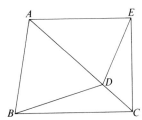

10. A boat sails from a port A for 10 km on a bearing of $135°$ to an island B and then 14 km on a bearing of $070°$ to a port C. Choose a suitable scale and draw an accurate scale drawing of the course sailed. If the boat then sails directly back to A, how far is the return journey and in what direction?

11. On graph paper draw the x-axis from -4 to 6 and the y-axis from -8 to 8. Draw the triangle ABC where A is $(-2, 2)$, B is $(-3, 3)$ and C is $(-1, 6)$.
The triangle ABC is translated 7 units parallel to the x-axis and 2 units parallel to the y-axis to form triangle $A_1B_1C_1$. State the coordinates of A_1, B_1 and C_1.
The triangle $A_1B_1C_1$ is transformed into triangle $A_2B_2C_2$ by reflection in the x-axis. State the coordinates of A_2, B_2 and C_2.
The triangle $A_2B_2C_2$ is transformed by a translation which maps A_2 into A, with B_2 into B_3 and C_2 into C_3. Describe the translation.
Describe a single transformation which would map triangle ABC into triangle AB_3C_3.

12. Solve the equations

   1 $4(x-4) = 5(13-x)$ **2** $x+4 = 2(x-4)$ **3** $\dfrac{3x}{4} - \dfrac{2x}{3} = 3$

13. Find the lengths of DE and DF.

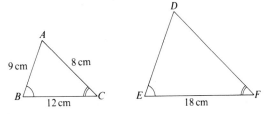

14. A and B are two points on horizontal ground. A kite attached to A by a string 80 m long is at D, vertically above B, and its angle of elevation from A is $20°$. Find the height of the kite above the ground, and the distance AB, giving answers to the nearest metre.

15.　A boy is playing near a circular pool of diameter 20 m. He sends his toy boat across the centre of the pool from A to B at a speed of 2.5 m/s, and at the same time as the boat leaves A he starts to run round the edge of the pool from A to B at a speed of 4 m/s. Which gets to B first, the boy or his boat? Take π as 3.14.

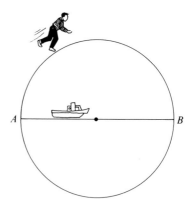

Exercise D5　Practical work and Investigations

1.　**My House**

Imagine that it is a few years into the future and you are about to buy a house. Design the house and draw a plan of each floor.

Then draw the plan of each room, showing where the doorways and windows are, and where each item of furniture will go.

Find the approximate cost of each item of furniture (by looking in shops, catalogues or advertisements).

For each room make a list of the furniture and fittings you will need and find the total cost. Find the total cost for all the rooms in the house.

If you intend to have a garden you could include a plan for this, and add on the costs of garden tools and garden furniture.

Find the up-to-date price of a similar house by looking at advertisements, and find the total cost of everything.

Cut pictures from magazines and catalogues to illustrate your booklet, and make an attractive cover for it.

This is your dream house so you need not be too practical about being able to afford it, if you wish to design a really luxurious one, on the other hand you may prefer to be practical and plan for an inexpensive one. You may prefer to choose a flat, or a bungalow, instead of a house.

2.　**Savings**

Investigate the different places or ways in which money can be saved or invested, such as banks, building societies, shares, savings certificates, life insurance policies, or hidden in the house.

Consider the advantages and disadvantages of each, such as

1　safety of your money,
2　interest gained (a) if you are a taxpayer or (b) if you are not,
3　easy access to your money.

Does it make any difference if you have

(a) only a small amount of money,
(b) quite a large sum of money?

If someone saves regularly out of his or her wages, e.g. saving £10 per week for several years, make a table or graph to show how this money would grow if invested in a regular savings' scheme.

3. **Planning a Day's Sightseeing Trip**

Choose an interesting place which you have never visited, but which is near
enough to your school or home for a day's outing. Suggestions include London,
Stratford-on-Avon or York, but there are many more possibilities, depending on
where you live.

Find a guide book of that city, town or area, and decide what you would like
to see. If you can find a street map you can make your own sketch map and mark
on it where these places are, and then plan your route for visiting them in a
sensible order.

Decide how you are going to get to the place, by train, bus, coach or other
means. Make a timetable for the day, including the times of the journeys there
and back, and approximate times of visiting each place. Remember to allow time
for getting from one site to another, and include time for a lunch break. Will you
take a packed lunch, and if so, where will you eat it, or will you buy a meal?
Calculate an approximate cost for the day, including fares, admission charges
and possibly refreshments and pocket money for souvenirs.

Instead of a sightseeing trip in a city or town you could plan a similar outing to
an outdoor region such as Snowdonia. You might prefer to make a plan for a
trip lasting more than one day, in which case you will have to plan for overnight
accommodation, and include the cost of it.

4. **Estimation**

It is useful to be able to make good estimates of weights and measurements. Here
are some suggestions to improve your skill. You should think of others.

Lengths. Find out the measurements of your thumb as far as the knuckle, the
width of your hand across four fingers, the length of your hand-span, the length
of your foot with a shoe on, your height, the distance you can reach with arms
stretched out, the height you can reach on tiptoe, and so on. Use a measured
distance of 100 m to find the length of your pace when you walk normally, and
how long your stride is. Practise estimating distances by comparing them with
these lengths.

Time. See how many times you take a breath normally, in 1 minute, and then
practise estimating 1 minute by counting your breathing.

Weight. Get used to the weight of 1 kg (a bag of sugar) and 2.5 kg (a bag of
potatoes). Find your own weight in kg and the weight of a small child. Estimate
other weights by comparing them with these known weights.

Capacity. Estimate how much water various containers hold and check by using
a measuring jug, a litre bottle (or a pint bottle for British measures). A bucket
or a watering can may have measuring lines marked on it. It is useful to
remember that 1 litre of water weighs 1 kg. In British measures 1 gallon of water
weighs 10 lb.

Area. Find the area of a local football pitch and compare other large areas with
that. For smaller areas, compare with $1 \, m^2$ or $1 \, cm^2$.

Angles. Practise drawing an angle of $45°$ by eye by cutting a right angle in half.
Then practise making angles of $30°$ and $60°$ by cutting a right angle into 3 equal
parts. Practise guessing the sizes of angles, then check with your protractor.

If you cannot find a measurement directly, there are various methods you could
use, relying on scale drawing, trigonometry or similar triangles.

A clinometer

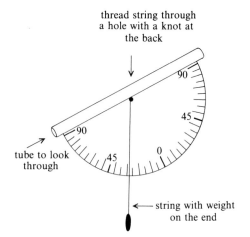

Make one of these to measure angles of elevation and depression. Mark the angles as on a protractor edge but put 0° in the centre and 90° at each end.

When you look at an object through the tube the string will hang vertically and measure the angle of elevation or depression.

Here are some practical problems. There are several possible solutions. See how many you can think of. Make up similar problems to solve.

1 An explorer in unknown territory discovers a deep gorge. He needs to report on its width but it is too wide to get across to measure it. How can he estimate its width?
2 He can see the bottom and wants to estimate its depth. How can he do this?
3 On the other side of the gorge is a very tall unusual tree. How can he estimate its height?

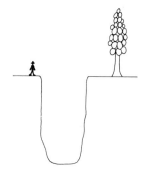

4 He has been travelling from his base camp in a north-easterly direction so he knows he has to go in a south-westerly direction to return to camp. Unfortunately, he has dropped his compass down the gorge. How can he find out which direction to go in?

5. Pascal's Triangle

```
                    1
                1       1
            1       2       1
        1       3       3       1
    1       4       6       4       1
1       5       10      10      5       1
    .   .   .   .   .   .   .
```

Pascal was a French Mathematician who lived in the 17th century. See if you can find out more about him from library books.

This triangle of numbers is named after him, although it was known long ago in Ancient China.

Decide how each number is formed from the numbers in the row above, and copy the triangle and continue it for a few more rows. (As a check, a later row is 1   8   28   56   70   56   28   8   1)

What do you notice about the sum of each row?

What do we call the numbers in the diagonal which begins 1, 3, 6, 10?

Diversions:

1   If you toss three coins in turn, there are 8 possible results, HHH, HTH, etc. which can be summarised like this.

	0 heads	1 head	2 heads	3 heads
Number of ways	1	3	3	1

Investigate the results when 4, or more, coins are tossed.

2   Suppose there are 7 people and 3 of them have to be selected for some purpose. How many ways are there of making the selection? First select 3 from 3, (1 way), then 3 from 4, (4 ways) and so on.

See how this connects with Pascal's triangle.

6.   **The cost of keeping a pet**

Make a survey of your friends and relatives to find out the sort of pets people have. You could also work out the average number of pets per family. Then ask these people about the costs of keeping their various pets. Here are some of the costs to consider:

Somewhere for the pet to live—hutch, cage, fish tank, stable.

Weekly food bill, including different sorts of food for a healthy diet.

Costs of cleaning out—cat litter, sawdust for cage, straw for stable.

Necessary Vet's bills, for inoculations, etc.

Unexpected Vet's bills, an average cost of treatment for illnesses.

Insurance, and any other costs.

You could also make a survey asking people what sort of pet they would like to own.

You could also ask about the amount of time people spend each week on looking after their pets, from the goldfish which needs very little attention to the dog or pony which need regular exercise.

7. **Make your own Maths Magazine**

Or at least, issue No. 1. for a beginning.

Don't be too ambitious. Use a plain sheet of A4 paper and fold it down the middle to make a leaflet.

On the first page you need a title in the top half, and then an article or a puzzle. On the next three pages you need further articles, puzzles, cartoons or jokes. You could make up a Maths cross-figure, similar to a crossword but with numbers instead of words for the answers. Articles could be about something you have learnt recently, or you could use library books to find out about great Mathematicians and their discoveries. You could describe how to do paper folding or how to make Maths models.

Try to keep some variety in your magazine. Keep your writing neat and perhaps use plenty of colour, unless you intend to make photocopies, when you should use black ink only.

You could have a display in your class if you all made magazines.

Alternatively you could combine together as a class and all produce articles, puzzles, etc, which could be sorted out and put together as a class Maths magazine.

8. **Curves of pursuit**

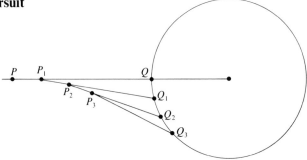

e.g. A dog at P chases a rabbit at Q, which is running along a circular track. Mark PQ to represent the dog's intended path. The rabbit runs to Q_1 whilst the dog reaches P_1. Mark P_1Q_1 which is the dog's new direction. In the next interval the rabbit reaches Q_2 and the dog reaches P_2, and so on.

Decide on their speeds, e.g. represent the dog's speed by 1 cm so that $PP_1 = P_1P_2 = P_2P_3 = \cdots = 1$ cm. If you want the rabbit to be slower choose a length such as 0.7 cm. Mark $QQ_1 = Q_1Q_2 = Q_2Q_3 = \cdots = 0.7$ cm, using compasses to mark off the distances along the circle.

When the rabbit is caught, or the dog gives up the chase, go over PP_1, P_1P_2, P_2P_3, . . . in colour as this is the curve of pursuit.

What happens if (1) the speeds vary, in relation to each other, (2) the rabbit starts from a different part of the circle, (3) the dog starts nearer to the circle, (4) the rabbit runs along a line instead of a circle?

Try the curve of pursuit for 3 dogs A, B, C starting from the 3 corners of an equilateral triangle with equal speeds, if A is chasing B, B is chasing C and C is chasing A.

Make up some other investigations for yourself.

9. **A snowflake curve**

Draw an equilateral triangle with sides 8.1 cm long (or 10.8 cm, 13.5 cm or 16.2 cm. A multiple of 2.7 is useful.)

Divide each side into 3 equal parts. Use compasses to construct an equilateral triangle on the outside of the middle third of each side, then rub out that middle third.

(Now the figure is a 6-pointed star and has 12 sides.)

Repeat the last instruction for each of the 12 sides.

(The figure is beginning to look like a snowflake. It has 48 sides.)

Repeat the last instruction for each of the 48 sides as accurately as you can.

This process should go on for ever. You may be able to take it one stage further if you started with a large enough triangle. Now colour the snowflake and this will hide the traces of the rubbing-out.

Work out the ratio, perimeter of curve : perimeter of original triangle, for each stage of the drawing.

Using similar triangle properties you may be able to work out the ratio, area of curve : area of original triangle, for each stage of the drawing.

For an anti-snowflake curve the triangles are drawn on the inside of the existing figure, so that the area shrinks. Try drawing it.

10. **For the Computer Programmer**

More suggestions for programs:

1   To find unknown sides or angles in right-angled triangles, by trig.
2   To plot shapes and transformations of these shapes.

To the student:

5   Learning formulae. Practice Exams.

Learning Formulae

There are certain formulae which you will need to know by heart. The best way to learn a formula is to know where it comes from.

e.g. The sum of the angles of a triangle is 180°.

Sketch this diagram.
Colour red $\angle A$ and an angle that is equal to it. (Why are they equal?)
Colour green $\angle B$ and an angle that is equal to it. (Why are they equal?)
Colour yellow the (interior) angle C.
Now can you see why
$\angle A + \angle B + \angle C = 180°$?

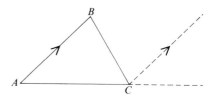

There is a formula checklist on page 406. Copy the list, completing each formula, then check your answers from the relevant chapters of the book. Learn those you do not know.
(There may be certain formulae which you do not need to learn as they will be given to you in the examination, either on the paper itself or on an accompanying leaflet. You could ask your teacher which these are, then you do not need to learn them. They vary for the different Examination Boards, so I cannot list them here.)

Learning formulae in isolation is not very useful. You need to link this with learning methods, so that you can use the formulae correctly.

Practice Exams

You may have a Practice Exam at school. This will give you some idea of your present standard. It will show you that you can do well if you have learnt the work. It will give you practice in working to time and working under pressure.

After the exam, you will be told your marks or grade and given back your paper. Perhaps your teacher will go through all the questions with the class or you may have to correct them yourself. Ask about anything you do not understand.

If you get a low mark, do not be too discouraged if you know that you can do better next time. But decide what you are going to do to improve your standard.

In an exam it is the marks which count. Could you have got more marks if you had spent less time on some questions and more on others? Should you have revised some topics more thoroughly?

Did you throw away any marks by:
not reading a question carefully enough,
not showing the necessary working with the answer,
writing so badly that the marker could not read it,
writing so badly that **you** could not read it and copied it wrongly on the next line,
not checking an answer that was obviously wrong,
not giving an answer to the accuracy asked for, e.g. to the nearest cm?

Since this was a practice exam, having made some of these mistakes, you can see that by avoiding them in future you can gain more marks.

Make a list of topics you still need to revise, and plan how you will use the remaining time before the proper examination.

Your teacher may give your further practice papers to do at home. If not, you may like to give yourself some. You can use the revision papers in this book, doing 12 of the 15 questions in each. Try to do them as in a proper exam, spending the correct time on them and working in a quiet room without referring to books or notes.

About Chapters 21 to 25

Chapter 21 is mainly about Functions and their graphs. You have met these functions throughout the algebra chapters. Here they are summarised and some extra ones are included.
Chapter 22 is about Sets. (This may not be needed for your syllabus. If it is, here is an easy chapter to enjoy.)
Chapter 23. Here is another easy chapter, all about Patterns. Perhaps you can discover or invent some patterns for yourself.
Chapter 24 includes more graphs, mainly conversion graphs and travel graphs.
In Chapter 25, just to finish the course, there is a section to make sure that you have no problems with calculations.

After these chapters you will have covered everything. Well done!

21 Functions and graphs

Functions

If a set of values, x, is connected to another set of values, y, and for each value of x there is only one value of y, then y is said to be a function of x.

A function can be represented by ordered pairs of numbers.
e.g. (1, 1), (2, 4), (3, 9), (4, 16).
The 1st number of each pair is the value of x, the 2nd number is the value of y.

A function can be represented by a mapping diagram.
e.g.

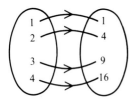

A function can be represented by a table.

e.g.

x	1	2	3	4
y	1	4	9	16

A function can be represented by an equation. The equation for this function is $y = x^2$.

If the values of x are continuous, the function can be represented by its graph. This is the graph of $y = x^2$.

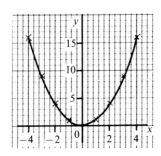

Graphs of functions

These have been drawn in Chapters 10 and 13. They are repeated here, with some other functions.

Linear functions

The graph of $y = mx + c$ is a straight line with gradient m, meeting the y-axis at $(0, c)$.

Example 1

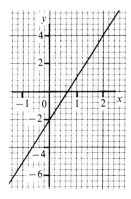

$y = 3x - 2$
Some corresponding values of x and y are

x	-1	0	1	2
y	-5	-2	1	4

The graph of the function is a straight line with gradient 3, meeting the y-axis at $(0, -2)$.

A quadratic function of the type $y = ax^2$

The graph is a parabola.
The y-axis is an axis of symmetry.

curve when a is positive

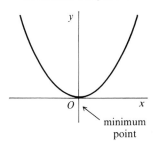

minimum point

curve when a is negative

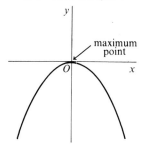

maximum point

Example 2

The graph of $y = 3x^2$
Some corresponding values of x and y are

x	-3	-2	-1	0	1	2	3
y	27	12	3	0	3	12	27

Draw the x-axis from -3 to 3 and the y-axis from 0 to 27 (or 30) using a smaller scale.
Plot the points and join them with a smooth curve.

Example 3

The graph of $y = -2x^2$
Some corresponding values of x and y are

x	-3	-2	-1	0	1	2	3
y	-18	-8	-2	0	-2	-8	-18

Draw the x-axis from -3 to 3 and the y-axis from 0 (downwards) to -18 (or -20)
Plot the points and join them with a smooth curve.

The function $y = \dfrac{a}{x}$ where a is a positive number.

(This curve is called a rectangular hyperbola.)

Sketch graph

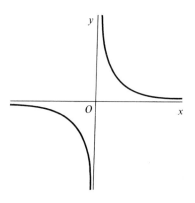

$y = \dfrac{a}{x}$ where a is a negative number.

Sketch graph

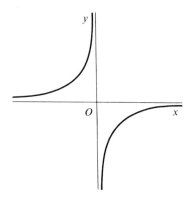

Example 4

$$y = \frac{4}{x}$$

Some corresponding values of x and y are

x	-8	-4	-2	-1	$-\frac{1}{2}$	$\frac{1}{2}$	1	2	4	8
y	$-\frac{1}{2}$	-1	-2	-4	-8	8	4	2	1	$\frac{1}{2}$

Draw x and y axes from -8 to 8 with equal scales on both axes. Plot these points and possibly other points such as (5, 0.8). The graph has two separate parts.

Draw a smooth curve through the points where x is positive, and a separate curve through the points where x is negative.
The graph has a point of symmetry. Which point is this?
The graph has two axes of symmetry. They are $y = x$ and $y = -x$. You could draw these lines on your graph to show this.

Other quadratic functions

The graph of $y = x^2 + bx + c$ is a parabola.
There is an axis of symmetry parallel to the y-axis.

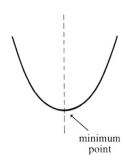

minimum
point

Example 5

Draw the graph of $y = x^2 - 5x + 2$, for values of x from -1 to 6.

Make a table of values, working out x^2 and $-5x$, and then $x^2 - 5x + 2$ for each value of x.

x	-1	0	1	2	3	4	5	6
x^2	1	0	1	4	9	16	25	36
$-5x$	5	0	-5	-10	-15	-20	-25	-30
2	2	2	2	2	2	2	2	2
$y (=x^2 - 5x + 2)$	8	2	-2	-4	-4	-2	2	8

(Since y is symmetrical about the line $x = 2\frac{1}{2}$ we will find the value of y on this line, to add this point to the graph.
When $x = 2\frac{1}{2}$, $x^2 = 6\frac{1}{4}$, $-5x = -12\frac{1}{2}$, $y = x^2 - 5x + 2 = 6\frac{1}{4} - 12\frac{1}{2} + 2 = -4\frac{1}{4}$.)

On the graph we draw the x-axis from -1 to 6 and the y-axis from -5 to 8. Plot the points and join them with a smooth curve.

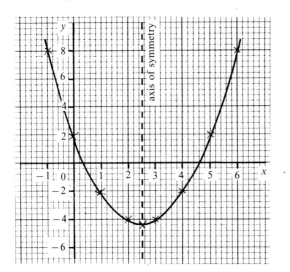

The axis of symmetry is the line $x = 2\frac{1}{2}$. The minimum point is the point $(2\frac{1}{2}, -4\frac{1}{4})$. (The minimum value of y is $-4\frac{1}{4}$.)

To solve the equation $x^2 - 5x + 2 = 0$, we must find where $y = 0$, i.e. where the curve crosses the x-axis. The solution (to 1 decimal place) is $x = 0.4$ or $x = 4.6$.

Example 6

Draw the graph of $y = (x + 2)(x - 3)$ for values of x from -3 to 4.

Make a table of values, working out $x + 2$, $x - 3$ then the product $(x + 2)(x - 3)$ for each value of x.

x	-3	-2	-1	0	1	2	3	4
$x + 2$	-1	0	1	2	3	4	5	6
$x - 3$	-6	-5	-4	-3	-2	-1	0	1
$y(= (x + 2)(x - 3))$	6	0	-4	-6	-6	-4	0	6

An extra value which might be helpful is when $x = \frac{1}{2}$, $y = 2\frac{1}{2} \times (-2\frac{1}{2}) = -6\frac{1}{4}$. Complete the question. Draw the x-axis from -3 to 4 and the y-axis from -7 to 6. Plot the points and join them with a smooth curve. From your graph find the axis of symmetry, and the minimum point on the curve.

We can use the graph to solve an equation such as $(x + 2)(x - 3) = -2$. For this, $y = -2$.

Draw the line $y = -2$ on your graph and find the two points where it meets the curve. Draw dotted lines to the x-axis at these points to read the values of x. The solution is $x = -1.6$ or 2.6.

The function $y = \sqrt{x}$

x has to be positive.

Make a table of values for x from 0 to 16, beginning like this:

x	0	1	2	3	4	5	. . .
$y = \sqrt{x}$	0	1	1.41	1.73	2	2.24	. . .

Sketch graph

Draw the graph, with x-axis from 0 to 16 and
y-axis from 0 to 4.
(Where the square roots are not exact, use
your calculator to find them to 1 or 2 decimal
places, depending on your scale and how
accurately you can plot them.)

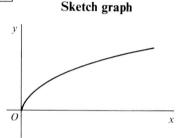

Gradients

Gradient of a chord

A line joining two points on a curve is called a chord of the curve.

$$\text{Gradient of chord } AB = \frac{y\text{-coordinate of } B - y\text{-coordinate of } A}{x\text{-coordinate of } B - x\text{-coordinate of } A}$$

(This method was explained in Chapter 10.)

Gradient of the curve at a point

Draw the tangent to the curve at the point. (The tangent is the line which touches the
curve at that point.)
Find the gradient of the tangent, by taking any two points on it and using their
coordinates.
The gradient of the curve = the gradient of the tangent to the curve.

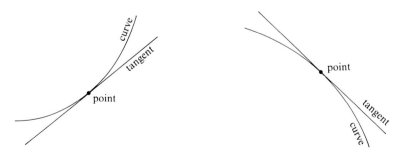

In the 1st diagram the gradient is positive, in the 2nd diagram it is negative.
The gradient measures the rate at which the curve is increasing or decreasing.

Example 7

In the diagram, find the gradient of the curve at the point $P(3\frac{1}{2}, 3)$.

Draw the tangent to the curve at P. Choose 2 points on the tangent and call them A and B. Find their coordinates. (It simplifies the calculation if you choose points with integer x-values.)
Here, A is (1, 4.5), B is (6, 1.6).

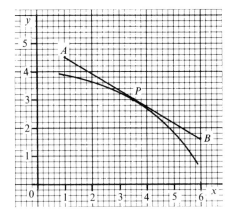

$$\text{Gradient of tangent at } P = \frac{y\text{-coordinate of } B - y\text{-coordinate of } A}{x\text{-coordinate of } B - x\text{-coordinate of } A}$$

$$= \frac{1.6 - 4.5}{6 - 1} = \frac{-2.9}{5} = -0.58$$

The gradient of the curve at P is -0.58.
It is negative because the curve is sloping downwards.
At the point P the curve is decreasing at the rate of 0.58 units of y per unit of x.

Sketch graphs

These are drawings which show the general shape of the function and its main details. The type of equation will tell you the general shape of the graph, whether it is a straight line, a parabola or some other curve.
If it is a straight line, by finding the value of x when $y = 0$ you can show on your graph the point where the line crosses the x-axis. By finding the value of y when $x = 0$ you can show on your graph the point where the line crosses the y-axis.

Exercise 21.1

1. Find the equation in the form $y =$ 'expression involving x' for these tables of values.

   1 | x | 0 | 1 | 2 | 3 | 4 |
      |-----|---|---|---|---|---|
      | y | 0 | 3 | 6 | 9 | 12 |

   4 | x | 1 | 2 | 3 | 4 | 5 |
      |-----|----|----|----|----|----|
      | y | 60 | 30 | 20 | 15 | 12 |

   2 | x | 0 | 1 | 2 | 3 | 4 |
      |-----|---|---|---|----|----|
      | y | 0 | 2 | 8 | 18 | 32 |

   5 | x | 0 | 1 | 2 | 3 | 4 |
      |-----|---|---|---|---|----|
      | y | 3 | 5 | 7 | 9 | 11 |

   3 | x | 0 | 1 | 2 | 3 | 4 |
      |-----|----|---|---|---|---|
      | y | 10 | 9 | 8 | 7 | 6 |

2. Find the equation in the form $y =$ 'expression involving x' for these ordered pairs.

    1 $(-2, 4)$, $(-1, 1)$, $(0, 0)$, $(1, 1)$, $(2, 4)$

    2 $(1, \frac{1}{2})$, $(2, 1)$, $(3, 1\frac{1}{2})$, $(4, 2)$, $(5, 2\frac{1}{2})$

    3 $(1, 24)$, $(2, 12)$, $(3, 8)$, $(4, 6)$, $(5, 4.8)$

    4 $(0, 10)$, $(1, 8)$, $(2, 6)$, $(3, 4)$, $(4, 2)$

    5 $(0, 0)$, $(1, 3)$, $(2, 12)$, $(3, 27)$, $(4, 48)$

3. Make a table of values for $x = 0, 1, 2, 3, 4$ for these functions.

    1 $y = 4x - 2$ **4** $y = \dfrac{6}{x}$ (not for $x = 0$)

    2 $y = \dfrac{x + 3}{2}$ **5** $y = 9 - 3x$

    3 $y = 5x^2$

4. Make a table of values for $x = 0, 1, 2, 3, 4$ for these functions.

    1 $y = (x - 1)(x + 3)$

    2 $y = x^2 - 2x$

    3 $y = x^2 - 1$

    4 $y = (x - 2)^2$

    5 $y = x^2 - 7x + 12$

5. Make a table of values for $x = -5, -1, 3, 7$ for the function $y = \dfrac{3(x + 1)}{4}$.

    Draw the x-axis from -5 to 7 and the y-axis from -3 to 6. Plot the points from the table and draw the graph.

6. Make a table of values for $x = -4, -3, -2, -1, 0, 1, 2, 3, 4$ for the function $y = \frac{1}{2}x^2$.

    Draw the x-axis from -4 to 4 and the y-axis from 0 to 8. Plot the points from the table and draw the graph.

7. Make a table of values for $x = 1, 1.5, 2, 3, 4, 5, 6, 7.5, 9$ for the function $y = \dfrac{9}{x}$.

    Draw both axes from 0 to 9. Plot the points from the table and draw the graph for values of x between 1 and 9.

8. Draw axes with x from -4 to 4, and y from -9 to 7.
    Copy and complete this table of values for the graph of $y = x^2 - 9$.

x	-4	-3	-2	-1	0	1	2	3	4
x^2	16							9	
-9	-9							-9	
$y(= x^2 - 9)$	7							0	

Draw the graph of $y = x^2 - 9$.
What is the least value of y on the curve?

9. Draw axes with x from -2 to 5 and y from -4 to 10.
    Copy and complete this table of values for the graph $y = x^2 - 3x$.

x	-2	-1	0	1	$1\frac{1}{2}$	2	3	4	5
x^2	4				$2\frac{1}{4}$		9		
$-3x$	6				$-4\frac{1}{2}$		-9		
$y\ (= x^2 - 3x)$	10				$-2\frac{1}{4}$		0		

Draw the graph of $y = x^2 - 3x$.
What is the equation of the axis of symmetry of the curve?
Use your graph to solve the equation $x^2 - 3x = 6$.

10. Draw axes with x from -3 to 4 and y from -6 to 8.
    Copy and complete this table of values for the graph $y = x^2 - x - 5$.

x	-3	-2	-1	0	1	2	3	4
x^2	9				1			
$-x$	3				-1			
-5	-5	-5	-5	-5	-5	-5	-5	-5
y	7				-5			

Draw the graph of $y = x^2 - x - 5$.
Write down the equation of the line about which the curve is symmetrical.
Use your graph to solve the equation $x^2 - x - 5 = 0$.

11.   Draw axes with x from -3 to 4 and y from -3 to 10. Copy and complete this
      table of values for the graph of $y = (x + 1)(x - 2)$.

x	-3	-2	-1	0	1	2	3	4
$x + 1$	-2				2			
$x - 2$	-5				-1			
$y(= (x + 1)(x - 2))$	10				-2			

Draw the graph of $y = (x + 1)(x - 2)$.
What are the coordinates of the point on the graph where y has its lowest value?
What is the equation of the axis of symmetry of the curve?
By finding where the line $y = 6$ cuts the curve, find the solutions of the equation
$(x + 1)(x - 2) = 6$.

12.   Draw axes with x from 0 to 9 and y from 0 to 4.
      Make a table of values for $x = 0, 1, 2, 3, 4, 5, 6, 7, 8, 9$ for the function $y = \sqrt{x}$,
      giving the values of y to 2 decimal places if they are not exact.
      Draw the graph of $y = \sqrt{x}$ for x from 0 to 9.
      Find y when $x = 0, 4, 8$ for the function $y = \dfrac{8 - x}{2}$. Draw this line on the same
      graph.
      Find the coordinates of the point where the graphs intersect.

13.   Identify these sketch graphs from this list:

$y = \dfrac{3}{x}, \ y = \dfrac{x}{3}, \ y = 3 - x, \ y = 3x^2$

14.   Draw the x and y axes from 0 to 6. Find a triangle whose sides lie on the three
      lines $x = 6$, $y = 4$ and $y = x$.

15.   Draw the x-axis from 0 to 4 and the y-axis from 0 to 3. Plot the points A, B, C,
      D where A is (3, 0), B is (4, 1), C is (1, 3) and D is (0, 2).
      Find the gradients of AB, BC, AD and DC.
      What sort of quadrilateral is $ABCD$?

16. Using the graph drawn in question 6, draw a tangent to the curve, touching the curve at the point (1.6, 1.28).
    Let A be the point on the tangent where $x = 1$. What is its y-value?
    Let B be the point on the tangent where $x = 3$. What is its y-value?
    Find the gradient of the tangent using the points A and B. (This is the gradient of the curve at the point (1.6, 1.28).)
    Without drawing the tangent, say what the gradient of the curve will be at the point $(-1.6, 1.28)$.

17. Using the graph drawn in question 7, draw a tangent to the curve, touching the curve at (5, 1.8).
    Let A be the point on the tangent where $x = 0$. What is its y-value?
    Let B be the point on the tangent where $x = 8$. What is its y-value?
    Find the gradient of the tangent using the points A and B. (This is the gradient of the curve at the point (5, 1.8).)

Expanding Brackets

The diagram shows the geometrical illustration of $(x + 6)^2$.

Total area $= (x + 6) \times (x + 6) = (x + 6)^2$

4 separate areas $= x^2 + 6x + 6x + 36$

$$= x^2 + 12x + 36$$

So $(x + 6)^2 = x^2 + 12x + 36$

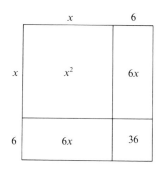

Examples

8   $(x + 8)(x - 10) = x(x - 10) + 8(x - 10)$
$$= x^2 - 10x + 8x - 80$$
$$= x^2 - 2x - 80$$

9   $(x - 1)(x - 3) = x^2 - 3x - x + 3$
$$= x^2 - 4x + 3$$

10   $(x - 3)(x + 5) = x^2 + 5x - 3x - 15$
$$= x^2 + 2x - 15$$

11   $(x + 2)^2 = (x + 2)(x + 2)$
$$= x^2 + 2x + 2x + 4$$
$$= x^2 + 4x + 4$$

Exercise 21.2

1. Illustrate geometrically these identities.

    1 $(x + 4)(x + 6) = x^2 + 10x + 24$

    2 $x(x + y) = x^2 + xy$

    3 $(x + 1)(x + 2) = x^2 + 3x + 2$

    4 $(x + 5)^2 = x^2 + 10x + 25$

    5 $3(x + 4) = 3x + 12$

2. Expand the following.

1 $(x + 5)(x + 1)$	**6** $(x + 4)(x - 3)$	**11** $(x - 4)(x + 5)$
2 $(x - 6)(x - 2)$	**7** $(x - 1)(x - 4)$	**12** $(x + 3)(x - 1)$
3 $(x + 4)(x - 4)$	**8** $(x + 1)(x - 1)$	**13** $(x + 1)(x + 6)$
4 $(x + 3)^2$	**9** $(x - 5)(x + 3)$	**14** $(x - 4)(x - 7)$
5 $(x + 2)(x + 7)$	**10** $(x - 1)^2$	**15** $(x - 5)(x + 1)$

Exercise 21.3

1. If $y = x^2 + 5x + 10$, find the values of y when $x = 2$ and $x = 5$.

2. If $y = 3(x - 1)^2 + 4$, find the values of y when $x = 0, 1, 2, 3$. What is the least value of y?

3. These sketch graphs represent the functions $y = 2$, $y = 2x$, $y = x + 2$, $y = 2x + 2$, $y = 2 - x$, $y = 2 - 2x$. Identify each graph.

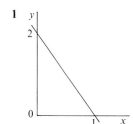

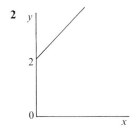

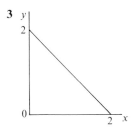

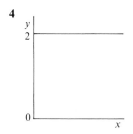

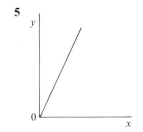

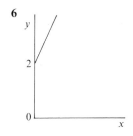

4. Which of these sketches can represent the graph of $y = 4x^2$?

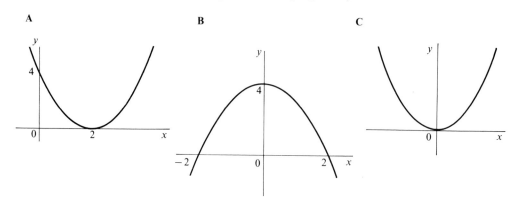

5. Draw axes with x and y from 0 to 8 and equal scales on both axes.
    With compasses, centre at the origin, radius 6 units, draw the quarter-circle which lies within the graph.
    Let A, B and C be points on the circumference of the quarter-circle where $x = 1$, 3 and 5 respectively.
    Draw the tangents to the circle at A, B and C and find their gradients.

6. Draw axes with x from -1 to 5 and y from -4 to 5.
    Make a table of values for the graph $y = x^2 - 4x$ for values of x from -1 to 5.
    Draw the graph.
    For the line with equation $y = x - 3$, find the values of y when $x = -1, 0, 5$, and draw the line on the same graph. Find the values of x and y at the two points where the line cuts the curve.
    This is the graphical method for solving the simultaneous equations $y = x^2 - 4x$ and $y = x - 3$.

7. Draw axes with x from -2 to 5 and y from -7 to 6. Make a table of values for the graph $y = (x + 1)(x - 4)$, for values of x from -2 to 5. Draw the graph. Draw also the line $y = -x$ on the same graph.
    Use your graphs to solve the simultaneous equations $y = (x + 1)(x - 4)$, $y = -x$.

8. Draw the graph of $y = x^2 - 7x + 10$ for values of x between 0 and 7. (Draw the x-axis from 0 to 7 and the y-axis from -4 to 10.)
    Use your graph to solve the equation $x^2 - 7x + 10 = 0$.

9. A trainee is tested on two pieces of work. In order to pass the test he must spend at least 1 minute on the first piece of work but complete it within 5 minutes, and take between 2 and 7 minutes on the second piece of work.
    If the time in minutes taken for the 1st piece is represented by x and the time in minutes taken for the 2nd piece is represented by y, write down the conditions which must be satisfied by x and y.
    Draw x and y axes from 0 to 8 and draw the lines representing the boundaries of these conditions. Identify the region representing the times which are satisfactory.

10. Mrs Parmar wants to buy some biscuits for a children's party. She decides to get at least 4 packets of cream biscuits, and not more than 7 packets of chocolate biscuits, but more packets of chocolate biscuits than cream biscuits.

If she buys x packets of chocolate biscuits and y packets of cream biscuits, write down the conditions satisfied by x and y.

On graph paper, draw x and y axes from 0 to 8, and draw lines giving the boundaries of these conditions. Identify the region containing the set of points (x, y) satisfying all these conditions.

List the possible combinations of packets she could buy, e.g. 5 packets of chocolate biscuits and 4 packets of cream biscuits.

11. Expand the brackets.

   1 $(x + 4)(x + 2)$

   2 $(x + 7)^2$

   3 $(x - 2)(x - 3)$

   4 $(x + 10)(x - 10)$

   5 $(x + 8)(x - 6)$

   Give geometrical illustrations for parts **1** and **2**.

12. The diagram represents a square $ABCD$ of side $(x + 4)$ cm.
    What is the area of $ABCD$?
    What is the total area of the 4 triangles?
    Hence find the area of the square $PQRS$ by subtraction. Simplify your answer and verify that the answer is the same as that found by using Pythagoras' theorem.

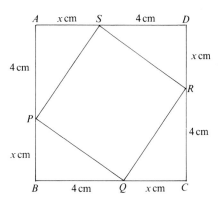

13. Write down an equation connecting the lengths of the sides of this right-angled triangle. Simplify the equation and solve it, to find x. What is the numerical value of the area of the triangle?

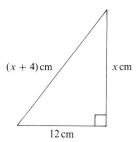

22 *Sets*

e.g. The set of days of the week is written as {days of the week}, i.e. {Sun, Mon, Tues, Wed, Thurs, Fri, Sat}.

The universal set, symbol $\mathscr{E}$, is the set consisting of all elements under consideration.

Example 1

This question is about the whole numbers from 1 to 10 so this is the universal set.
i.e. $\mathscr{E} = \{1, 2, 3, 4, 5, 6, 7, 8, 9, 10\}$

If $A = \{1, 3, 5, 7, 9\}$, $B = \{\text{multiples of 3}\}$, $C = \{\text{square numbers}\}$ and $D = \{\text{multiples of 11}\}$ then

A can be described as {odd numbers}.
The number of elements in set A is 5.
$B = \{3, 6, 9\}$, and the number of elements in set B is 3.
$C = \{1, 4, 9\}$, and the number of elements in set C is 3.
$D = \{\ \}$. This set has no elements and is called 'the empty set'.

Venn diagrams

These represent sets by enclosed regions, which can be any shape so they are often drawn roughly circular. $\mathscr{E}$ is often drawn rectangular. $\mathscr{E}$ need not be included if it is not relevant to the question.

The area outside A, within $\mathscr{E}$, represents the elements of $\mathscr{E}$ which are not members of A.

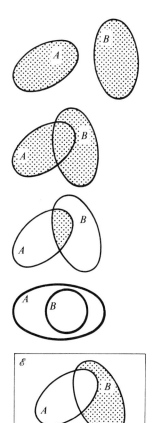

Two sets A, B which have no elements in common.
All elements which are members of A or B lie in the shaded region.

Two sets A, B which have some elements in common.
All elements which are members of A or B (or both) lie in the shaded region.

The shaded region here represents elements which are members of both A and B.

Two sets A, B where all the members of B are also members of A. B is called a **subset** of A.

The shaded region here represents elements which are members of B but not also of A.

Venn diagrams with 3 sets

Example 2

$\mathscr{E}$ is {students in a form}
A is {students taking Art}
B is {students taking Biology}
C is {students taking Commerce}
The numbers in each section represent the numbers of students studying that combination, thus 6 students study only Art, 7 study Art and Biology but not Commerce, and 5 study all three subjects.

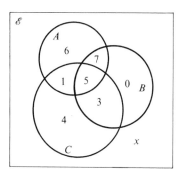

If there are 28 students in the form and x represents the number of students who take none of these three subjects, what is the value of x?
How many students take Biology and either Art or Commerce (but not both)?

The numbers in the diagram add up to 26 and there are 28 students altogether, so $x = 2$. There are 7 students who take Biology and Art but not Commerce, and 3 students who take Biology and Commerce but not Art, so altogether 10 students take Biology and either Art or Commerce (but not both).

Probability and Venn Diagrams

If the relationship between events A and B is represented on a Venn Diagram then

1 the probability of A and B happening can be found from the number of elements which are in A and in B.
2 the probability of A or B (or both) happening can be found from the number of elements which are in A or in B (or both).

Example 3

The number of students in a form who study Chemistry or Physics is shown in the Venn diagram, where $\mathscr{E} = \{$students in the form$\}$

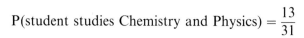

From the diagram:

$$P(\text{student studies Chemistry}) = \frac{24}{31}$$

$$P(\text{student studies Physics}) = \frac{16}{31}$$

$$P(\text{student studies Chemistry and Physics}) = \frac{13}{31}$$

$$P(\text{student studies Chemistry or Physics}) = \frac{11 + 13 + 3}{31} = \frac{27}{31}$$

Exercise 22.1

1. Name 4 members of each of these sets.

    1 {solid figures}
    2 {points on the line $y = 5 - x$}
    3 {measures of length}
    4 {months of the year with 31 days}
    5 {television channels}

2. List the members of the sets A to E, as described. If there are more than 3 members, list any 3.

    1 $\mathscr{E} = \{$quadrilaterals$\}$, $A = \{$polygons with all angles equal$\}$
    2 $\mathscr{E} = \{$measures of weight$\}$, $B = \{$metric measures$\}$
    3 $\mathscr{E} = \{$parts of a circle$\}$, $C = \{$words beginning with C$\}$
    4 $\mathscr{E} = \{$points on the curve $y = x^2\}$, $D = \{$points such that $y = x\}$
    5 $\mathscr{E} = \{$prime numbers$\}$, $E = \{$even numbers$\}$

3. Write 'belongs to' or 'does not belong to' in the space.

    1 moon   {planets}
    2 mean, median   (averages}
    3 39   {prime numbers}
    4 200   {square numbers}
    5 a triangle with angles of 50° and 80°   {isosceles triangles}

4. Find the number of elements in these sets, or say if they have an infinite number of elements.

    1   A = {months of the year}
    2   A = {square numbers}
    3   A = {points which lie on the line $y = 5 - x$}
    4   A = {multiples of $7 \leqslant 70$}

5. List the members which belong to set A or set B (or both).
    The universal set = {positive integers from 1 to 10}.

    1   A = {odd numbers}, B = {even numbers}
    2   A = {square numbers}, B = {multiples of 3}
    3   A = {factors of 60}, B = {factors of 42}

6. List or describe the members which belong to both set A and set B.

    1   A = {rectangles}, B = {rhombuses}
    2   A = {factors of 30}, B = {factors of 80}
    3   A = {regular polygons}, B = {triangles}
    4   A = {prime numbers}, B = {numbers between 50 and 60}

7. If A = {2, 4, 6, 8, 10}, B = {3, 6, 9} and C = {1, 2, 4, 8}, list the members which belong to

    1   set A but not to set C,
    2   set A or set B, but not to set C.

8. If $\mathscr{E}$ = {letters of the alphabet}, A = {a, b, c, d, e}, B = {vowels}, C = {b, u, s}, list the members which belong to

    1   set A and set B.
    2   set C but not set B.
    3   How many elements belong to set A or set B (or both)?
    4   How many elements of $\mathscr{E}$ do not belong to set B?

9. $\mathscr{E}$ = {positive integers}, A = {even numbers},
    B = {multiples of 5}, C = {prime numbers}.

    Describe these sets.

    1   {numbers which belong to A and to B},
    2   {numbers which belong to C but not to A},
    3   {numbers which belong to B but not to C}.

10. $\mathscr{E}$ = {all triangles}, A = {isosceles triangles},
    B = {right-angled triangles}, C = {equilateral triangles},
    D = {obtuse-angled triangles}.
    Describe these sets.

    1   {triangles which belong to A and B}
    2   {triangles which belong to A and C}
    3   {triangles which belong to C and D}
    4   {triangles which belong to B and C}

11. If $\mathscr{E}$ = {positive integers < 10}, A = {even numbers} and B = {multiples of 3}, show each number in its correct region on a Venn diagram.

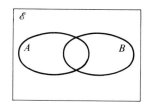

12. If $\mathscr{E}$ = {children in a class}
A = {children who can swim}
and B = {children who can skate},
on separate diagrams shade the regions representing these sets.

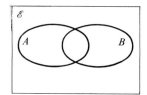

  1 {children who can swim and skate},
  2 {children who can't swim},
  3 {children who can skate or swim (or both)},
  4 {children who can swim but can't skate},
  5 {children who can't swim and can't skate}.

13. In a Youth Club with 60 members, everyone attends either on Tuesdays for Drama or on Thursdays for Sports, or on both evenings. If 48 attend for Drama and 44 attend for Sports, show these data on a Venn diagram, and find how many members attend for both Drama and Sports.
If a member of the Club is chosen at random, what is the probability that that person attends on both evenings?

14. If $\mathscr{E}$ = {integers from 2 to 10 inclusive}, A = {prime numbers},
B = {multiples of 5},
draw a Venn diagram and write each number in the correct region.

15. There are two shops in the village, the Post Office and the grocer's. In a survey on shopping habits, 100 people were asked which shops they had used in the past week.
31 had been in the Post Office, 54 had been in the grocer's and of these, 10 had been in both shops.
Draw a Venn diagram showing this information and find

  1 the number who only went into the Post Office,
  2 the number of those interviewed who did not go into either of the shops.
  3 If one of those interviewed was picked at random, what is the probability that that person had been in one (or both) of the shops?

16. $\mathscr{E}$ = {positive integers $\leqslant 12$},
A = {even numbers},
B = {multiples of 4}.
Copy the Venn diagram and write the numbers 1 to 12 in their correct regions.

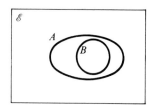

17. In a group of 25 students, 11 study Art and 12 study Craft. 2 of these students take both Art and Craft. Represent this information on a Venn diagram and find how many students do not study either of these subjects.

18. In a class of 22 children, 10 children can play the recorder and 12 children can play the piàno. 4 can play neither the recorder nor the piano. Show this information on a Venn diagram. How many children can play both the recorder and the piano?

19. In a certain school, students must study either French or Spanish (or both). If 85% of the students study French and 25% study Spanish, show this information on a Venn diagram and find what percentage study both subjects. If 84 students study both French and Spanish, how many students are there altogether? If a student of the school is chosen at random, what is the probability that this student studies both French and Spanish? If a student is chosen at random from those who study Spanish, what is the probability that this student also studies French?

Exercise 22.2

1. If $\mathscr{E} = \{$months of the year$\}$, $A = \{$months beginning with the letter J$\}$, $B = \{$months with 31 days$\}$, $C = \{$months ending with the letter y$\}$, list the members which

   1 belong to A and to B,
   2 belong to A and to C,
   3 belong to B but not to C,
   4 belong to C but not to A.

2. In a certain road with 40 householders, 25 householders had an evening paper delivered, and 10 of these householders also had a morning paper. 8 householders did not have any paper delivered. Show this information on a Venn diagram.

   1 How many householders had a morning paper only?
   2 How many householders did not get a morning paper?

3. In a class of 33 girls, 18 study Cookery, 10 study Commerce and 9 do not study either. Draw a Venn diagram to represent these facts.
   If a girl is chosen at random from the class what is the probability that

   1 she studies both Cookery and Commerce,
   2 she studies Commerce but not Cookery?
   3 If a girl is chosen at random from those who take Commerce, what is the probability that she also studies Cookery?

4. A is a set with 10 members. B is a subset of A with 4 members. If a member of set A is chosen at random what is the probability that this member belongs to subset B?

5. $\mathscr{E} = \{$positive integers from 1 to 50$\}$,
    $A = \{$multiples of 9$\}$,
    $B = \{$square numbers$\}$.
    List the members of A and of B.
    List the members which belong to A and to B.
    Copy the Venn diagram and fill in the number of
    members in each section.

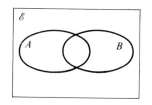

If 50 discs labelled 1 to 50 are put in a bag and one is drawn out at random, what
is the probability that

1   it is a multiple of 9,
2   it is a square number,
3   it is either a multiple of 9 or a square number,
4   it is a multiple of 9 and a square number,
5   it is not a multiple of 9 nor a square number?

6. $\mathscr{E} = \{$triangles$\}$, $I = \{$isosceles triangles$\}$, $R = \{$right-angled triangles$\}$.
    Draw a Venn diagram showing $\mathscr{E}$, I and R in their correct relationship.
    Mark these triangles in their correct regions on the diagram.

1   $\triangle ABX$, if $ABCD$ is a rectangle with diagonals intersecting at X.
2   $\triangle EFY$, if $EFGH$ is a square with diagonals intersecting at Y.
3   $\triangle KLZ$, if $KLMN$ is a rhombus with diagonals intersecting at Z.

7. The sets A, B and C have members as
    shown.

1   Who belongs to set A and set B,
2   who belongs to set A and set C,
3   who belongs to all three sets,
4   who belongs to only one set,
5   which sets does Eve belong to?

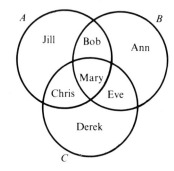

8. $\mathscr{E} = \{$students in a form$\}$,
    $F = \{$students learning French$\}$,
    $G = \{$students learning Geography$\}$,
    $H = \{$students learning History$\}$.
    The number of students in each section are shown
    in the diagram.

1   How many students are there in the form?
2   How many students learn both French and
    History?
3   How many students learn Geography, and
    either French or History but not both?
4   How many students do not learn History?
5   How many students learn all three of these
    subjects?
6   How many students learn only one of these
    subjects?

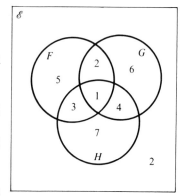

9. In a village, the bank opens on Mondays, Wednesdays and Fridays. The shop opens on Mondays, Wednesdays, Thursdays and Saturdays. The cafe opens on Wednesdays, Saturdays and Sundays.

    If $\mathscr{E}$ = {days of the week}, copy the diagram and write the days in their correct spaces according to which places are open.

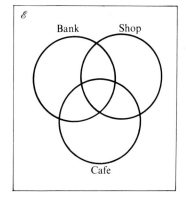

10. In a survey of 36 boys, the numbers playing football, cricket and rugby are given in the Venn diagram.

    If a boy is picked at random from this group what is the probability that he plays

    1 football,
    2 cricket and football but not rugby,
    3 only rugby?
    4 If a boy who plays cricket is chosen at random, what is the probability that he also plays football?

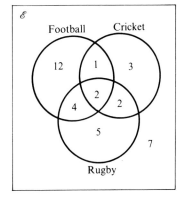

PUZZLES

61. Whilst Mr Mercer's car was being repaired, he travelled to and from work either by train or by bus. When he went to work on the train, he came home on the bus. If he came home on the train, he had taken the bus to work. During this time he travelled on the train 9 times and travelled on the bus 10 times going to work and 15 times coming home from work. For how many days was his car off the road?

62. Using the figures 1 to 7 and the multiplication sign, as in these examples, 6 × 325 714, 341 × 5276, 21 × 56 × 473, which arrangement gives the largest product?

63. The ages of my father, my son and myself total 85 years. My father is just twice my age, and the units figure in his age is equal to the age of my son. How old am I?

23 *Patterns*

Number Patterns

There are many patterns in numbers which you can notice.

For example $3 \times 37 = 111$

$6 \times 37 = 222$

$9 \times 37 = 333$

. . .

Copy and continue this pattern to 27×37.

Sequences of numbers

Whole numbers 1, 2, 3, 4, . . .

Odd numbers 1, 3, 5, 7, . . .

Even numbers 2, 4, 6, 8, . . .

Multiples of 5. 5, 10, 15, 20, . . .

Prime numbers 2, 3, 5, 7, 11, . . . (These do not follow a regular pattern, but apart from 2 and 5 they all have unit figures of 1, 3, 7 or 9.)

Square numbers 1, 4, 9, 16, . . . from 1^2, 2^2, 3^2, 4^2, . . .

(What are the differences between successive numbers, 1 and 4, 4 and 9, 9 and 16, etc? Another pattern emerges.)

Square numbers can be represented by dots arranged in the form of squares.

Triangular numbers 1, 3, 6, 10, 15, . . .

These can be represented by dots in the form of triangles.

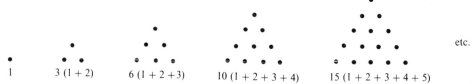

(What do you notice about the sum of two successive triangular numbers? Can you show why this is so, using a dots pattern?)

Cube numbers 1, 8, 27, 64, . . . from 1^3, 2^3, 3^3, 4^3, . . .

There are many other sequences of numbers.
If you have to identify a sequence and continue it, see if you can recognise anything special about it. Also look at the differences between successive terms.

e.g. 8, 17, 26, 35, . . .
You might notice that the difference between successive numbers is always 9. You get the next term by adding on 9.
You might notice that the unit figures go down in 1's and the ten's figures go up in 1's, so the next term is 44. This will give you terms up to 80, although the sequence continues beyond that.
You might notice that the digits add up to 8 each time.

e.g. 6, 12, 24, 48, 96, . . .
The differences between successive terms are 6, 12, 24, 48. These are the same numbers as in the sequence, so the sequence is a doubling one. The next term is $96 \times 2 = 192$.

e.g. $\frac{1}{2}$, $\frac{1}{4}$, $\frac{1}{6}$, $\frac{1}{8}$, . . .
These are fractions which are getting smaller. The numerators are all 1. The denominators in turn go 2, 4, 6, 8 so they increase by 2 each time and the next one is 10. So the next number in the sequence is $\frac{1}{10}$.

e.g. 2, 3, 5, 9, 17, 33, . . .
The sequence is growing more and more rapidly and after 2 the numbers are all odd. Investigate the differences between successive terms. They are 1, 2, 4, 8, 16. These are always doubled, the next difference is 32 and the next number in the sequence is $33 + 32 = 65$.

You can discover a general formula to give the terms of a sequence if it follows a regular pattern.
This is often given in terms of n (rather than x) because the terms are found by substituting whole numbers only.

e.g. The n'th term of a sequence is $n^2 - n$.

This means, putting $n = 1, 2, 3, . . .$ in turn,
the 1st term of the sequence is $1^2 - 1 = 0$,
the 2nd term of the sequence is $2^2 - 2 = 2$,
the 3rd term of the sequence is $3^2 - 3 = 6$,
the 4th term of the sequence is $4^2 - 4 = 12$, and so on.
The sequence is 0, 2, 6, 12, 20, . . .
(Do you recognise any connection with this and the sequence of triangular numbers?)

e.g. Consider the sequence of 3, 10, 17, 24, 31, . . .
The numbers go up by 7's. In this case investigate a general term with $7n$ involved.
If the n'th term of a sequence is $7n$ then the sequence is 7, 14, 21, 28, 35, . . .
The numbers we want are all 4 less than the corresponding terms here, so the general formula is
n'th term $= 7n - 4$.
Check this by putting $n = 1, 2, 3, . . .$
(You should have often noticed the numbers 3, 10, 17, 24, 31 in a column or a row on a calendar.)

The Fibonacci Sequence

Every term of this sequence is obtained from the sum of the previous two terms.
The sequence is 1, 1, 2(1 + 1), 3(2 + 1), 5(3 + 2), 8(5 + 3), and so on.

Other sequences could be made in the same way, e.g. 10, 3, 13, 16, 29, 45, 74, . . .

Other sequences can go in pairs, e.g. 14, 10, 20, 16, 32, 28, 56, . . .
Here the rule is: 1st time subtract 4, next time multiply by 2, and repeat these two
operations in order.

Exercise 23.1

1. Find the next 2 numbers in these sequences.

   1 4, 10, 16, 22, 28, . . .   **6** 3, 4, 6, 9, 13, . . .

   2 3, 6, 9, 12, 15, . . .   **7** 3, 1, $\frac{1}{3}$, $\frac{1}{9}$, $\frac{1}{27}$, . . .

   3 5, 10, 20, 40, 80, . . .   **8** 3, 7, 15, 31, 63, . . .

   4 3, 9, 27, 81, 243, . . .   **9** 3, 8, 18, 38, 78, . . .

   5 3, 0, -3, -6, -9, . . .   **10** 1, 2, 6, 24, 120, . . .

2. Find the 1st 5 terms in these sequences.

   1 n'th term is $2n + 5$

   2 n'th term is $n^2 + 1$

   3 n'th term is $\dfrac{n}{n + 1}$

   4 n'th term is 2^n

   5 n'th term is $n(n + 1)$

3. Give an expression for the n'th term in these sequences.

   1 1, 3, 5, 7, 9, . . .

   2 1, 8, 27, 64, 125, . . .

   3 1, $\frac{1}{2}$, $\frac{1}{3}$, $\frac{1}{4}$, $\frac{1}{5}$, . . .

   4 2, 8, 14, 20, 26, . . .

   5 100, 95, 90, 85, 80, . . .

4. There is one mistake in this pattern. Copy the pattern, replacing the wrong number by the correct one.

    $$1 \qquad\qquad = 1$$
    $$1 + 3 \qquad\;\; = 4$$
    $$1 + 3 + 5 \quad\; = 8$$
    $$1 + 3 + 5 + 7 = 16$$

    Fill in the next 3 rows of the pattern.
    What do you notice about the totals?
    If this pattern was continued, what would be the total of numbers in the 20th row?

5. Copy and complete this number pattern to the row which begins 123456789

    $$1 \times 8 + 1 \quad\; = 9$$
    $$12 \times 8 + 2 \quad = 98$$
    $$123 \times 8 + 3 \;=$$
    $$1234 \times 8 + 4 =$$

    . . .

6. Copy these sequences, correcting the mistake in each one.

    1 $(0, 1)$, $(1, 3\frac{1}{2})$, $(2, 6)$, $(3, 8\frac{1}{2})$, $(4, 10)$.

    2 $(2, 4)$, $(3, 9)$, $(4, 16)$, $(5, 24)$, $(6, 36)$

    3 $-1, 3, -9, 27, -81, 243, 729$.

7. **Magic Squares**

    Rearrange these numbers so that each row, each column and each diagonal add up to 15.
    (Leave 5 in the centre and put 4 in a corner.)

1	2	3
4	5	6
7	8	9

8. This is a multiplication table pattern using the numbers 1, 3, 5, 7 only.
    Make a similar table but instead of writing the answer down, for numbers greater than 7, divide them by 8 and just write the remainder down.
    e.g. $5 \times 7 = 35$ and $35 \div 8 = 4$ remainder 3, so write down 3.
    Do you notice any patterns?

	1	3	5	7
1	1	3	5	7
3	3	9	15	21
5	5	15	25	35
7	7	21	35	49

    Make a similar table for the numbers 1, 3, 7, 9 just writing the units figures down, and another one for the numbers 2, 4, 6, 8 just writing the units figures down.

    Make a similar table for the numbers 1, 2, 3, 4, dividing the answers by 5 and just writing the remainders down.

    Do you notice any similarities?

9. Copy and complete the table, of the number of lines needed to join 2, 3, 4, . . . points. (The diagrams may help you to discover the pattern.)

Number of points	2	3	4	5	6	7	8	9	10
Number of lines needed	1	3	6						

2 points
1 line

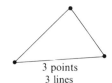

3 points
3 lines

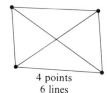

4 points
6 lines

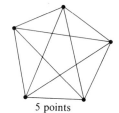

5 points

10. **Number chains** These change a number into another number by a certain rule. Then the new number is changed and the process is repeated.
    Rule For 2-figure numbers, multiply the 10's digit by 4 and add to the units digit. Stop the chain when you get a single figure.
    e.g. $29 \rightarrow (2 \times 4) + 9 = 17 \rightarrow (1 \times 4) + 7 = 11 \rightarrow (1 \times 4) + 1 = 5$.
    $94 \rightarrow (9 \times 4) + 4 = 40 \rightarrow (4 \times 4) + 0 = 16 \rightarrow (1 \times 4) + 6 = 10 \rightarrow (1 \times 4) + 0 = 4$.

    Carry out this rule for some 2-figure multiples of 6. What do you notice?
    Try it out for other 2-figure numbers.
    Make other number chains using different rules.

11. Copy and fill in this table, but write in the units figures only.
    e.g. $9^2 = 81$ so the units figure is 1.
    $8^3 = 512$ so the units figure is 2.
    Do you notice any patterns?

x	x^2	x^3	x^4	x^5
0	0			
1				
2				
3				
.				
.				
9	1			

Inequalities

$<$ is the symbol for 'is less than', so $3 < 4$ means '3 is less than 4'.
$>$ is the symbol for 'is greater than'.
$\leqslant$ is the symbol for 'is less than or equal to'.
$\geqslant$ is the symbol for 'is greater than or equal to', so $x \geqslant 3$ means 'x is greater than or equal to 3'.

Also $\neq$ is the symbol for 'is not equal to', e.g. $3.3 \neq 3\frac{1}{3}$.

Example 1

If x is an integer, what are the possible values of x if $-1 \leqslant x < 5$?

x is greater than or equal to -1
x is less than 5
The possible values of x are $-1, 0, 1, 2, 3, 4$.

Inequalities on the number line

Example 2

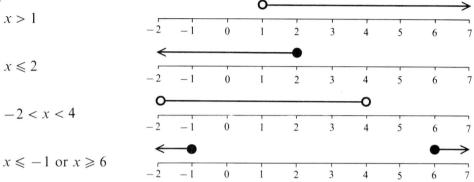

$x > 1$

$x \leqslant 2$

$-2 < x < 4$

$x \leqslant -1$ or $x \geqslant 6$

We have used the symbol ● if the end point is included and the symbol ○ if the end point is not included.

Exercise 23.2

1. Describe these statements in words.

    1 $x > 7$ **4** $1 < x < 4$

    2 $x \leqslant 8$ **5** $x \geqslant -5$

    3 $x \neq 1$

2. Write these statements in symbols.

    1 x is less than 6.
    2 x is greater than or equal to -2.
    3 x is not equal to 0.
    4 x is less than 10 but greater than -3
    5 x is less than or equal to 5.

3. Show these inequalities on the number line.

    1 $x > -3$ **6** $-2 < x < -1$

    2 $x < -1$ **7** $-3 \leqslant x \leqslant 4$

    3 $x \geqslant 0$ **8** $x < -3$ or $x > 2$

    4 $x < 3$ **9** $x \leqslant 1$ or $x \geqslant 2$

    5 $x \leqslant 2$ **10** $-1 < x < 1$

4. Write a statement linking a, b, c by $<$ signs, e.g. $b < a < c$, if

    1   $a = -2, b = 4, c = -1$ 4 $a = -3, b = 1\frac{1}{2}, c = 1\frac{3}{4}$

    2   $a = 3, b = 0, c = -4$ 5 $a = 4, b = -4\frac{1}{2}, c = -3\frac{1}{2}$

    3   $a = -1, b = 5, c = -6$

5. If x is an integer, what are the possible values of x if

    1   $3 < x < 7$ 4 $-8 < x < -4$

    2   $4 \leqslant x < 6$ 5 $0 \leqslant x \leqslant 5$

    3   $-2 \leqslant x \leqslant 2$

Geometric Patterns

We see many examples of patterns in our daily lives.
Notice the patterns on wallpaper and fabric and see how they involve reflections, rotations and translations.
Look for symmetry in buildings and in natural objects such as flowers.

Tessellations

These are congruent shapes arranged in a pattern to cover an area.
At every point where shapes join, for them to fit exactly, the sum of the angles is 360°.

examples

triangles covering a surface   hexagons   rhombuses

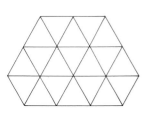
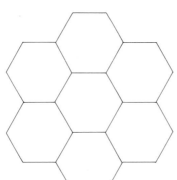
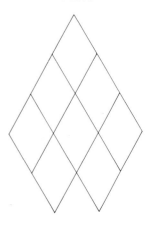

If we take triangles or other shapes out of 2 sides of a square and add them to the other 2 sides

the shapes will still fit together, and make a more interesting pattern.

The second pattern takes out equal curved shapes.

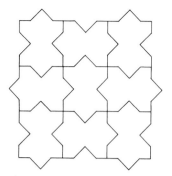
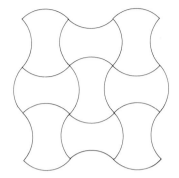

Tessellations can also be made using combinations of regular polygons.

examples

equilateral triangles and
regular hexagons

regular octagons
and squares

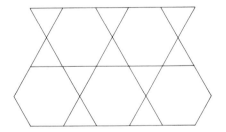
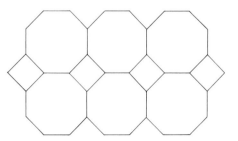

The possibilities are endless. Notice any tessellations you see, for example, on tiled floors.
Make up your own designs.

Exercise 23.3

1. Patterns made with triangles. Copy and continue these patterns and design others.

   1 Reflection and translation.

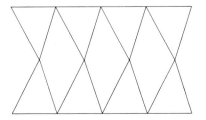   or   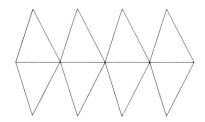

2   Rotation and translation.

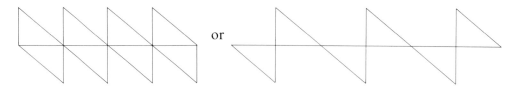

or

2.   Patterns made with circles. Copy these patterns and design others.

   1 Keep the same radius   **2**   Extend to outer circles

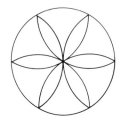

3.   Start with a square with sides divided into 4 equal parts. By joining points make
     a symmetrical pattern.
     Here is one idea.

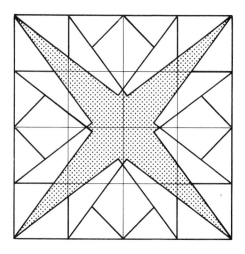

4. Start with a circle and mark 12 equally-spaced points round the circumference.
    By joining some of these points make a symmetrical pattern.
    Here is one idea.

5. Copy and continue these patterns, or design similar patterns for yourself.

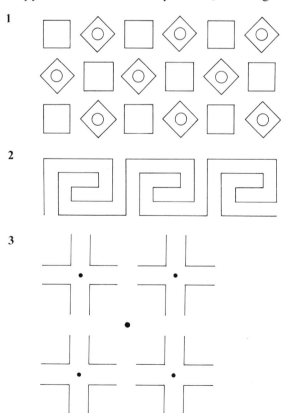

6. Draw on squared paper and cut out several pieces of each of these shapes. Draw outlines on squared paper to show how each shape can be used to tessellate an area.

1 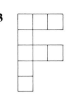   2 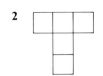   3 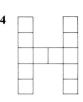   4

7. Draw a regular hexagon with side 4 cm on thick card. Cut it out. By drawing round the outside, make several more hexagons. Also make some equilateral triangles and some squares of side 4 cm.
Draw sketches of these tessellated areas.

   1 Use equilateral triangles and regular hexagons, so that every point is the join of 1 hexagon and 4 triangles.

   2 Use equilateral triangles, regular hexagons and squares. How many of each meet at every point?

   3 Use equilateral triangles and squares.

Exercise 23.4

1. Find the next 2 numbers in these sequences.

   1 1, 2, 5, 10, 17, . . .   6 $\frac{1}{3}, \frac{1}{6}, \frac{1}{9}, \frac{1}{12}$, . . .

   2 288, 144, 72, 36, . . .   7 45, 36, 27, 18, . . .

   3 2, 4, 8, 16, . . .   8 1, -2, -5, -8, . . .

   4 81, 27, 9, 3, . . .   9 1, 10, 100, 1000, . . .

   5 3, 7, 11, 15, . . .   10 100, 91, 82, 73, . . .

2. Copy and complete the 1st 9 rows of this pattern.

   $$1 \qquad = \frac{1 \times 2}{2} = 1$$

   $$1 + 2 \qquad = \frac{2 \times 3}{2} = 3$$

   $$1 + 2 + 3 \qquad = \frac{3 \times 4}{2} = 6$$

   $$1 + 2 + 3 + 4 = \qquad =$$

   . . .

   Now using the method of this pattern, work out the sum of the numbers from 1 to 40.

3. Three coins are to be arranged in a row in as many different ways as possible. Three examples in which **H** represents heads and **T** tails are shown.

   T H T   H T T   H H H

   Write down the other 5 possible arrangements in the same way.
   List the number of arrangements when this investigation is done with different numbers of coins.

Number of coins		1	2	3	4	5	6
Total number of arrangements	2		8				

   If there were 1024 different arrangements how many coins would be used?

4. Write down a formula for the n'th term of these sequences.

   1   2, 4, 8, 16, 32, . . .   **4**   21, 25, 29, 33, 37, . . .

   2   100, 93, 86, 79, 72, . . .   **5**   3, 12, 27, 48, 75, . . .

   3 $\frac{1}{2}, \frac{2}{3}, \frac{3}{4}, \frac{4}{5}, \ldots$

5. 6 is called a **perfect number** because its factors are 1, 2, 3 and when you add them up their sum equals 6.
   12 has factors 1, 2, 3, 4, 6 and their sum equals 16, not 12, so 12 is not a perfect number.
   However, there is one other number less than 50 which is a perfect number. Which is it?

6. Copy and complete this number pattern.

   $142857 \times 1 = 142857$
   $142857 \times 5 =$
   $142857 \times 4 =$
   $142857 \times 6 =$
   $142857 \times 2 =$
   $142857 \times 3 =$

   What do you notice about the answers?

7. Copy and complete this magic square which uses numbers 1 to 16.
   All rows, columns and the main diagonals add up to 34.

			12
3	16		
15		14	

8. Mrs Jones makes toy animals, dogs and elephants, to sell. She can make not
    more than 10 of these animals in a week. There is more demand for elephants
    so she always makes at least 6 elephants, although she also makes at least 2 dogs.
    If in one week she makes x dogs and y elephants, write down inequalities
    satisfied by x and y.
    List the possible combinations of animals she could make, e.g. 2 dogs and 6
    elephants.
    If she makes £3 profit on each dog and £2 profit on each elephant, consider the
    possible combinations and decide what she should make to get most profit. How
    much profit will this be?

9. Start with an equilateral triangle of
    side 8 cm.
    Mark points every 2 cm along each
    side.
    By joining points, design a pattern.
    Here is one idea.

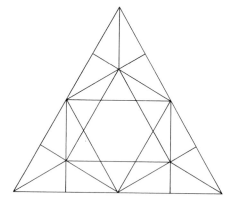

10. Draw a regular octagon as follows:
    From a point O draw 8 lines $OA, OB, OC, OD, OE, OF, OG, OH$ each 4 cm long
    with an angle of 45° between each two adjacent lines.
    Join $AB, BC, CD, DE, EF, FG, GH, HA$. Measure these lines which should be
    equal.
    Cut out the octagon, and make several more of the same size.
    Make several squares with sides the same length as AB.
    Arrange the octagons and squares to make a tessellated area and show your
    design on a sketch.

There are other patterns and suggestions for patterns in the practical exercises. There
is unlimited scope for discovery, investigation and invention both with number
patterns and with geometric patterns.

24 Graphs of numerical data

Conversion Graphs

Example 1

Draw a graph to convert kilometres into miles, given that 1 km ≈ 0.62 miles.
Draw the 'kilometres' axis horizontally, label from 0 to 100.
Draw the 'miles' axis vertically, label from 0 to 70.
You know that 0 km = 0 miles so plot a point at (0, 0).
Also 100 km = 100 × 0.62 miles = 62 miles, so plot a point at (100, 62).
A third point would be useful as a check.
50 km = 50 × 0.62 miles = 31 miles, so you can plot a point at (50, 31).
Join the points with a straight line.
You can use this graph to convert km into miles or miles into km.

1 Convert 22.5 km into miles.   2 Convert 50 miles into km.

Time-distance graph

Example 2

This graph represents a boy's journey from a town P.
He leaves at 12 noon and walks for 30 minutes at a steady speed. This is represented by the line AB. The gradient of the line gives the speed.
At what speed does he walk?
The line BC represents the next stage, where he cycles.

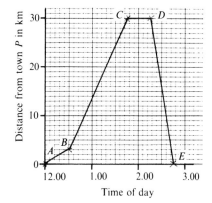

For how long does he cycle?
What distance does he travel?
At what average speed does he cycle?
The line CD represents a rest of 30 minutes.
How far is he away from P?
The line DE represents his journey home by bus.
What time does the bus journey begin?
How long is the bus journey?
What is the average speed of the bus?
(The gradient of the line DE gives the velocity which is negative because the direction of motion is in the opposite direction to that at first.)
The **average speed** from A to C can be found by joining A and C with a straight line and finding its gradient. It is $\dfrac{30}{1\frac{3}{4}}$ km/hour = 17.1 km/hour.

Time–Speed Graph

Example 3

Draw a graph to represent the journey of a car which starts from rest and increases its speed uniformly for 10 seconds, reaching a speed of 30 m/s. It maintains this speed for 30 seconds and then decreases its speed uniformly at the rate of 2 m/s per second until it comes to rest.

Put time on the horizontal axis, from 0 to 55 s.
Put speed on the vertical axis, from 0 to 30 m/s.
For the first part of the journey, join the point (0, 0) to the point (10, 30) with a straight line.
Then draw a straight line with the speed 30 for the next 30 seconds.
Finally, the slowing-down period from 30 m/s to 0 at the rate of 2 m/s per second will take 15 seconds. Draw in the line to represent this.

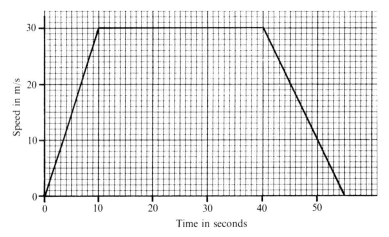

Use your graph to find the speed of the car at time 6 seconds, and at time 42 seconds.

Acceleration

The rate at which speed increases with time is called acceleration.
If the speed is decreasing then there is a negative acceleration, sometimes called deceleration or retardation.

The formula is

$$\text{acceleration} = \frac{\text{increase in speed}}{\text{time}}$$

If the speed is in m/s and time in seconds then the acceleration is measured in metres per second per second, which is abbreviated to m/s^2 or ms^{-2}.
On a time–speed graph the gradient gives the acceleration.
(More precisely, acceleration is the rate of change of **velocity**, but we will consider only cases where the speeds are measured in the same positive direction.)

In example **3**, in the first part of the journey, the car increases speed from 0 to 30 m/s in 10 seconds, so that there is an acceleration of 3 m/s per second, (written as $3 \, \text{m/s}^2$ or $3 \, \text{ms}^{-2}$).

In the middle part of the graph the speed is steady, there is no slope on the graph and no acceleration.

In the last part of the graph there is a negative acceleration (or deceleration or retardation) of $2 \, \text{m/s}^2$.

Exercise. 24.1

1. Draw a graph to convert U.S. dollars into £'s at a time when the rate of exchange was 1 dollar = £0.69. Draw the 'dollars' axis horizontally, label from 0 to 100. Draw the £'s axis vertically, label from 0 to 70. Plot the point representing 100 dollars on the graph and join it to the origin (0, 0) with a straight line.
   Use your graph to convert

   1   75 dollars into £'s,
   2   £22 into dollars.

   (If you know the up-to-date rate of exchange you may prefer to use that.)

2. Draw a graph to convert gallons into litres.
   Draw the 'gallons' axis horizontally, label from 0 to 10.
   Draw the 'litres' axis vertically, label from 0 to 50.
   10 gallons is equivalent to 45.5 litres.
   Plot this point on the graph and join it to the origin (0, 0) with a straight line.
   Use your graph to convert 6.5 gallons into litres, and to convert 10 litres into gallons.

3. Draw a graph to convert metres/second into km/hour for speeds up to 50 m/s. Label the horizontal axis from 0 to 50 (m/s) and the vertical axis from 0 to 180 (km/hour). Use the information that 0 m/s = 0 km/hour and 50 m/s = 180 km/hour to draw the straight-line graph.
   What speed is equivalent to   1   13 m/s,   2   100 km/hour?

4. The diagram represents the journeys of 4 trains, 3 of them travelling from town *A* to town *B*, 100 km away, and one going in the opposite direction.

   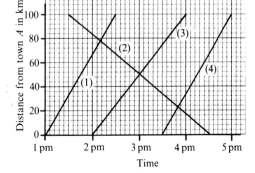

   1   Which two trains travel at the same speed? What speed is it?

   2   Which train has the slowest speed? What speed is it?

   3   Train (2) should have been travelling at a speed of 40 km/hour. How many minutes late was it on reaching town *A*?

5. Dhiren leaves village *A* on his bicycle at noon and cycles at a speed of 15 km/hour towards a town *B*. After an hour he has 30 minutes rest and then continues at a speed of 12 km/hour, reaching *B* at 3 p.m. His father leaves town *B* by car at 1.45 p.m., driving towards *A* at a steady speed, and arrives at *A* at 2.30 p.m.
    Represent this information on a time-distance graph, drawing the time axis from noon to 3 p.m. and the distance axis showing distances from *A* from 0 to 40 km.

    1   How far apart are *A* and *B*?

    2   How far from *B*, and at what time, did his father pass Dhiren?

6. A train leaves town *A* for town *B* at 1 p.m. and maintains a steady speed of 60 km/hour. At 2 p.m. another train leaves *B* for *A* maintaining a steady speed of 72 km/hour. The distance between *A* and *B* is 180 km.
    Draw the time-distance graphs for these two trains using the same axes.
    Draw the time axis with times from 1 p.m. to 5 p.m. and the distance axis with distances from *A* from 0 to 180 km with *A* at 0 and *B* at 180.
    When do the trains pass one another and how far are they from *A* at this time?

7. The table gives the heights of an object projected vertically upwards from ground level.

Time in seconds	0	1	2	3	4	5
Height in metres	0	20	30	30	20	0

    Draw a horizontal axis from 0 to 5 (for time, in seconds) and a vertical axis from 0 to 40 (for height, in metres). Plot the points and join them with a smooth curve. Estimate the height the object attains. At what times is the object 10 m above the ground?
    The speed is constantly changing but the speed at any point on the curve can be found from the gradient of the tangent to the curve at that point. By drawing a tangent to the curve and calculating its gradient, find an estimate of the speed of the object at time $1\frac{1}{2}$ seconds.

8. An object moves from rest so that its distance, *y* m, travelled in time *t* seconds is shown in this table.

t	0	0.5	1	1.5	2	2.5	3
y	0	0.8	3.3	7.4	13.2	20.6	29.7

    Draw a time-distance graph, joining the points with a smooth curve.
    Draw the *t*-axis from 0 to 3 and the *y*-axis from 0 to 30.
    Estimate the time needed to travel 25 m.

9. The graph shows the speed of an object over 10 seconds.
    Find

    1   the distance travelled in the first 6 seconds,

    2   the retardation over the last 4 seconds.

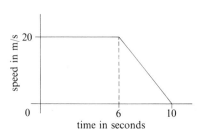

10. A train starts from rest at a station *A* and increases speed at a steady rate for 2 minutes until it reaches a speed of 100 km/hour. It maintains this steady speed for 12 minutes, and then slows down at a steady rate of 20 km/hour per minute until it comes to a stop at station *B*.
Represent this information graphically on a time–speed graph.
Draw the time axis from 0 to 20 minutes and the speed axis from 0 to 100 km/hour.

   1 How far does the train travel at its highest speed?

   2 What is its speed after $\frac{1}{2}$ minute, and at what time is it next travelling at this speed?

11. The table shows the speed of a train at various times as it travels between two stations.

Time from start, in seconds	0	15	30	45	60	75	90	105	120
Speed, in m/s	0	9	14	18	21	21	18	11	0

Draw a time–speed graph, joining the points with a smooth curve.
Draw the time axis from 0 to 120 seconds and the speed axis from 0 to 24 m/s (or 25 m/s).
Find from the graph

   1 the greatest speed,

   2 the two times when the train was travelling at half its greatest speed.

   3 By drawing a tangent to the curve, find the retardation 105 seconds after the start.

12. These times are taken from a table of 'lighting-up times for vehicles', on the Sunday of each week.

Week number	1	2	3	4	5	6	7	8
Time of day	16.32	16.40	16.50	17.02	17.14	17.26	17.39	17.52

Plot these values on a graph. Draw the 'week number' axis horizontally with 2 cm to each unit. Draw the 'time of day' axis vertically, from 16.00 hours to 18.00 hours taking 1 cm to 10 minutes. Join the plotted points with a smooth curve.
These lighting-up times are worked out as half-an-hour after sunset. On the same axes draw the graph showing times of sunset during the same weeks.

Sketch Graphs

These can show the general relationship between two variables, without showing the exact details.
A good way to decide what the graph looks like is to make a possible table of values, even though you are not going to plot them exactly.

Examples

4   A man's wages stay constant over several years.

        Make a table of values. Suppose he earns £5000 per year.

Year	1	2	3	4	5
Wage (£)	5000	5000	5000	5000	5000

        The graph looks like this.

5   The distance travelled by a car going at a constant speed, at different times.

        Make a table of values. Suppose the speed is 30 miles/hour.

Time (hours)	0	1	2	3	4
Distance (miles)	0	30	60	90	120

        The graph looks like this.

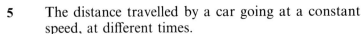

6   The level of water in a rectangular tank at different times if it is being drained and running out at a constant rate.

        Make a table of values. Suppose the level is falling 10 cm/minute and it is 60 cm deep at the beginning.

Time (min)	0	1	2	3	4	5	6
Level (cm)	60	50	40	30	20	10	0

        The graph looks like this.

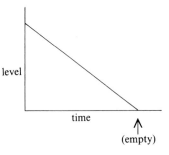

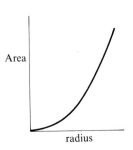

7   The connection between the area and radius of a circle.

        $A = \pi r^2$ but take π as 3 to get a rough idea, in the table of values.

r	0	1	2	3	4
A	0	3	12	27	48

        The graph is of the form $y = ax^2$ and looks like this.

8   The connection between the length and breadth of a
rectangle with a fixed area.

Make a table of values. Suppose the area is $12\,\text{cm}^2$.
Then length × breadth = 12, so length $= \dfrac{12}{\text{breadth}}$.

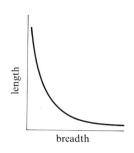

Breadth	1	2	3	4	6	8	10	12
Length	12	6	4	3	2	1.5	1.2	1

This is an inverse relationship so the graph is of the
form $y = \dfrac{a}{x}$ and looks like this.

Exercise 24.2

1.   These sketch graphs show the costs of running a business over several months.
Identify which sketch matches each of these statements.

   1   The costs are rising steadily.

   2   The costs are falling after having reached a peak.

   3   The costs are rising at an increasing rate.

   4   The costs have been rising but now seem to have levelled out.

A

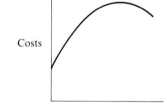

B

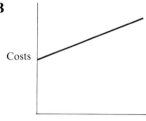

C

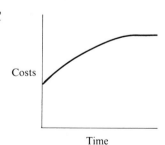

D

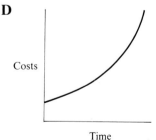

2.   A train starts from rest and for the first 70 seconds its speed increases steadily
until it reaches $15\,\text{m/s}$. Then the speed immediately decreases at a constant rate
until the train stops in a further 50 seconds. Sketch the time–speed graph for the
train.

3. Show the general relationship between these quantities by a sketch graph. Put the first quantity mentioned on the vertical axis.

    1   The areas of squares with edges of different lengths.
    2   The amount of VAT payable on goods of different prices.
    3   A man's wages over several years if he gets a fixed rise each year.
    4   A man's wages over several years if he gets a 5% rise each year.
    5   The number of passengers compared with the number of empty seats in a minibus over several journeys.

4. Three workmen charge for doing a job as follows:
    Mr *A* charges £120 for the 1st 40 hours and £5 an hour for any hours over 40.
    Mr *B* charges a flat-rate of £6 per hour.
    Mr *C* charges £150 for the job regardless of how long it will take.
    Draw sketch graphs showing the relationship between time taken and cost, for jobs taking up to 50 hours, for each of the three men. Put time on the horizontal axis and cost on the vertical axis.

Scatter Diagrams (used in Statistics)

A scatter diagram is used when there is some relationship between 2 sets of variables.

A line of best fit is a line which seems to fit the trend of the data best, so that points on one side of it are balanced by points on the other side.

Example 9

The length and width of 10 leaves from a bush.

length (in cm)	6.4	7.5	6.7	7.3	6.8	5.6	5.1	4.7	5.5	6.2
width (in cm)	2.6	3.9	2.8	3.4	3.7	2.1	2.3	1.5	2.2	2.6

Scatter diagram of the lengths and widths of 10 leaves

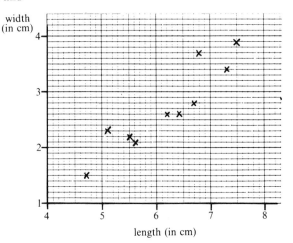

Note that the labelling on the axes need not start at 0.

The 1st set of data is usually plotted on the horizontal axis.

The diagram shows that there is some relationship between length and width. Longer leaves tend to be wider, although the relationship is not exact. We can draw a line of best fit, although we may not all agree on what is the 'best' line. This line can be used to estimate the likely width of a leaf with a certain length, but the result will only be a 'best estimate', not a fixed measure.
For a leaf of length 7 cm the estimate for the width is 3.3 cm.

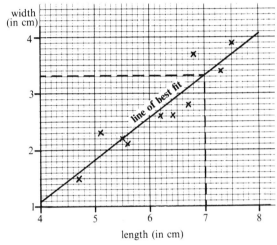

length (in cm)

Exercise 24.3

1. The marks of 10 students in a Maths exam were as follows:

Paper 1	32	38	42	45	48	51	57	62	70	72
Paper 2	45	44	49	51	50	55	60	60	68	70

Plot the points on a scatter diagram and draw the line of best fit.
Another student scored 55 marks on paper 1 but was absent for paper 2.
Use your diagram to estimate what he might have scored in paper 2.

2. The heights of 10 boys and their fathers are given in this table.

Height of father (in cm)	167	168	169	171	172	172	174	175	176	182
Height of son (in cm)	164	166	166	168	169	170	170	171	173	177

Plot the points on a scatter diagram and draw the line of best fit. Use your diagram to estimate the height of a boy of this age if his father is 1.7 m tall.

3. The heights and weights of 8 young men are given in this table.

Height (in cm)	168	170	173	178	181	182	183	185
Weight (in kg)	68	70	70	74	75	76	78	79

Plot the points on a scatter diagram and draw the line of best fit.
Estimate the likely weight of a young man if he is 1.75 m tall.

4. The average prices of houses for five districts is given in this table.
    (Prices are in £1000's, to the nearest £1000.)

Detached house	37	41	48	62	80
Semi-detached house	23	25	30	38	51

    Plot the points on a scatter diagram and draw the line of best fit.

5. A group of 6 children held a money-raising event and raised £90, which they
    decided to split between 2 charities, X and Y.
    They each wrote down the amounts they wanted to send to each.

Child	Adam	Ben	Claire	Donna	Edward	Farida
To charity X	50	85	20			
To charity Y	40	5		55		

    Edward wanted to send equal amounts to each charity. Farida wanted to send
    twice as much to charity X as to charity Y.
    Copy and complete the table.
    Plot the data on a scatter diagram with charity X on the horizontal axis and
    charity Y on the vertical axis.
    The children found the mean of the amounts they wished to send to X, and this
    was the money they sent, with the rest going to Y. Draw a line on your graph and
    represent these amounts by a point on the line. How much did each charity
    receive?

6. You can try to find data which has some sort of paired relationship, but do not
    be too disappointed if your scatter diagrams do not show a good relationship.

    Some suggestions are:
    Heights and weights of children of the same age.
    Heights of mothers and their 16 year old daughters.
    Ages of young children and their bedtimes.
    Heights and arm-spans.
    Exam marks in similar subjects such as Maths and Science, French and German,
    or in different subjects such as Art and Science.
    Times spent learning a piece of work, and marks gained in a test on it.
    Times taken to do a piece of work using (1) normal hand and (2) other hand.
    Shoe sizes and collar (or hat) sizes.
    Amounts of pocket money and amounts saved.

Exercise 24.4

1. Draw a graph to convert temperatures from °F to °C.
    Draw the °F axis horizontally, label from 0 to 240, and draw the °C axis vertically, label from 0 to 120.
    When the temperature is 32°F, it is 0°C. (Freezing point.)
    When the temperature is 212°F, it is 100°C. (Boiling point.)
    Plot these two points on the graph, and join them with a straight line.
    Use your graph to convert 70°F into °C, and to convert 80°C into °F.
    A person's 'normal' temperature is 98.4°F. What is the approximate value in °C?

2. Draw a graph to convert between British and Yugoslavian currency at a time when the rate of exchange was £1 = 580 dinars.
    On the horizontal axis, for £, label from 0 to 10 with 1 unit to 1 cm.
    On the vertical axis, for dinars, label from 0 to 6000 with 500 units to 1 cm.
    Plot the point representing £10 in dinars and join this to the origin with a straight line.
    From your graph find

    1   the amount you would get if you changed £3 into dinars,

    2   the value in British money of a present which cost you 4500 dinars.

    (If you know the up-to-date rate of exchange you may prefer to use that.)

3. The graph shows the journeys of 2 girls, Pam and Ruth.
    Pam cycles from town *A* to village *B*, stopping for a rest on the way. Ruth cycles from village *B* to town *A*.

    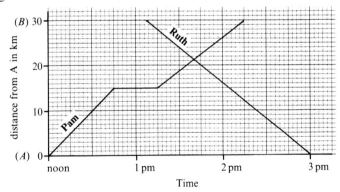

    1   For how long did Pam rest?

    2   What was Pam's average speed on the part of her journey after her rest?

    3   When did the two girls pass each other and how far from *B* were they at this time?

    4   What was Ruth's average speed?

    5   How far apart were the girls at 2.00 p.m.?

4. Alan lives in village A and Bill lives 20 miles away in village B. They plan to cycle
    to meet each other.
    Alan's average cycling speed varies between 8 and 13 miles/hour.
    Bill's speed varies between 12 and 18 miles/hour.
    Alan leaves village A at 1 p.m. Bill leaves village B at 2 p.m.
    Draw two time–distance graphs for each person using their greatest and least
    speeds.
    From your graphs estimate

    1   the earliest time they could meet,

    2   the nearest possible distance to A at which they could meet.

5. The table shows the distances reached by a train at different times after leaving
    a station.

Time in minutes	0	10	20	30	40	50	60
Distance in km	0	4	13	15	22	33	50

    Show the data on a time–distance graph, joining the points by a curve.
    Find from your graph

    1   the distance travelled in the first 45 minutes,

    2   the time when the train was 10 km from the station.

    3   By drawing a tangent to the curve and finding its gradient, estimate the
        speed of the train 50 minutes from the start (in km/hour).

6. The following values of the speed y m/s of an object at times t seconds are
    obtained by experiment. Plot the values of y against t and show that they lie
    approximately on a straight line. Use the line to estimate the value of y when
    $t = 3.5$.

t	1	2	3	4	5	6
y	2.05	2.75	3.6	4.45	5.3	5.9

7. The speed of a racing-car during the first minute after starting from rest is given
    in this table.

Time in seconds	0	10	20	30	40	50	60
Speed in m/s	0	28	46	51	47	43	46

    Draw the time–speed graph, joining the points with a smooth curve.
    Use the graph to estimate the speed 15 seconds after the start.

8. Two vehicles *A* and *B* start moving from rest at the same time, and *A*'s speed in the next 20 seconds is given in this table.

Time in seconds	0	4	8	12	16	18	20
Speed in m/s	0	1	3	7	13	15	16

The speed of *B* increases steadily during the first 20 seconds and reaches a speed of 15 m/s.
Draw the time–speed graphs for *A* and *B*.
Draw the time axis from 0 to 20 seconds and the speed axis from 0 to 16 m/s.
From the graphs find the time when *A* and *B* are moving at the same speed.

9. The temperature of water in a jug is shown in this table.

Time in minutes	0	2	4	6	8	10	12
Temperature in °C	100	60	40	30	25	23	21

Plot the points on a graph with time on the horizontal axis and join them with a smooth curve.
Find the average rate of cooling in the first 10 minutes (in ° per minute).
By drawing a tangent to the curve, estimate the rate of cooling at time 2 minutes.

10. Draw sketch graphs to show the daily attendances at a show at a theatre over 6 weeks, for the following descriptions.

    1   We started off with half-full attendance, but the attendances rose steadily and we have had a full house for the last two weeks.
    2   We started off with a full house for the first three weeks but then the numbers started falling and we are now running to a nearly empty theatre.
    3   We started off with half-full attendances. The numbers rose quite rapidly and we had a full house after two weeks. This state lasted for two weeks but now the numbers are falling slowly. We are still quite full, though.

11. Which of these graphs shows the true relationship between the perimeter of a square and the length of an edge?

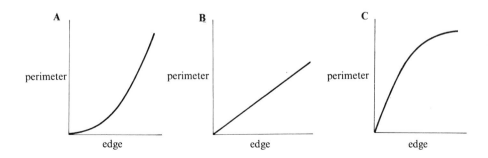

12. An experiment is carried out with readings of values of x and y. Here are the results.

x	8	17	30	42	54	66	78
y	46	71	94	118	142	176	190

Plot these values on a graph and draw the line of best fit. Find an approximate value for y when $x = 60$.

13. The diameter and circumference of different-sized circular objects were measured, with the following results:

Diameter, d, in cm	2.6	5.4	8.2	13.2	15.8
Circumference, c, in cm	7.8	17.5	26.2	41.0	49.5

Plot the values of c (vertical axis) against d (horizontal axis), and show that they lie approximately on a straight line.
Draw a line of best fit through these points. This line should pass through the origin. Find the gradient of this line.
What is the equation connecting c and d?

14. The exam marks for 10 students for Maths and Physics are as follows:

Maths mark	63	89	53	45	47	74	69	79	64	37
Physics mark	44	65	38	32	35	53	50	59	51	26

Plot these marks on a scatter diagram and draw the line of best fit.
Another student scored 56 in Maths but was absent for the Physics exam. Use the diagram to give an estimated mark for Physics.

15. A manufacturing company gives these figures for each quarter in a two-year period.

Quarter	1	2	3	4	1	2	3	4
Output units	10	20	40	25	30	40	50	45
Total cost (in £1000's)	41	48	67	53	61	70	79	73

Draw a scatter diagram for the data, with output units on the horizontal axis and total cost on the vertical axis. Draw a line of best fit. What is the estimate for the total cost likely to be incurred at an output level of 35 units?

16. 8 plots were treated with different amounts of fertilizer and the crop yield recorded.

Amount of fertilizer (units/m²)	1	2	3	4	5	6	7	8
Yield (in kg)	36	41	58	60	70	76	75	92

Plot a scatter diagram of these results and draw a line of best fit.

25 *Calculating*

As you have worked through this book you have had a great deal of practice in doing arithmetic mentally, and you must continue to maintain the standards you have achieved as you will need to work out simple sums all your life.

For more complicated calculations you have had practice in using a calculator, and you should be very efficient in its use. This simple, cheap tool has made a great difference to our lives. Answers which would have taken too long to work out twenty years ago can now be found at the touch of a few keys. Do not lose your skills with a calculator. Whether you need to use it in your future work, or just use it to keep track of your personal finances, you will need to keep it available, and use it.

The computer is also making a great impact on our lives. Here the changes are coming so rapidly that machines which were so special a few years ago may now be out-of-date as they have been replaced by better ones. If you have access to a computer, do make use of it, either to run programs designed by someone else, perhaps teaching programs on some aspect of Maths, or try to write some of your own programs, or amend existing ones to improve them.

Here are some ideas to improve your speed and accuracy in mental arithmetic. First read the beginning of Chapter 1 again and work through Exercise 1.1.

1. **Multiplying pence by 100**

   Since $100 \times 1\,p = £1$, multiplying by 100 changes pence into £'s.
   If a packet of sweets cost 12p, then 100 packets cost £12.
   If the coach fare per child is 75p, then for 100 children it is £75.
   If 1 pencil costs 6p, then 100 cost £6, so 200 cost £12.

2. **Multiplying grams by 1000**

   Since $1000 \times 1\,g = 1\,kg$, multiplying by 1000 changes grams into kg.
   If 1 article weighs 12g, then 1000 of them weigh 12kg.

3. **Articles costing 99 p, £1.99, £2.99, etc**

   To find the cost of 7 articles at 99p each, this is 7 at £1 less
   $7 \times 1\,p = £7 - 7\,p = £6.93$.
   To find the cost of 4 articles at £5.99 each, this is 4 at £6 less
   $4 \times 1\,p = £24 - 4\,p = £23.96$.

4. **Multiplying by 5**, especially for even numbers. Halve the number and then multiply by 10, since $x \times 5 = \dfrac{x}{2} \times 10$.

    $82 \times 5 = 41 \times 10 = 410$
    $38 \times 5 = 19 \times 10 = 190$
    $23 \times 5 = 11\frac{1}{2} \times 10 = 115$

    Some other numbers can be multiplied more quickly by halving one number and doubling the other, since $a \times b = \frac{1}{2}a \times 2b$ or $2a \times \frac{1}{2}b$.

    12×15 (halve 12, double 15) $= 6 \times 30 = 180$
    30×18 (double 30, halve 18) $= 60 \times 9 = 540$

    Multiplying by 25. Divide by 4 and multiply by 100, since $x \times 25 = \dfrac{x}{4} \times 100$.

    $28 \times 25 = 7 \times 100 = 700$
    $63 \times 25 = 15\frac{3}{4} \times 100 = 15.75 \times 100 = 1575$

5. **Multiplying 2-figure numbers by 11**

    Add the 2 figures together and put the total in the middle of the 2 figures.

    $32 \times 11 = 3\ 5\ 2$ Put $3 + 2 = 5$ in the middle of 3 and 2.
    $63 \times 11 = 693$

    If the figures add up to 10 or more, you must carry 1 onto the left-hand figure.

    $87 \times 11 = 9\ 5\ 7$ $8 + 7 = 15$. Put 5 in the middle, carrying 1 changes 8 into 9.
    $68 \times 11 = 748$.

6. **Squaring $1\frac{1}{2}$, $2\frac{1}{2}$, $3\frac{1}{2}$, etc**

    For $3\frac{1}{2}^{2}$ multiply 3 by 4 and add $\frac{1}{4}$.
    $3\frac{1}{2}^{2} = 3 \times 4 + \frac{1}{4} = 12\frac{1}{4}$
    $8\frac{1}{2}^{2} = 8 \times 9 + \frac{1}{4} = 72\frac{1}{4}$

7. **Subtraction** by the method of adding on. This is useful when subtracting from a number such as 100, 200, . . .
    $100 - 63$. To make 63 into 70 you need 7, then to make 70 into 100 you need 30. The answer is 37.
    $300 - 51$. To make 51 into 60 you need 9, to make 60 into 100 you need 40 and to make 100 into 300 you need 200. The answer is 249.

    This is the way a shopkeeper would count out the change.
    £5 − £1.83. £1.83 and 7 p makes £1.90, and 10 p makes £2, and £3 makes £5. You receive £3.17 in change.

8. **Learn the equivalent fractions** for simple percentages, especially that 10% is $\frac{1}{10}$. (But 5% is $\frac{1}{20}$, not $\frac{1}{5}$, of course.)

    Learn the fractions equivalent to 50%, 25%, 75%, $33\frac{1}{3}$%, $66\frac{2}{3}$%, 20%, 40%, 60%, 80%, 5%, $12\frac{1}{2}$%.

    $33\frac{1}{3}$% of $123 = \frac{1}{3}$ of $123 = 41$

    $12\frac{1}{2}$% of $56 = \frac{1}{8}$ of $56 = 7$

    Money. 1% of £1 is 1 p so 6% of £1 is 6 p.
    To find 8% of £8.50.

    1% of £8.50 is $8\frac{1}{2}$p so 8% is $8 \times 8\frac{1}{2}$p $= 4 \times 17$p $= 68$p

    VAT. (If it is at 15%)
    Find the VAT on £7.

    1% of £7 $= 7$p so 15% of £7 $= 15 \times 7$p $= £1.05$.
    Another way to do this is to find 10%, then 5%, and add these together.
    10% of £7 $= \frac{1}{10}$ of £7 $= 70$p
    5% is $\frac{1}{2}$ of 10% $= 35$p
    Tax at 15% $= £1.05$, and price + tax $= £7 + £1.05 = £8.05$.

9. When adding a long list of small numbers, look for pairs of numbers making 10 and add these together.

    $9 + 2 + 5 + 8 + 1 = (9 + 1) + (2 + 8) + 5 = 10 + 10 + 5 = 25$

10. 20 articles at 7 p + 20 articles at 23 p

    1 article at 7 p + 1 article at 23 p $= 30$ p, so 20 of each $= 20 \times 30$p $= £6$.

11. **Practise taking numbers from 180** as you use this when finding the 3rd angle of a triangle. Use the method of adding on.

    $180 - 57$. To make 57 into 60 you need 3, then to make 60 into 80 you need 20, then to make 80 into 180 you need 100. The answer is 123.

    Practise dividing numbers into 360 as this is used in pie charts and polygons. Divide 360 by 2, 3, 4, 5, 6, 8, 10 and 12.

    Practise squaring numbers mentally up to 13^2 and possibly up to 20^2. Note that all square numbers end with unit figures of 0, 1, 4, 5, 6 or 9, never 2, 3, 7 or 8. 13^2 is needed for Pythagoras' theorem.

    Practise cubing numbers mentally up to 10^3 and then recognise the cube roots of 1, 8, 27, . . . , 1000.

    Learn the 13 times table up to 13×4. This is needed for probability questions involving a pack of 52 cards, with 13 in each suit.

Practise recognising simple fractions as decimals and vice versa.

$\frac{1}{2} = 0.5$, $\frac{1}{4} = 0.25$, $\frac{3}{4} = 0.75$, $\frac{1}{5} = 0.2$, ...

Practise multiplying decimals

$0.1 \times 0.2 = 0.02$.
$0.35 \times 10 = 3.5$

12. Learn the simpler sets of numbers which give whole numbers for lengths of sides in right-angled triangles.

    1   3, 4, 5, since $3^2 + 4^2 = 5^2$
        Multiples of this such as 6, 8, 10; 9, 12, 15; 30, 40, 50.
        If a triangle has one side 9 cm and hypotenuse 15 cm, you can immediately recognise that the other side is 12 cm.
    2   5, 12, 13, since $5^2 + 12^2 = 13^2$
        Multiples of this such as 10, 24, 26.
    3   8, 15, 17.
    4   7, 24, 25.
    There are many more but they involve larger numbers so they are less likely to be needed.

Use of a Calculator

Here are some further points about using your calculator. Read the details given in Chapter 1 and Chapter 5 again, and make sure you can do the basic operations with your calculator. Also look again at Chapter 20 to make sure you can use the trig. functions correctly.

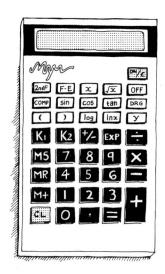

13. To enter a negative number, use the $\boxed{+/-}$ key.
    To enter -3, press $3\boxed{+/-}$
    To change -3 into 3, press $\boxed{+/-}$

14. The key marked $\boxed{1/x}$ can be used to change simple fractions $\frac{1}{3}$, $\frac{1}{4}$, $\frac{1}{5}$, . . . to decimals. To find $\frac{1}{3}$ as a decimal, press $3\boxed{1/x}$

15. **Mixed operations**

Not all calculators work in the same way in a calculation where plus and minus operations are mixed with multiplication and division operations. Some calculators deal with the operations in the order in which they are entered, some do the multiplication and division operations first, as if they were in brackets. Try a simple question such as $3\boxed{\times}$ $4\boxed{+}$ $5\boxed{\times}$ $6\boxed{=}$ to see how your calculator reads this.
If it gives the answer 102, it is doing each operation in order.
$3 \times 4 = 12$, $12 + 5 = 17$, $17 \times 6 = 102$.
If it gives the answer 42, it is reading the question as
$(3 \times 4) + (5 \times 6)$.
When you have found out how your calculator works, you can decide on the sequence of keys you need to do questions of the types

$$33 - (4 \times 5), \quad (3 + 4) \times 5, \quad \frac{3+4}{5}, \quad 3 - \frac{4}{5}, \quad (3 \times 4) - (2 \div 6).$$

You may have to use brackets, or enter partial answers into the memory.

16. **To find the remainder in a division sum**

e.g. $79 \div 19$.
Press $79\boxed{\div}$ $19\boxed{=}$ getting $4.157 \ldots$ So 19 divided into 79 goes 4 times.
Now find out what 4×19 equals.
$4 \times 19 = 76$ and $79 - 76 = 3$, so the remainder is 3.

A simpler way to do this is:
$79\boxed{\div}$ $19\boxed{=}$ $4.157 \ldots$
Keeping this number on the calculator, subtract 4 to leave the decimals, then multiply by 19.
This should give the remainder, 3, but due to rounding errors it may not give 3 exactly. So count a number such as $2.999 \ldots$ or $3.000 \ldots$ as 3.

17. **Numbers in standard form**

There may be a key labelled $\boxed{\text{EXP}}$ or $\boxed{\text{EE}}$ on your calculator.
To enter a number in standard form, e.g. for 1.23×10^3, press $1.23\boxed{\text{EXP}}3$, then pressing $\boxed{=}$ will give you its value which is 1230.
For 4.56×10^{-2}, press $4.56\boxed{\text{EXP}}2\boxed{+/-}$, then pressing $\boxed{=}$ will give you its value which is 0.0456.
(You can also use the same key to enter numbers which are not in standard form, such as 789×10^3.)

To turn a number into standard form

On some calculators there is a key labelled $\boxed{\text{F} \leftrightarrow \text{E}}$
To turn 1230 into standard form press $1230\boxed{=}\boxed{\text{F} \leftrightarrow \text{E}}$ and you get $1.23 \quad 03$ which means 1.23×10^3.
To turn 0.0456 into standard form press $0.0456\boxed{=}\boxed{\text{F} \leftrightarrow \text{E}}$ and you get $4.56 - 02$ which means 4.56×10^{-2}.

Pressing $\boxed{F \leftrightarrow E}$ again will turn the number back again into its original form. On some calculators where there is not a key labelled $\boxed{F \leftrightarrow E}$ there may be an

inverse function on the $\boxed{EXP}$ or $\boxed{EE}$ key. So try 1230 $\boxed{\substack{\text{INVERSE} \\ \text{EXP}}}$ and you

should get 1.23 03 (To get the inverse function, press the $\boxed{F}$ key then the $\boxed{EXP}$ key.)
If you have difficulty with your calculator look in the instruction booklet to see how it works.

Very large or small numbers.

If a calculation requires too many figures for the calculator to display, it may turn the answer into standard form.
For example, 4 000 000 × 6 000 000 is displayed as 2.4 13, meaning 2.4×10^{13}.
0.000 000 4 × 0.000 000 6 is displayed as 2.4 − 13, meaning 2.4×10^{-13}.
0.000 000 6 ÷ 4000 is displayed as 1.5 − 10 meaning 1.5×10^{-10}.
Try some questions on your calculator to see if it works in this way.

Accuracy of Measurements

If we were measuring the width of a field to the nearest metre and it came to between 66.5 m and 67.5 m then we would give the answer as 67 m. The boundaries of the range of measurement if the result is 67 m are 66.5 m and 67.5 m. So if we measure to the nearest metre we are accurate to within $\frac{1}{2}$ metre above or below.
If we were measuring the length of a room, for most purposes it would be sufficient to give it to the nearest 0.1 m (that is, to the nearest 10 cm). However, if we were measuring it to buy a fitted carpet, we would need the measurement to the nearest cm. If we were timing someone in running 200 m we would give the time to the nearest second, but a more serious runner would want his time to the nearest 0.1 second and in an important race he would be timed to 0.01 second.
When weighing ingredients for baking, precise measurements are not needed. If we need 250 g of sugar, it is sufficient to weigh this on scales to the nearest 50 g, that is to within 25 g above or below, but if we were doing a chemical experiment we would use a more accurate balance.

If we are using exact numbers then we can give an exact answer,
e.g. 4.1 × 3.2 = 13.12. But if the numbers are measurements correct to 1 decimal place then we are not justified in giving more decimal places in the answer, so an answer of 13.1 would be sensible and even that is only an average answer. (4.1 could be anywhere between 4.05 and 4.15, 3.2 between 3.15 and 3.25 and the product could be as small as 12.76 or as large as 13.49.)

Accuracy of Answers

When you are doing calculations for practical purposes you will give answers to a sensible degree of accuracy.
'It will take me about 20 minutes to get there, I will spend about £10 on food, there are about 800 pupils in our school, the car is travelling at about 50 miles an hour.'
However, if you are giving an answer in an examination, the examiner will want to check that you can do an accurate calculation, so first you must give that answer before you correct it up to a sensible degree of accuracy.
So, as a general guide,

1   Give the exact answer if there is one, but if the answer fills the calculator, give the answer correct to 4 significant figures at this stage.
2   **Read the question** to see if there are any instructions about giving the answer to 3 significant figures, 2 decimal places, the nearest whole number, etc, and **carry these out**.
3   If there are no instructions, then you will have to decide on how many figures it is sensible to leave in your final answer. Make sure you leave the answer from 1 legible as well, in case it is needed.

Exercise 25.1

Questions 1 to 15 are for practice in quick calculations, without using a calculator.

1.   If 1 article costs 4 p, what do 100 cost?

2.   Find the cost of 6 articles at 99 p each.

3.   If 1 washer weighs 3 g, what do 1000 weigh?

4.   Multiply these numbers by 5.

  28,   62,   96,   17,   89.

5.   Multiply these numbers by 25.

  24,   32,   46,   81,   39.

6.   Subtract these numbers from 100.

  55,   22,   76,   87,   18.

7.   Find the change from £5 if I spend

  84 p,   £2.33,   £4.61,   £1.11,   £3.30.

8.   State the fractions which are equivalent to

  10%,   75%, $33\frac{1}{3}$%,   60%, $12\frac{1}{2}$%.

9.   Find 12% of £1, and 23% of £2.

10.   Give the squares of these numbers.

  7,   9,   12,   13,   6.

11. Give the cubes of these numbers.

   3, 5, 1, 10, 2.

12. By changing the decimals into fractions, find the values of

   0.5×18, 0.75×44, 0.25×32, 0.2×55, 0.05×80.

13. Find the total cost of 20 cups at 48 p and 20 saucers at 32 p.

14. Find the total amount if VAT at 15% is added to £12.

15. Find the 3rd angle in a triangle if the other 2 angles add up to

   $163°$, $121°$, $55°$, $97°$, $101°$.

Questions 16 to 18 are for practice in using a calculator.

16. Work out the following, giving the answers correct to 3 significant figures.

   1 $\dfrac{249 \times 0.0084}{0.064}$

   2 $(35 - 29.73) \times 61.39$

   3 $1.932 + (0.22 \times 8.64)$

   4 $\sqrt{23.75} - \sqrt{1.671}$

   5 $4.78 \times (-3.16)$

17. Work out the following, giving answers **1**, **2**, **3** to 3 significant figures and the angles in degrees, to 1 decimal place.

   1 $4 \times \sin 25.1°$ **2** $2.1 \times \tan 63.9°$

   3 $\frac{1}{3}\cos 40°$

   4 the acute angle whose sine is $\frac{8}{11}$

   5 the acute angle whose cosine is 0.723

18. Change these numbers into standard form.

   1 53870   **4** 15.7×10^{-2}

   2 0.00479   **5** $(8.57 \times 10^3) - (4.52 \times 10^2)$

   3 12.3×10^3

19. For these statements 4 alternatives are given in brackets. Which one makes the most sensible statement?

   1 Jim's 20-year old brother is (1.2) (1.8) (2.4) (6) metres tall.
   2 Mary's baby sister weighs (35 g) ($3\frac{1}{2}$ kg) (35 kg) (350 lb). Her other young sister weighs (35 g) ($3\frac{1}{2}$ kg) (35 kg) (350 lb).
   3 Tessa measured one of the angles of a regular polygon and it was (50°) (72°) (100°) (108°).
   4 Sam's car does 40 miles to the gallon. On his holiday he expects to drive about 600 miles, and he estimates that he will need about (£3) (£20) (£30) (£300) for petrol, which costs £1.90 per gallon.
   5 The height of the oak tree in the field is (1.5) (20) (50) (75) metres.

20. The radius of a circle, measured to the nearest metre, is 11 m. Find

    1 the largest possible length of the circumference,
    2 the smallest possible length of the circumference,
    3 the largest possible area of the circle,
    4 the smallest possible area of the circle.

Take π as 3.14 and give answers correct to 3 significant figures.

Exercise 25.2

Questions 1 to 15 are for practice in quick calculations, without using a calculator.

1. If 1 article costs 11 p, what do 200 cost?

2. Find the cost of 5 articles at £3.99 each.

3. If 1 cm^3 of liquid weighs 1.1 g, what will 1000 cm^3 of the liquid weigh?

4. Multiply these numbers by 11.

    26, 61, 83, 45, 29.

5. Multiply these numbers by doubling the first one and halving the second one.

    6×14, 15×16, 30×24.

6. Find the values of $6\frac{1}{2}^{2}$ and $4\frac{1}{2}^{2}$.

7. Work out the values of $300 - 51$, $200 - 45$, $500 - 92$.

8. Find the change from £1 if I spend

    87 p, 62 p, 56 p, 13 p, 47 p.

9. Subtract these fractions by the method of adding on.

    $1 - \frac{3}{5}$, $3 - \frac{7}{10}$, $3 - \frac{1}{6}$, $2 - \frac{3}{8}$, $5 - \frac{5}{12}$.

10. Find the values of the following by turning the percentages into fractions.

    10% of £9.60, 25% of £5.20, $66\frac{2}{3}$% of £1.50, 80% of £2.50.

11. Work out these decimal questions.

    0.3×0.4, 0.71×10, 0.03×0.1, 0.7×0.8, $1.4 \div 10$, 0.2^2, 0.5×0.6,
    0.03×100, 0.6^2, $4.2 \div 100$.

12. Find the total cost of 12 bags of crisps at 13 p and 12 bottles of lemonade at 17 p.

13. Give the square roots of these numbers.

    64, 121, 49, 1, 100.

14. Give the cube roots of these numbers.

    216, 8, 1000, 125, 64.

15. Find these fractions of 360°.

    $\frac{1}{2}$, $\frac{1}{10}$, $\frac{1}{12}$, $\frac{1}{8}$, $\frac{1}{5}$.

16. These sets of numbers are sides in a right-angled triangle. The 3rd one in the set is the hypotenuse. Give the missing number.

   1 3, −, 5   **5** 6, 8, −   **8** 10, 24, −

   2 9, 12, −   **6** 15, 20, −   **9** −, 40, 50

   3 −, 24, 25   **7** 8, 15, −   **10** 12, 16, −

   4 −, 12, 13

17. Work out the following. (If you use your calculator, take care with the mixed units.)

   1 2 hr 56 min + 1 hr 23 min + 5 hr 48 min

   2 12 hr 18 min − 5 hr 42 min

   3 12 yr 9 mths × 5

   4 40 yr 3 mths ÷ 7

   5 (2 hr 14 min × 5) + (7 hr 12 min × 4)

18. Find the value of

   1 1.83×10^{-2} **4** $(4.63 \times 10^2) + (2.81 \times 10^3)$

   2 6.01×10^3 **5** $(8.21 \times 10^{-1}) - (4.9 \times 10^{-2})$

   3 5.5×10^{-1}

19. Find the remainders when

   1 371 is divided by 12
   2 827 is divided by 23
   3 1024 is divided by 13
   4 7 is divided into 2000
   5 60 is divided into 400

20. Find approximate answers to the following, then use your calculator to work out the exact answers.

   1 1.4×2.32 **4** 6.3^2

   2 $203.7 - 114.9$ **5** $\sqrt{79.21}$

   3 $8.74 \div 3.8$

21. Write down the number and the unit which together make the most sensible statement.

   1 To knit a pair of gloves you will need (2, 10, 60)   (g, kg) of wool.
   2 A good runner can run a mile in about (4, 20, 60)   (seconds, minutes, hours).
   3 If 200 new pencils were placed end-to-end to make a long straight line, the line would stretch for about (2, 10, 30)   (cm, m, km).

22. The sides of a rectangle, each measured to the nearest cm, are 6 cm and 4 cm. Find
   1 the largest possible length of the perimeter,
   2 the smallest possible length of the perimeter,
   3 the largest possible area of the rectangle,
   4 the smallest possible area.

23. In each of these calculations a mistake has been made. Find the correct answers. Can you also discover what mistake was made in each case?
   1 $1.32 + 2.5 + 3.79 = 7.09$ 4 $5.32 \times 6.15 = 34.6332$
   2 $10 - 0.918 = 0.82$ 5 $1234 \div 0.032 = 3856.25$
   3 $(13.1 + 17.9) \times 1.2 = 34.58$

PUZZLES

64. Make 12 pieces like this (with 3 squares) out of cardboard.

Colour them red (R), yellow (Y), blue (B) as follows.

   3 of these   2 of these   3 of these   2 of these   1 of this   1 of this

Rearrange the pieces to form a rectangle. How many different-sized rectangles can you make?
Now rearrange the pieces to form a rectangle such that only two of the three colours appear on the perimeter.

65. Mrs Richards left her umbrella on the bus so she went into the local gift shop to buy a new one at £6.75. She paid with a £20 note, but since it was early in the morning, Mr Jenkins who owned the gift shop had no change so he took the £20 note next door to Mrs Evans at the confectioner's, and got £20 in change. Then he gave Mrs Richards her £13.25 change and she went on her way.
Later on, Mrs Evans came in, very worried, because she had just discovered that the £20 note was a forgery. Mr Jenkins had to give her a cheque for £20, and give the forged note to the police. Later on he told his wife the sad tale—that he had lost a good umbrella, £13.25 in change and a cheque for £20, total value £40.
Was he correct?

66. How far would someone have to travel to get to 'the opposite end of the Earth' assuming that the Earth is a sphere of diameter 12 750 km?
If instead of travelling over the surface, the person went by plane which travelled at a height of 10 km over the earth, how much further would the journey be?

Miscellaneous section E

Exercise E1   Aural practice
If possible find someone to read these questions to you.
You should do all of them within 10 minutes.
Do not use your calculator.
Write down the answers only.

1. The sides of a triangle have lengths 5 cm, 7 cm and 8 cm. What is its perimeter?
2. How many minutes are there from 11.20 a.m. to 12.15 p.m.?
3. A man buys a bicycle for £36 and sells it to gain $33\frac{1}{3}\%$. What is the selling price?
4. 3 cups of tea and a cake cost 90 pence. If the cake cost 30 pence, what is the cost of a cup of tea?
5. What is 8% of £2?
6. What is 0.05 as a fraction in its lowest terms?
7. If today is June 24th, what will be the date this day next week?
8. Two boys share £1.40 in the ratio 5 : 2. What is the smaller share?
9. What is the total surface area of a cube of edge 2 cm?
10. What is the next prime number after 47?
11. There are 120 eggs in a box. One-twelfth are cracked. How many are whole?
12. 8 men can build a wall in 10 days. How long would 4 men take?
13. What is the smallest number which must be added to 50 in order to make it exactly divisible by 6?
14. What is the total cost of 200 badges at 9 pence each?
15. How many minutes will it take to travel 8 km when cycling at an average speed of 24 km per hour?

Exercise E2   Multi-choice Exercise

Select the correct answer to each question.

1. The number 5.2749 when written correct to three significant figures is

   A   5.27   **B**   5.28   **C**   5.274   **D**   5.275   **E**   5.30

2. If $V = \frac{1}{3}x^2h$, what is the value of V when $x = 9$ and $h = 10$?

   A   37   **B**   60   **C**   90   **D** $91\frac{1}{3}$ **E**   270

3. The line OP is reflected in the y-axis and the image line OP_1 is then rotated in an anticlockwise direction through $90°$ about the origin. The coordinates of the final position P_2 of P are

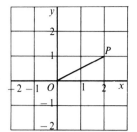

A $(2, -1)$ B $(1, 2)$ C $(-1, 2)$

D $(-1, -2)$ E $(-2, -1)$

4. If $\dfrac{2x - 3}{8} = 4$, then the value of x is

A $\frac{7}{16}$ B $1\frac{3}{4}$ C $14\frac{1}{2}$ D $17\frac{1}{2}$ E 28

5. What is the value of x if $6(2x - 1) - 5(x - 3) = 2$?

A -1 B 0 C $\frac{6}{7}$ D 1 E $3\frac{2}{7}$

6. The cost of a apples at b pence each will be

A $£\dfrac{a + b}{100}$ B $£\dfrac{ab}{100}$ C £ab D £$100ab$ E £$100(a + b)$

7. Village Q is due North of P. Village R is on a bearing of $028°$ from P. The distances PQ and PR are both 10 km. What is the bearing of R from Q?

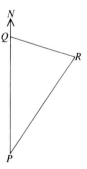

A 076° B 104° C 118°

D 194° E 284°

8. A man earns £7500, and he gets a pay-rise of 6%. The following year he gets a pay-rise of 4%. What does he earn then?

A £7950 B £8250 C £8268 D £10 625 E £10 937.50

9. In this triangle, the value of $\tan P = \frac{3}{4}$. The length of QR is

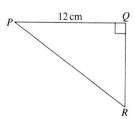

A 7.2 cm B 9 cm C 15 cm

D 16 cm E 20 cm

10. A man travelled by car for 30 km at an average speed of 45 km/hour and then, on the motorway, another 100 km at an average speed of 80 km/hour. If he started his journey at 9 a.m., he finished at

   A   10.55 a.m.   B   11.00 a.m.   C   11.15 a.m.

   D   11.18 a.m.   E   11.55 a.m.

11. The angles of a triangle are $(x + 10)°$, $(2x - 40)°$ and $(3x - 90)°$. Which of the following accurately describes the triangle?

   A   It has 3 angles of different sizes and no right angle.

   B   It is isosceles, but not right-angled.

   C   It is right-angled, but not isosceles.

   D   It is right-angled and isosceles.

   E   It is equilateral.

12. This rectangle, with sides 4 cm and 3 cm, is inscribed in a circle centre O. What is the area of the circle, in cm²?

   A $6\frac{1}{4}\pi$ B 9π C 12π

   D 16π E 25π

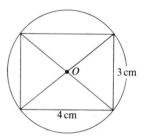

13. The area of a square is 900 cm². What is its perimeter?

   A   30 cm   B   120 cm   C   900 cm   D   1200 cm   E   3600 cm

14. The diagram shows the goals scored by some football teams. The total number of goals was

   A   15   B   16   C   21

   D   28   E   32

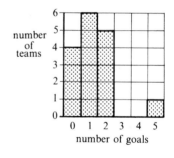

15. In this triangle, $\sin Q = 0.6$ and $\tan Q = 0.75$. What is the length of QR?

   A   7.2 cm   B   9 cm   C   15 cm

   D   16 cm   E   20 cm

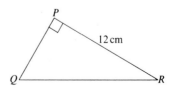

16. The graph represents the journey of a boy who cycles from a town A to a town B, and after a rest there, cycles back to A. By how many km/hour was his speed greater on the return journey, than on the outward journey?

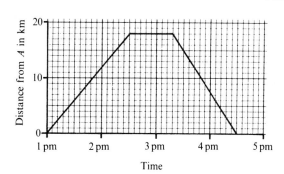

    A 0   B 3

    C 12   D 15

    E 30

17. The value of x is

    A 10   B 30   C 50

    D $\sqrt{70}$ E $\sqrt{700}$

18. How many axes of symmetry has a regular octagon?

    A 0   B 2   C 4   D 8   E 16

19. There are a lot of coloured beads in a bag, and some of them are green ones. When picking a bead at random the probability that it is green is 0.64. The probability of picking a bead that is not green is

    A 0.32   B 0.36   C $\dfrac{1}{0.64}$ D 0.64   E 0.64^2

20. Which of these triangles are congruent to each other?

    A I and II only

    B I and III only

    C II and III only

    D I, II and III

    E no two of them

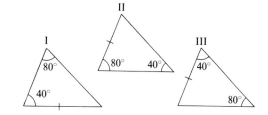

21. In the diagram, where AB is vertical and BC horizontal, what is the angle of depression of D from A?

    A 10°   B 18°   C 28°

    D 44°   E 46°

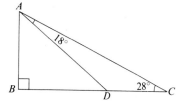

22. Which statement best describes this graph, showing profits of a firm over several months.

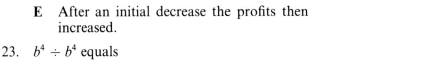

A The profits of the firm show a steady increase.

B The firm's profits are increasing at an increasing rate.

C Although the profits are increasing, the rate of increase is slowing down.

D The firm is making a steady profit.

E After an initial decrease the profits then increased.

23. $b^4 \div b^4$ equals

A b^{-4} B 0   C 1   D b E b^{16}

24. Three men invest £2000, £3000 and £4000 in a business. They share the profits in the same ratio as their investments. If the total profit is £2700, what does the man who invested £2000 receive?

A £600   B £900   C £1200   D £1350   E £2000

25. Which diagram represents the locus of points inside the triangle PQR which are equidistant from PQ and QR?

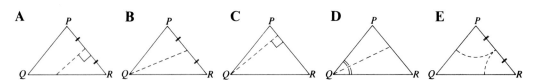

26. The size of angle a is

A 18°   B 46°   C 58°

D 62°   E 67°

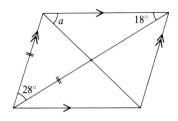

27. Which point does **not** lie on the line $3y = 7 - x$?

A $(-5, 4)$ B $(-2, 1\frac{2}{3})$ C $(0, 2\frac{1}{3})$ D $(1, 2)$ E $(4, 1)$

28. On a map a distance of 48 km is represented by a line of 2.4 cm. What is the scale of the map in ratio form?

A 1 : 200   B 1 : 2000   C 1 : 20 000

D 1 : 200 000   E 1 : 2 000 000

29. If $y = mx + c$, the expression for m in terms of x, y, c is

    A $y - c - x$ **B** $x(y - c)$ **C** $\dfrac{y + c}{x}$ **D** $\dfrac{y}{x} - c$

    E $\dfrac{y - c}{x}$

30. The graph shows the speed of a train which starts from A and increases speed steadily until it reaches 20 m/s. After keeping a steady speed for some time it then decreases its speed steadily until it stops at B. For how long altogether was its speed greater than 12 m/s?

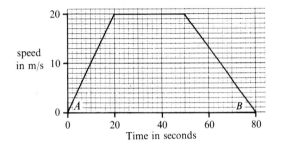

    A   12 s   **B**   30 s   **C**   50 s

    D   55 s   **E**   62 s

Exercise E3   Revision

1.   **1**   Find 36% of $2\frac{1}{2}$ hours.

    2   What percentage is 40 cm of 5 m?

2. One number in each of these sequences is incorrect. Copy them, replacing the wrong number by the correct number.

    1   1,   3,   6,   9,   15,   21,   28.
        What is this sequence of numbers called?
        Write down the next 3 numbers in the sequence.

    2   1,   1,   2,   3,   5,   8,   13,   22,   34.
        (Each number is connected to the previous two numbers.)
        Write down the next 3 numbers in the sequence.

    3   1,   6,   27,   64,   125,   216.
        Is 1000 a member of this sequence?

    4   100,   93,   86,   79,   72,   66,   58,   51.
        Write down the next 3 numbers in the sequence.

3. Find the values of

    1 $0.07 + 0.05$

    2 0.07×0.05

    3 $0.07 \div 0.05$

4. A road slopes at a steady angle of 17° to the horizontal. Calculate the increase of height of the road over a distance of 2 km.

5. Divide £14.85 in the ratio 4 : 5.

6. Calculate the length of AB and state as fractions the values of $\sin A$, $\cos A$ and $\tan A$.

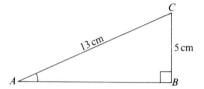

7. The number of insects in a colony doubles each week. If there were 100 insects initially, how many would there be after 5 weeks?

8. Find the positive value of $\sqrt{b^2 - 4ac}$ when $a = 3$, $b = -5$ and $c = -8$.

9. Write these numbers correct to 3 significant figures.

    1 35 840   **2** 3.0783   **3** 0.002 155 3

10. Simplify

    1 $2\frac{1}{2} + 1\frac{2}{3}$ **4** $3\frac{1}{2} - 1\frac{2}{3}$

    2 $2\frac{2}{3} \times 1\frac{1}{2}$ **5** $3\frac{1}{2}^2$

    3 $1\frac{2}{3} \div 2\frac{1}{2}$

11. 35 packets of sweets cost £3.15. What will be the cost of 42 similar packets?

12. In each diagram, the angle marked x is 52°. Find the size of the angle marked y. O is the centre of the circle.

    1   **2**

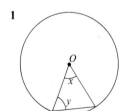

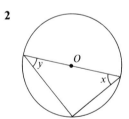

13. **1** If $0.023\,45 = 2.345 \times 10^n$, what is the value of n?

    2 If $4970 = 4.97 \times 10^n$, what is the value of n?

    3 Express 0.852 and 19.7 in standard index form.

14. A rectangular lawn 9 m by 8 m has a path $\frac{1}{2}$ m wide surrounding it. Find the area of the path.

15. A boy, John, goes jogging and leaves his home A at 6 p.m. on a straight run of 8 km to a village B, which he reaches at 6.45 p.m. Assuming that he jogs at a steady speed, draw a time–distance graph to represent his journey.
Another boy, Ken, leaves B at 6 p.m., cycling towards A, at a steady speed of 24 km/hour. Draw on the same graph a line to represent his journey.
When and where do the two boys pass each other?

Exercise E4 Revision

1. Write in order of size, smallest first, $\frac{3}{8}$, 0.4, $\frac{3}{10}$, $\frac{1}{3}$, 38%.

2. A batsman had an average of 18 runs per innings after 10 innings and was out on each occasion. In his next innings he was out after making 40 runs. What was his new average?

3. A hair shampoo is sold in two sizes costing 46 p and 67 p. The cheaper bottle is marked as holding 110 ml and the other one holds 150 ml. Which bottle is the better value for money?

4. Copy and complete this table showing the size of an interior angle of a regular polygon.

Number of sides	3	4	5	6	8	9	10
Size of each interior angle (in degrees)	60						144

On graph paper, label the horizontal axis for 'number of sides' from 3 to 10, and label the vertical axis for 'size of angle in degrees' from 0 to 180.
Plot the values in the table on the graph.
Join the points with a smooth curve. (Note that intermediate points on the curve have no meaning, except where the number of sides is 7.)
Estimate the size of an interior angle of a regular polygon with 7 sides.

5. The marks of 12 students in a test are 5, 5, 6, 6, 6, 7, 8, 8, 10, 10, 14, 17. Find
   1 the mode,
   2 the median,
   3 the mean,
   4 the range, of the marks.

6. Find the values of 2^3, 3^0, 5^{-2}, 10^{-3}, 8^{-1}.

7. Find the Simple Interest on £220 invested for 5 years at 9% per annum.

8. A shopkeeper buys a radio for a cost price of £20.00 and sells it for £32.00.
   1 Express the shopkeeper's profit as a percentage of his cost price.
   2 Express the profit as a percentage of the selling price.

9. *ABCD* is a square and *CDE* is an equilateral triangle. Find the sizes of

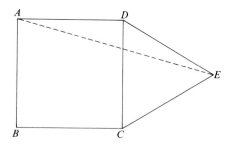

   1 $\angle ADE$,

   2 $\angle AED$,

   3 $\angle AEC$.

10. Use your calculator to find the price of fuel in pence per litre, to the nearest penny, when it is £2 per gallon. (Take 1 gallon as equivalent to 4.55 litres.)

11. Given the set of numbers

   4, $\sqrt{25}$, $\sqrt[3]{6}$, π,   0.3, $\frac{3}{4}$, $3\frac{1}{7}$,   3.142, -5,

   write down

   1 the positive integers,

   2 the integers,

   3 the rational numbers which are not integers,

   4 the irrational numbers.

12. An explorer setting out from his base camp *C* walks due West for 8 km and then due North for 5 km. Use trig. to find on what bearing he must now travel to go directly back to camp.

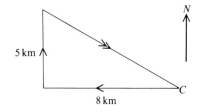

13. A rectangular shallow tray is 1.2 m long, 80 cm wide and 5 cm high. How many litres of water will it hold?

14. The following numbers were written on pieces of paper, put into a hat, and drawn out at random.

   10, 13, 16, 17, 21, 25, 30, 36, 39, 49, 110, 121.

   What is the probability of drawing out

   1 a number greater than 100,

   2 a number less than 20,

   3 a prime number,

   4 a number which is not a square number?

   5 If an odd number is drawn out and not replaced, what is the probability of drawing out a second odd number?

15. The bar chart shows sales of 5 products *A, B, C, D* and *E*, by a manufacturing company in two years, this year and last year.

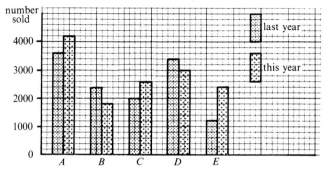

1   How many items of product *A* were sold last year?

2   Which products sold less this year than last year?

3   Of which product were approximately 2000 sold last year?

4   Find the total sales of all 5 products this year, to the nearest 1000.

Exercise E5   Revision

1.   30 kg of fertilizer costing 22 p per kg is mixed with 70 kg of fertilizer costing 12 p per kg. What is the cost per kg of the mixture?

2.   Find the value of *x*.

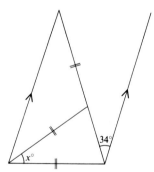

3.   Identify these sketch graphs. The first quantity named is measured on the horizontal axis.

1   The relationship between the radius and the volume in a cylinder with constant height.

2   The relationship between speed and the time taken to travel a fixed distance.

3   The relationship between money invested and Simple Interest gained per year, when the rate of interest is constant.

4   The relationship between children present and children absent in a class of 30 pupils on different days.

4. Here is one quarter of a symmetrical pattern. Copy it and complete the other three quarters to match, so that the dotted lines are axes of symmetry.

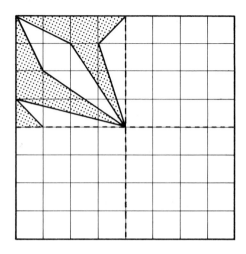

5. The points $A(1, 2)$, $B(3, -2)$, $C(-4, -1)$ and $D(-2, 4)$ are transformed by the transformations Q, R, S, T, U.
    Q is 'reflect the point in the y-axis'.
    R is 'rotate the point about the origin through $180°$'.
    S is 'move the point until it is twice as far from the origin in the same direction'.
    T is 'translate the point 2 units parallel to the x-axis'.
    U is 'reflect the point in the line $y = x$'.
    Copy the table below and fill in the coordinates of the new positions of A, B, C and D.

		Q	R	S	T	U
A	$(1, 2)$	$(-1, 2)$	$(-1, -2)$			
B	$(3, -2)$			$(6, -4)$		
C	$(-4, -1)$				$(-2, -1)$	
D	$(-2, 4)$					$(4, -2)$

6. Draw the x-axis from -3 to 4 and the y-axis from -6 to 6. Draw the graphs of $y = 2 - x$ and $y = \frac{1}{2}(3x - 2)$.
    Use the graphs to solve the simultaneous equations $y = 2 - x$, $y = \frac{1}{2}(3x - 2)$.

7. There are 7 discs in a bag numbered from 1 to 7. A disc is drawn (and not replaced) and a second disc is drawn. Show the sample space of all possible pairs of results and find the probability that

    1   the sum of the numbers drawn is odd,

    2   the product of the numbers drawn is odd.

8. A television set costs a total of £81 if bought on a hire-purchase agreement. The same set costs £72 if bought for cash.

1 If the hire-purchase agreement is for a deposit of £12 followed by 12 equal monthly payments, how much would be paid each month?

2 Find the extra cost involved in buying on hire-purchase, as a percentage of the cash price.

3 During a sale the cash price of all goods is reduced by 5%. How much is deducted from the cash price of the television set?

4 If the cash price of £72 represents a profit of 20% on the shopkeeper's cost price, how much did he pay for the television set?

9. On a stretch of straight coastline there is a coastguard station at *A*. Their rescue boats patrol a region within 10 km of the coast, and there is a lookout at the station who can see a distance of 15 km through a telescope.
Using a scale 1 cm to 2 km, copy the diagram and mark in
(1) the boundary of the patrolled region, and
(2) the boundary of the region at sea that the lookout can see.
Shade the region of the sea which is not patrolled, but is visible to the lookout.

10. This shows the reading when Bert had filled his car with some petrol.

1 How many litres had he bought?
2 He paid for the petrol with a £20 note. How much change did he get?
3 What is the price per gallon, to the nearest penny, if 1 gallon = 4.546 litres?

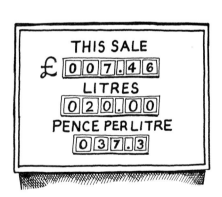

11. *A* and *B* are two harbours 15 km apart on a straight coastline running West–East. A ship *C* out at sea is seen from *A* on a bearing of 056° and from *B* on a bearing of 288°. Use scale drawing to find the distance of the ship from *B*, to the nearest 0.1 km.

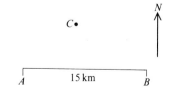

12. If $AX = 4$ cm and $XB = 3$ cm, what are the ratios of

   1 $AX : AB$,
   2 $XY : BC$.

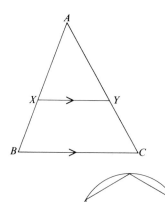

13. The circle centre O, radius 5 cm, has a regular hexagon inscribed in it.

   1 Find the circumference of the circle. Take π as 3.14.
   2 What is the size of $\angle AOB$?
   3 What kind of triangle is $\triangle AOB$?
   4 What is the length of the chord AB?

14. Rearrange these formulae to give expressions for x.

   1 $a = b + cx$

   2 $a = \sqrt{x} + b$

   3 $\dfrac{a}{x} = b$

   4 $a = bx - c$

15. The angles of a quadrilateral, in order, are $(x + 5)°$, $(x - 25)°$, $(2x - 95)°$ and $(175 - x)°$. Write down an equation and solve it to find the value of x. What are the numerical values of the sizes of the angles? What sort of quadrilateral is it?

Exercise E6   Revision

1. 1 Simplify $2(x^2 - 5x + 3) - (2x^2 + 4x - 1)$ and factorise your answer.
    2 Solve the equation $3(2x + 1) - 2(x + 3) = 33$ and check your answer.

2. A man went abroad taking £200 which he changed into francs at the rate of 12.5 francs to the £. He stayed 7 days in a hotel for 180 francs per day, and his other expenses averaged 60 francs per day. In addition he spent 340 francs on presents. After 7 days how many francs had he left? On his return he changed his remaining money back into £'s but the rate this time was 12 francs to the £. How much did he get?

3. The table shows the heights of 120 seedlings.

Height in cm	0–2	2–4	4–6	6–8	8–10	10–12
Number	14	34	22	30	18	2

Draw a histogram of the data.
What is the modal class?
Using the centres of intervals, which are 1, 3, 5, 7, 9 and 11 cm, calculate the mean height of the seedlings.

4. Copy this drawing of a prism on your own squared paper, then using the squares to help you, draw an enlargement of your prism with scale factor 2.

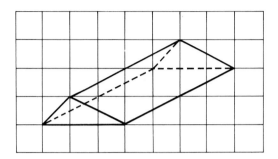

5. The air service between London and 'Kereva', together with connecting train services to 'Veefield', are given in a time-table as follows:

London dep.	23.00	10.20	11.20	15.25	16.55
Kereva airport arr.	00.30	11.40	12.50	16.45	18.10
Kereva station dep.	04.30	13.31	15.17	17.55	20.01
Veefield arr.	06.13	14.43	16.25	19.03	21.09

1 What is the time of departure from London of the fastest service to Kereva?

2 What is the time taken for the slowest journey from London to Veefield?

3 The single fare from London to Kereva is £95, and the distance is 760 km. How much is the cost per km?

4 From Kereva to Veefield is 84 km. What is the average speed of the 13.31 train.

6. A triangular field has sides 900 m, 700 m, 600 m. Treasure is hidden in the field (1) 200 m from the longest side, (2) equidistant from the two other sides. Draw a scale drawing using a scale of 1 cm to represent 100 m, showing the loci for (1) and (2). Mark the position of the treasure. Find its distance from the nearest corner of the field, to the nearest 10 m.

7. Draw the graph of $y = x^2 + x - 3$ for values of x from -4 to 3.

1 What is the least value of y?

2 Use your graph to solve the equation $x^2 + x - 3 = 0$, correct to 1 decimal place.

8. A householder paid £360 in rates last year. This compound bar chart shows how this money is used by the County.

    1 How much goes into the Reserve Fund?
    2 What percentage of the rate is spent on Education?
    3 Show the data on a pie chart.

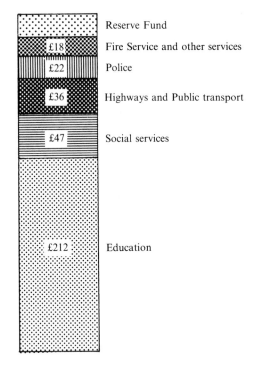

Reserve Fund

£18   Fire Service and other services

£22   Police

£36   Highways and Public transport

£47   Social services

£212   Education

9. *P* is a point 12 cm away from the centre *O* of a circle. *PT* is a tangent touching the circle at *T*.

    1 What is the size of $\angle OTP$?
    2 If $\angle OPT = 23°$, calculate the radius of the circle, to the nearest mm.

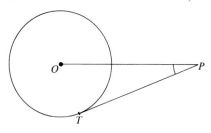

10. A cylindrical drum has a base radius of 30 cm and height 50 cm. What is its volume? (Take π as 3.14)
    The drum is full of liquid, and this is poured into an empty rectangular tank which has a square base of side 60 cm. What will be the level of the liquid in this tank, to the nearest cm?

11. Copy the figure except for triangles E and F, and add these triangles:
    Triangle B, in the position of triangle A reflected in the line $y = 1$.
    Triangle C, in the position of triangle A rotated about the origin through $90°$ clockwise.
    Triangle D, in the position of triangle A when it is reflected in the line $x = 0$.
    Describe in a similar way how triangle A can be transformed into the position of triangle E, and into triangle F.

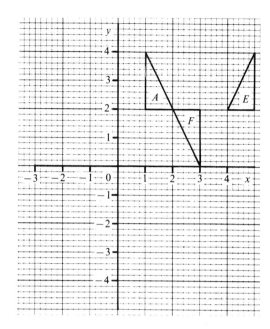

12. Here is a sequence of sets of numbers:

    $(3, 4, 5)$, $(5, 11, 13)$, $(7, 24, 25)$, $(9, 40, 41)$, $(11, 60, 61)$, . . .

    1 These numbers are connected with the sides of right-angled triangles. With which Mathematician are they associated?

    2 One number in the sequence above is incorrect. Which one is incorrect, and what is the correct number?

    3 By finding the connection between the first number of a set and the **sum** of the other two, deduce the next set of numbers in the sequence.

13. A man bought 600 eggs for £36 and planned to sell them at 90 p per dozen. What percentage profit would he have made on his cost price?
    However, 60 of the eggs were broken and he could not sell them. What was his percentage profit after he had sold the rest?

14. The costs for inland mail are as follows.

Not over	1st class	2nd class
60 g	18 p	13 p
100 g	26 p	20 p
150 g	32 p	24 p
200 g	40 p	30 p

(Note that these rates may not be up-to-date.)

A firm has the following items to post.
50 letters weighing less than 60 g, 20 letters weighing over 60 g but less than 100 g, 1 packet weighing 120 g and 1 packet weighing 130 g.
Find the costs of sending these items by 1st class, and by 2nd class post.
How much extra does it cost to send them all by 1st class instead of 2nd class post?

15. Draw axes as shown and show the journey of a boy on his bicycle and his father in the car. The boy starts from *A* at 1 p.m. and cycles at a steady speed of 10 km/hour for 2 hours. He then rests for $\frac{1}{2}$ hour and then continues cycling to *B*, which is 40 km from *A*, and he arrives at 6 p.m.

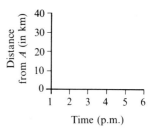

His father starts from *A* at 4 p.m. and arrives at *B* at 5.20 p.m., travelling at a steady speed.

1 On the second part of the journey the boy travelled at a steady speed. What was his speed?
2 What was his father's speed?
3 When and where did the father overtake his son?

Exercise E7   Practical work and Investigations

1. **A budget for a year**
    Imagine that in a few year's time you have moved away from home into your own flat.
    You have your wages from your work or your grant as a student and you plan ahead how you are going to manage.
    Total income for the year . . .
    Total spending for the year . . .

    Firstly, there is necessary spending on the flat—rent, rates, water rates, gas, electricity and other fuel, insurance, TV licence, phone bills, etc.
    Then there is the necessary spending on yourself—food, travelling expenses (including car expenses if you have one), clothes, etc.
    Then there are all the extras such as HP or loan repayments, things for the flat, holidays, presents, entertainment, sports or hobbies, etc.
    Make a complete list with estimated costs.
    If the spending total exceeds the income total you will have to decide what you can do about it.
    (If you prefer, instead of this do a similar budget for a family.)

2. **A scale model**
    Design a study-bedroom suitable for a teenager and make a scale model of the room, showing the door, windows and heating source. Make scale models of the furniture and include those. Show where the lighting is and where the power points are. Paint your model to show the colour scheme.
    A more ambitious project would be to make a model of a house, a famous building or a village.

3. **Planning a party for children**

Your party can be in your own home, for a younger brother or sister, or it may be a party for members of a children's club, held in the clubroom, or a party for the junior classes at your school. It can be a birthday party, a party at Christmas or some other festival time, or an end-of-term party.

First decide on what sort of party you are planning, how many children there will be, the ages of the children involved, when and where it will be held.

Decide how much you can spend on the party, perhaps as an over-all total or as 'so much a head'.

Plan a menu and decide how much of each item must be bought. Don't forget to include soft drinks.

Plan a timetable for the party with time of beginning and the time it will end, times for various activities such as games and entertainment, and time for eating.

Decide what other things must be bought, other than food, e.g. balloons, decorations, small prizes. Are there any other expenses such as hire of a disco or hire of a room? Find the total cost of everything.

Everything for the party has to be ready in time. Who is doing the shopping, and when? Who is making the sandwiches, and how long will this take? Plan the timetable for the time leading up to the party. (There are also details for tidying up after the party.)

Make a topic booklet about all this. Include a sample invitation, a copy of the menu, and illustrate it with pictures.

You might prefer to plan your party for a different age-group, a teenage party, a surprise party for your parents, or a party for the handicapped or for senior citizens living locally.

4. **The Fibonacci Series**

   1,   1,   2,   3,   5,   8,   13,   21, . . .

Discover how each number in the series is linked to the previous numbers and continue the series for several terms.

(As a check, 377 is a member of the series.)

Fibonacci was an Italian who lived in the 13th century. See if you can find out more about him.

1   His series is usually linked to 'the rabbit problem'.

'How many pairs of rabbits can be produced from a single pair in a year assuming that every month each pair gives birth to a new pair, which starts breeding from the second month?'

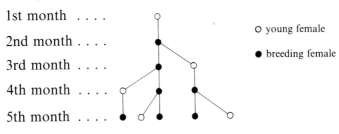

1st month . . . .
2nd month . . . .
3rd month . . . .
4th month . . . .
5th month . . . .

. . . .

○ young female

● breeding female

2   If you are paying out money using only 10 pence coins and 20 pence coins, and you take into account the order in which you pay the coins, then, for example, 50 pence can be paid in these ways

| 10, 10, 10, 10, 10 | 10, 10, 10, 20 | 10, 10, 20, 10 | 10, 20, 10, 10 |
| 20, 10, 10, 10 | 20, 20, 10 | 20, 10, 20 | 10, 20, 20 |

Altogether there are 8 ways. Investigate for other amounts.

3   Many natural objects have links with Fibonacci numbers. Count the number of petals on a daisy-type flower. Count the spirals on a pine cone, a pineapple or the centre part of a sunflower, and then count the spirals in the opposite direction.

4   Divide each number of the series by the preceding number, and then divide each number by the next one.

$\frac{1}{1} = 1$ $\frac{1}{1} = 1$

$\frac{2}{1} = 2$ $\frac{1}{2} = 0.5$

$\frac{3}{2} = 1.5$ $\frac{2}{3} = 0.667$

$\frac{5}{3} = 1.667$ $\frac{3}{5} = 0.6$

$\cdots$ $\cdots$

Continue these for about 20 terms. What do you notice?
Investigate the relationships between each number and the next alternate number.

5   Draw a regular pentagon and draw its diagonals.

Find the ratios $\frac{AB}{BC}$, $\frac{AC}{AB}$ and $\frac{AD}{AC}$, by measuring.

$\left(\text{These equal 1.618 or } \frac{\sqrt{5} + 1}{2} \text{ exactly.}\right)$

Find the ratios $\frac{BC}{AB}$, $\frac{AB}{AC}$ and $\frac{AC}{AD}$.

$\left(\text{These equal 0.618 or } \frac{\sqrt{5} - 1}{2} \text{ exactly.}\right)$

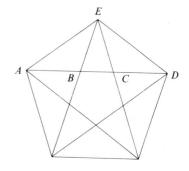

Is there a link with the Fibonacci series?
The ratio 1.618 : 1 or 1 : 0.618 is known as The Golden Section.
It is often used in Art and Architecture.

6 Golden section spiral

Start with a large rectangle with sides in the ratio 1.62 : 1
Mark off a square.
Starting from A, with centre A_1, draw a quarter circle, going to B.
Now join XY and A_1Z as guidelines as a corner of each following square lies on one of these lines.
Mark off a square including point B.
Starting from B, with centre B_1, which is on A_1B and on XY, draw a quarter circle, going to C.
Mark off a square including point C.
Starting from C, with centre C_1, which is on B_1C and on A_1Z, draw a quarter circle going to D.
Continue until the squares get too small to go any further. Where does it end?

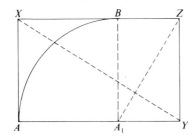 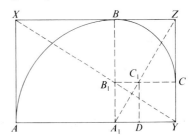

7 Pascal's Triangle

Start with Pascal's Triangle (see Exercise D5), move the numbers along so that the first number starts one column further along each time, and add the column totals.

```
        1              ⟶
      1   1            ⟶
    1   2   1          ⟶
  1   3   3   1        ⟶
 1  4   6   4   1      ⟶
1  5  10  10   5   1   ⟶
```

1									
	1	1							
		1	2	1					
			1	3	3	1			
				1	4	6	4	1	
					1	5	10	10	.
						.	.	.	.
1	1	2	3	5	8	.	.	.	.

8 Number patterns

Take every three consecutive numbers of the series. Multiply the two outside ones and square the middle one. What do you notice?
Investigate consecutive numbers 4 at a time, then 5 at a time.
Find the sums of $1, 1 + 1, 1 + 1 + 2, 1 + 1 + 2 + 3$, etc. What do you notice if you add 1 to each?
Investigate sums of squares of 2 consecutive numbers, and differences of squares of alternate numbers.

Investigate number patterns such as

$$
\begin{aligned}
8 &= 8 \times 1 + 5 \times 0 = 8 \times 1 - 3 \times 0 \\
13 &= 8 \times 1 + 5 \times 1 = 8 \times 2 - 3 \times 1 \\
21 &= 8 \times 2 + 5 \times 1 = 8 \times 3 - 3 \times 1 \\
34 &= 8 \times 3 + 5 \times 2 = 8 \times 5 - 3 \times 2 \\
55 &= 8 \times 5 + 5 \times 3 = 8 \times 8 - 3 \times 3 \\
89 &= \ldots \\
&\ldots
\end{aligned}
$$

5. **Palindromes**

A palindrome is a number which is the same when written down backwards such as 22, 353, 1441, 70607, etc.
In this investigation you are turning numbers into palindromes.

Write down the 2-figure numbers which are palindromes.

For the other numbers, e.g. 25,
Write the number down backwards and add to the number.
25
52
‾77   This is a palindrome, so stop.
Make a list of the 2-figure numbers which form palindromes after this one stage.

For the others, keep repeating the process and see how many stages are needed.
e.g. 69

  69
  96
‾165   Now write 165 backwards and add to 165
561
‾726   Now write 726 backwards and add to 726, and repeat until you get a palindrome.

(If the process seems to go on indefinitely you may have to abandon that particular number when it gets very big, unless you can program a computer to carry the investigation further.)

You can also investigate for 3-figure numbers.

6. **An ABC book**

You know many Mathematical facts now. You could make a 'Maths ABC' book. Put one letter on each page and choose a mathematical word beginning with that letter, e.g. A is for Angle. Then illustrate that page with an angle, if you want a simple, attractive book, or with facts about angles, such as types of angles, with illustrations, if you want to do more research. Even letters like Q, X, Y and Z give no difficulty. The most difficult letter to find a suitable word for seems to be J. There is 'join', as in 'Join the points', or 'Joule', whose name is used for a unit of work.

7. **To find the day of the week for any date (1800–2099)**

By using this method you will be able to find the day of the week for any date without looking at a calendar for that year.
On which day of the week does your 18th birthday fall?
On which day of the week were you born?
On which day of the week does 1st January, 2001 fall?
Work out these and other dates.

e.g. 12th September, 1987. This is written as 12.9.87
You are going to write down 5 numbers, add them up, divide by 7 and find the remainder.

(a) Add the three numbers for day, month and year together.   108
(b) Double the number of the month.   18
(c) Write down the special number (see below).   2
(d) Divide the last two figures of the year by 4, ignoring any remainder.   21
(e) Write down the century number. (For years 1800–1899 this is 6,
     for 1900–1999 it is 4, for 2000–2099 it is 3.)   4
                                                                                                                    ‾‾‾
                                                                                                                    153

$153 \div 7$ gives remainder 6.
This remainder gives the day of the week, using this list.

Remainder	0	1	2	3	4	5	6
Day	Sun	Mon	Tues	Wed	Thur	Fri	Sat

So 12th September, 1987 is a Saturday.

The special number is found by counting how many of the following list of imaginary dates would occur **after** the date you are using.

Feb 29,   Feb 30,   Feb 31,   Apl 31,   Jun 31,   Sep 31,   Nov 31.

(Do not count Feb 29 in a leap year as it is not an imaginary date.)

(In our example, after 12th September there are 2 imaginary dates, Sep 31 and Nov 31, so the special number is 2.)

8. **Centres of a triangle**

It is easy to find the centre of an equilateral triangle because there is only one. Investigate triangles of different shapes and find the following centres.
We are considering a triangle ABC.

1   O. Bisect AB and BC. These bisectors intersect at O. Can you prove that the bisector of AC will also pass through O?

2   I. Bisect angles A and B (internally). These bisectors intersect at I. Can you prove that the bisector of angle C will also pass through I?

3   G. Let the mid-points of BC, CA and AB be D, E and F respectively. Join AD and BE. These lines intersect at G. Show on your drawing that CF also passes through G. Can you discover any connection between the lengths of AG and GD (or BG and GE, or CG and GF)?

4   H. Draw the perpendicular line from A to BC, and the perpendicular line from B to AC. These lines meet at H. Show on your drawing that the perpendicular line from C to AB also passes through H.

5   Of the centres *O*, *I*, *G* and *H*, which centre is the incentre, the centre of the inscribed circle? Draw the inscribed circle of the triangle showing this centre.

6   Which centre is the circumcentre, the centre of the circumcircle? Draw the circumcircle of the triangle showing this centre.

7   Which centre is the centre of gravity (the balancing point) of the triangle? Draw triangles on thick cardboard, draw this centre on them, cut them out and try to balance them at this point on the flat end of a pencil.

8   Find points *O*, *G* and *H* in the same triangle. What do you notice about these points?

9   The 9-point circle

In one diagram, repeat part 1 to find *O*, and draw all three bisectors. Repeat part 4 to find *H*, and draw all three perpendiculars. Mark the mid-points of *AH*, *BH* and *CH*.

Find *N*, the mid-point of *OH*.

There is a circle, centre *N*, which passes through 9 special points of the triangle. Can you decide which points it should pass through? If so, find the required radius and draw the circle.

9.   3-d tessellation designs

1   Make 48 triangular prisms with square sides, suggested measurements, all edges 5 cm long.
Prepare a cardboard base 40 cm by 30 cm, divided into 5 cm squares.
Glue the prisms onto the base putting square faces on the base, with the top ridge in opposite directions in adjacent squares.

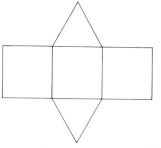

Put tabs on alternate edges

2   Make 16 pyramids with octagonal bases, suggested measurements, slant edges 8 cm, base edges 3 cm.
Make 21 pyramids with square bases, slant edges 5 cm and base edges 3 cm.
Arrange the pyramids on a cardboard base so that their bases form a tessellation of octagons and squares.

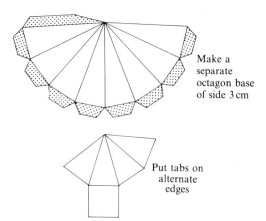

Make a separate octagon base of side 3 cm

Put tabs on alternate edges

3   A similar design can be made by using pyramids with hexagonal bases, on their own, or another one using pyramids with hexagonal bases and pyramids with triangular bases together.

10. **For the Computer Programmer**
   More suggestions for programs:

   1 To draw graphs of algebraic functions.
   2 To draw travel graphs or conversion graphs.
   3 To draw scatter diagrams.
   4 To make number patterns and investigate them.
   5 To make geometric patterns based on transformations and symmetry.

   These lists contain ideas related to the work in the main chapters of this book. In many investigations you do, you could make use of the computer.

PUZZLES

67. Copy and complete this magic square. All rows, columns and the main diagonals should add up to 111, and when complete all numbers from 1 to 36 are used.

1		24			31
35	8			26	
34		15	21		4
3		16		10	33
	11	14	20		
	7		18	25	36

68. By crossing out just SIX LETTERS in the following, leave the name of a topic in this book.

   P S R I O X B L A E B T I T L E I R T S Y

69. A farmer has 70 m of fencing available and he wants to enclose a rectangular area of 300 m². What measurements will his rectangle have?

70. Is it correct to say 'Half of 13 **is** $7\frac{1}{2}$' or 'Half of 13 **are** $7\frac{1}{2}$'?

Revision Checklist

If you will find this list helpful in planning your revision, then copy it out and tick off the topics when you are satisfied with them.
If you prefer to keep to the order of the textbook, use the list of contents of the book as your checklist.
You could also make your own checklist by using the printed syllabus of your Examination Board.

Tick when satisfied		Chapters
	Prime numbers, factors, number patterns	1, 23
	Fractions	1
	Decimals, significant figures, standard index form	5, 25
	Percentages	15
	Ratio and proportion	16
	Metric and British tables, money and time	1, 5
	Time, distance, speed	16
	Conversion graphs and travel graphs	24
	Use of calculator	1, 5, 20, 25
	Applications of arithmetic to everyday life	1, 5, 15, 16, 24, 25
	Algebraic expressions	2
	Directed numbers	2
	Laws of indices	2
	Simple equations	2, 13
	Removing brackets	2, 13
	Fractions in algebra	13
	Transformation of formulae	13
	Common factors	13
	Variation	16
	Functions	21
	Expanding brackets	21
	Inequalities	23

Tick when satisfied		Chapters
	Symmetry, patterns	3, 23
	Angles, and parallel lines	3
	Triangles, congruent triangles	3
	Quadrilaterals	7
	Polygons	8
	Solid figures and their nets	8
	Circles	11
	Similar triangles, similar figures	17
	Constructions	3, 11
	Loci	11
	Scale drawings, bearings	18
	Pythagoras' theorem	12
	Transformations: reflection, rotation, translation, enlargement	3, 17, 19
	Areas of plane figures	12
	Volumes and surface areas of solid figures	12
	Coordinates and straight line graphs	10, 21
	Graphs of quadratic functions	13, 21
	Graphs of other functions	13, 21
	Solution of simultaneous equations	10
	Gradient of a line	10
	Gradient of a curve	21
	Trigonometry	20
	Vectors	19
	Sets	22
	Statistics, collection of data and diagrams	4
	Averages: mean, median and mode	9, 14
	Frequency distributions and histograms	9, 14
	Dispersion: range	9
	Scatter diagrams	24
	Probability	6, 22

Formula Checklist

This list should remind you of the more important formulae. Read the notes on page 318 for suggestions on how to use it.

Chapter 2

Indices

1. $a^m \times a^n =$
2. $a^m \div a^n =$
3. $(a^m)^n =$
4. $a^0 =$
5. $a^{-n} =$

Chapter 3

Triangles

6. sum of angles =
7. exterior angle =

Chapter 5

Standard index form

8. The form of the number is:

Chapter 6

Probability

9. Probability of a successful outcome =
10. $\mathrm{P}(A \text{ or } B) =$
11. $\mathrm{P}(A \text{ and } B) =$

Chapter 7

Quadrilaterals

12. sum of angles =

Chapter 8

Polygons

13 to 17. Interior angle and exterior angle of a regular polygon with

13. 3 sides
14. 4 sides
15. 5 sides
16. 6 sides
17. 8 sides
18. Sum of exterior angles of a polygon =
19. Sum of interior angles of a polygon with n sides =

Chapter 9

Statistics

20. Mean of a set of numbers =
21. Definition of the median is
22. Definition of the mode is
23. Mean of a frequency distribution =
24. Range =

Chapter 10

Graphs

25. Gradient of a line =

Chapter 12

Areas and Volumes

26. Perimeter of a triangle =
27. Perimeter of a rectangle =
28. Circumference of a circle =
29. Length of arc =
30. Area of rectangle =
31. Area of square =
32. Area of triangle =
33. Area of parallelogram =
34. Area of trapezium =
35. Area of circle =
36. Area of sector =
37. Volume of cuboid =
38. Volume of cube =
39. Volume of prism or solid of uniform cross-section =
40. Volume of cylinder =
41. Curved surface area of cylinder =
42. Equation for Pythagoras' theorem:

Chapter 15

Simple Interest

43. $I =$

Chapter 16

Variation

Formulae for:

44. y is directly proportional to x

45. y is inversely proportional to x

Travel

46. speed =

47. time =

48. distance =

49. average speed =

Chapter 20

Trigonometry

50. $\sin A =$

51. $\cos A =$

52. $\tan A =$

Chapter 24

Travel

53. acceleration =

To the student:

6   The examination.

The day before

Get all your equipment ready:
Pen (and spare cartridges),
Pencil and sharpener,
Rubber,
Ruler,
Compasses, protractor, set square,
Calculator,
Watch.

For your calculator, buy new batteries and make sure they work. Spend a few minutes playing with your calculator to recall what functions you can get with the various keys. How do you find $\sqrt{40}$, $\sqrt[3]{64}$, 40^2, $\frac{1}{40}$, $\sin 40°$ and x where $\cos x° = 0.4$? Remove the instruction booklet which you must not take into the examination room.

Although there should be a clock in the examination room, you may not be able to see it from where you are sitting so it is advisable to wear your watch. Does it also need new batteries? If you have not got a watch, then borrow one or buy a cheap one.

You want to be comfortable in the exam room so plan to wear a jacket or pullover to keep you warm if it is cold, but which you can take off if you get too hot. (If it gets very stuffy during the exam, ask the invigilator if a window can be opened. If you are in a chilly draught, ask him if it can be closed.)

Check your exam timetable. If you think the exam is in the **afternoon**, check very carefully, because you will be too late if you turn up in the afternoon for an exam that actually took place that morning. Check with someone else in your class to make sure.

Have a last-minute glance at last year's paper or a practice paper. See what instructions were given on that. Plan ahead as to how you will allocate your time. Have a final look at your revision checklist and maybe do just a little more revision, but not too much, as this should be a time for relaxation. Get out into the fresh air and have some exercise. Then go to bed at a reasonable time.

The examination

Get to the exam room in good time, with all your equipment, and have nothing on your desk or in your pockets which you are not supposed to have with you.

When the exam begins, make a note of the time shown on your own watch, and note the time it is due to end.

Check the instructions at the beginning of the paper so that you know whether you must answer all the questions or whether you have to make a choice from one section. Note any other important points.

Do not rush into the first question too quickly. Read it very carefully. Decide how to answer it, then do so. If you have to show your working, set it down neatly. You have plenty of time. It is so easy to make a mistake at this stage as you have not settled down, so don't be in too much of a rush.

When you have finished this question, and this applies to all the other questions as well, read the printed question again. Have you done what you were asked to do? Have you answered all of it? Is the answer reasonable? (Should you check your calculations again?) Is the answer given to the accuracy required, e.g. to 3 significant figures, and have you given the units, e.g. cm^2?

Continue answering questions carefully until you have done a few. Then check the time. If you are going very slowly it might be sensible to leave out any long questions so as to do a few quick ones at this stage. Remember it is the marks which count so spend the time on what will gain you the most marks.

If you can't do a question, read it again carefully. What is it about? Are you using all the information given? Is there a diagram? Is there any other information you could deduce from the diagram? If there is not a diagram, would a sketch diagram help? If so, draw one. What facts or formulae do you know about this topic? Do they help? If the question is in several parts, often an answer to an earlier part may be needed in working out a later part. Even if you can't finish the question, put something down on paper because your attempt might be worth some marks and it cannot be marked if it is not written down. If you can't do part (1) of a question but can do part (2), then do part (2) so that you will get the marks for that. You can always go back to thinking about part (1) later if you want to, and have the time. If you cannot get any further on any part of the question then abandon it and try a different one.

If the numbers in a question turn out to be complicated it is possible that you have made a simple mistake. Check that you have copied the numbers or expression correctly, and check the signs in your working.

Keep your writing clear. Show all necessary working with your answer as you cannot gain marks for it if it is in a jumbled mess at the bottom of the page. You can do rough work at the side of the page near the answer, and then cross it out if you wish, but cross it out neatly so that it can still be read, in case it is worth some marks.

Do not use white paint correction fluid to blot out your mistakes. Some Examination Boards do not allow you to use this, but even if allowed, it wastes time, and if you write over it the new writing might get soaked up and be illegible by the time your script has reached the examiner.

Once the examination is over, forget it, until the results come out. You have done your best and that is all that matters. We hope you will be satisfied with your final grade. GOOD LUCK!

Index

This index refers to topics in the main chapters of the book.

acceleration, 356
accuracy of answers, 375
accuracy of measurements, 374
addition of vectors, 284
AND rule, 113
angle of depression, 269
angle of elevation, 269
angles, 36, 180
angles of circles, 176
        of polygons, 129
        of triangles, 41
appreciation, 224
approximations, 75, 80
arc of circle, 176, 191
area units, 79
areas of plane figures, 189
        of surfaces, 198
averages, 140, 214
average speed, 256, 355

bar chart, 58
bearings, 268, 273
bisectors, 52, 123, 179

calculator, 16, 74, 291, 372
capacity units, 15, 79
centre of enlargement, 264, 278, 281
chord of circle, 176
circle, 176, 190
circumference, 176, 190
collecting data, 66, 150, 220, 364
common factors, 208
compass directions, 268
compound interest, 223
cone, 134
congruent figures, 47
        triangles, 47
constructions, 44, 132, 179, 186
conversion graphs, 355
coordinates, 151
cosine ratio, 291
cube, 134, 197
cube numbers, 7, 343
cuboid, 134, 197

curves, 209, 320
cylinder, 134, 197

decimals, 70, 221, 372
depreciation, 224
diagonals of quadrilaterals, 123
diameter, 176, 190
directed numbers, 26
dispersion, 145
distance, 256, 355

enlargement, 260, 278
equations, linear, 23, 205
                simultaneous, 154
equilateral triangle, 40
estimations, 80
expanding brackets, 330
expressions in algebra, 22
exterior angle of polygon, 129
        of triangle, 41

factors in algebra, 208
factors in arithmetic, 6
foreign exchange, 255
fractions, 9, 221, 371
fractions in algebra, 204
frequency distributions, 142, 214
functions, 152, 209, 320

geometric patterns, 348
gradient of curves, 325
        of lines, 152, 154, 321, 325
graphs of linear functions, 152, 321
        of quadratic functions, 209, 321, 323
        of other functions, 210, 322, 325

heptagon, 129
hexagon, 129
highest common factor (HCF), 8
histograms, 143, 214
horizontal lines, 268
hypotenuse, 40, 195, 291

income tax, 225
indices, 22, 29
inequalities, 346
integers, 73
interest, 223
irrational numbers, 74
isosceles triangle, 40, 293

kite, 112

length units, 15, 79
line of best fit, 362
linear functions, 152, 321
loans, 224
locus, 183
lowest common multiple (LCM), 8

mapping diagram, 320
mean, 140, 142, 214
measurement units, 15, 79
median, 140, 144
mental arithmetic, 3, 369
meter dials, 81
metric system, 15, 79
misleading diagrams, 61
modal class, 214
mode, 140, 144
money, 13, 369

nets of solid figures, 134
number patterns, 342
numbers, 3, 26, 70, 73, 342

octagon, 129
OR rule, 113

parallel lines, 37, 44
parallelogram, 112, 189
patterns, 342
pentagon, 129
percentages, 221, 371
perimeter, 189
perpendicular lines, 37, 179, 181
π (pi), 74, 190
pictogram, 57
pie chart, 59
polygons, 129
prime factors, 6
prime numbers, 6, 342
prism, 134, 197
probability, experimental, 106
              theoretical, 111, 336
proportion, 249
pyramid, 134
Pythagoras' theorem, 195

quadratic functions, 209, 321, 323
            graphs, 209, 321, 323
quadrilateral, 122
questionnaire, 68

radius, 176, 190
random sample, 67
range, 145
rate, 253
rateable value, 254
rates of exchange, 255
ratio, 249
rational numbers, 74
rectangle, 122, 189
reflection, 34, 279
regular polygons, 129
removing brackets, 23, 204, 330
rhombus, 123
right angle, 36, 176, 182
rotation, 34, 280
rotational symmetry, 33

sample space, 112
sampling, 67
scale drawing, 269
scatter diagram, 362
sector, 176, 191
segment, 176
sequences of numbers, 342
sets, 334
significant figures, 73
similar figures, 260
        triangles, 262
simple interest, 223
simultaneous equations, 154
sine ratio, 291
sketch graphs, 326, 359
solid figures, 134, 197
speed, 256, 355
sphere, 134
square, 123, 189
square numbers, 7, 342
standard index form, 73, 373
statistics, 56, 140, 214, 362
straight line graph (algebraic), 152, 321
straight line graph (in statistics), 60
subtraction of vectors, 284
surface area, 198
symmetry, 33

tables, 3, 13, 79
tally table, 56, 143
tangent ratio, 291
tangent to a circle, 176
        to a curve, 325
temperature, 15
tessellations, 348

tests of divisibility, 7
tetrahedron, 134
time, 13, 256, 355
time-distance graph, 355
time-speed graph, 356
transformation of formulae, 207
transformations, 34, 48, 260, 278
translation, 48, 278, 283
trapezium, 122, 189
travel graphs, 355
tree diagram, 114
triangles, 40, 44, 47, 189, 195, 262, 291
trigonometry, 291

unitary method, 15
units of measurement, 15, 79

variation, 252
vectors, 283
velocity, 256, 355
Venn diagrams, 334
vertical line graph, 143
vertical lines, 268
volume units, 79
volumes of solid figures, 197

weight units, 15, 79

Answers

Some answers have been given corrected to reasonable degrees of accuracy, depending on the questions.
There may be variations in answers where questions involve drawings or graphs, or if trig. tables are used instead of a calculator.

Page 3   **Exercise 1.1**

1. 56, 24, 20, 60, 120, 15, 121, 8, 15, 6, 600, 12, 72, 0, 8, 13, 20, 106, 0, 144

2. 8, 6, 8, 7, 3, 12, 10, 12, 11, 8, 12, 5, 6, 5, 7, 12, 3, 7, 9, 9

3.
1	3	6	4
2	4	7	8
3	2	8	5
4	0	9	3
5	4	10	19

4.
1	265 384
2	12 040
3	1500
4	$30\frac{3}{4}$
5	4 440 404
6	One hundred thousand, five hundred, sixty
7	Two million, eight thousand

5.
1	15	6	188
2	0	7	36
3	19	8	12
4	8000	9	190
5	250	10	36

6.
1	4, 9	6	2, 3, 6
2	5, 6	7	3, 4, 5
3	2, 50	8	9, 8
4	1, 15	9	8, 3
5	4, 12	10	11, 7

7.
1	2	4	9, 10
2	4	5	3, 4, 5
3	5, 6		

8.
1	44, 9, 4, 7, 30, 12, 21, 26, 45, 48
2	6, 33, 20, 8, 15, 9, 1, 7, 13, 25
3	2, 7, 20, 25, 13, 11, 1, 6, 40, 9
4	12, 4, 9, 2, 20, 3, 7, 15, 11, 40
5	4, 10, 16, 6, 20, 40, 22, 60, 50, 12

9.
1	4	4	106
2	1024	5	105
3	8		

10.
1	8	2	4	3	10

11.
1	33	6	65
2	48	7	121
3	39	8	33
4	55	9	9
5	3	10	33

Page 7   **Exercise 1.2**

1. 23, 29

2.
1	31, 37	2	83, 89

3.
1	$2^4 \times 3$	9	2^6
2	$3^2 \times 11$	10	$2^2 \times 5^2$
3	$2^2 \times 13$	11	3×13
4	$2^2 \times 3 \times 5$	12	$2^4 \times 5$
5	$2^2 \times 3^2 \times 5$	13	11^2
6	$2^3 \times 3$	14	3^4
7	$2 \times 5 \times 7$	15	$2 \times 3 \times 5^2$
8	$2^5 \times 3$		

4.
1	132, 156, 400
2	135, 225, 400
3	132, 135, 156, 225

5.

1	11	6	8	11	21
2	20	7	3	12	4
3	5	8	13	13	12
4	3	9	2	14	8
5	4	10	7	15	5

6.

1	15	5	60	8	18
2	24	6	44	9	70
3	60	7	36	10	42
4	72				

7.

1	16	4	90
2	72	5	88
3	140		

8.
1 $2 \times 3 \times 5$
2 $2 + 11 + 17$ or $2 + 5 + 23$

9.

1	19	4	12
2	16	5	16, 20
3	20	6	8, 19

10.

1	19, 23	4	27
2	25	5	19, 25
3	18, 27		

11.

1	81	5	8
2	8	6	360
3	37, 73	7	81
4	91	8	50

12. 41

13. 66

14. 45

15.   1 7   2 3   3 3

16.   1 3×37 2 $7 \times 11 \times 13$

17.

1	81, 121	6	216, 343
2	21, 28	7	40, 35
3	32, 64	8	$\frac{5}{6}, \frac{6}{7}$
4	65, 58	9	14, 17
5	$\frac{1}{6}, \frac{1}{7}$	10	35, 48

18. $85^2 = 7225$

19.   1 60   2 13   3 17

20.

1	15	5	75	8	44
2	42	6	14	9	65
3	33	7	21	10	101
4	16				

Page 11   Exercise 1.3

1.

1	$\frac{3}{11}$	5	$\frac{1}{4}$	9	$\frac{4}{9}$
2	$\frac{5}{7}$	6	$\frac{7}{12}$	10	$\frac{2}{3}$
3	$\frac{2}{5}$	7	$\frac{3}{8}$		
4	$\frac{5}{8}$	8	$\frac{1}{10}$		

2.

1	$\frac{7}{4}$	5	$\frac{29}{6}$	9	$\frac{22}{7}$
2	$\frac{77}{12}$	6	$\frac{77}{10}$	10	$\frac{42}{5}$
3	$\frac{7}{3}$	7	$\frac{100}{11}$		
4	$\frac{67}{20}$	8	$\frac{47}{8}$		

3.

1	$4\frac{3}{5}$	5	$2\frac{3}{4}$	9	$33\frac{1}{3}$
2	$2\frac{5}{6}$	6	$6\frac{1}{9}$	10	$8\frac{3}{4}$
3	$3\frac{7}{10}$	7	$2\frac{3}{5}$		
4	$3\frac{1}{8}$	8	$3\frac{7}{11}$		

4.

1	$1\frac{1}{12}$	5	$4\frac{3}{4}$	9	$4\frac{11}{20}$
2	$\frac{19}{24}$	6	$7\frac{17}{24}$	10	$5\frac{17}{24}$
3	$4\frac{3}{10}$	7	$5\frac{13}{18}$		
4	$5\frac{7}{40}$	8	$3\frac{1}{3}$		

5.

1	$\frac{11}{24}$	5	$\frac{11}{20}$	9	$2\frac{4}{5}$
2	$2\frac{1}{24}$	6	$1\frac{1}{2}$	10	$3\frac{33}{40}$
3	$1\frac{7}{12}$	7	$\frac{1}{9}$		
4	$1\frac{19}{36}$	8	$\frac{2}{3}$		

6.

1	$\frac{1}{4}$	5	$1\frac{1}{2}$	9	$8\frac{1}{4}$
2	$\frac{35}{48}$	6	$\frac{3}{4}$	10	40
3	$\frac{3}{4}$	7	$11\frac{3}{7}$		
4	$4\frac{1}{5}$	8	$3\frac{3}{4}$		

7.

1	$\frac{20}{21}$	5	$\frac{5}{8}$	9	$\frac{10}{27}$
2	$\frac{9}{35}$	6	$\frac{2}{5}$	10	$5\frac{1}{7}$
3	$1\frac{1}{2}$	7	$1\frac{9}{16}$		
4	4	8	$\frac{16}{21}$		

8.

1	$5\frac{1}{12}$	5	$2\frac{3}{5}$	9	$4\frac{11}{12}$
2	$\frac{2}{3}$	6	$\frac{1}{2}$	10	$1\frac{1}{7}$
3	$7\frac{1}{3}$	7	2		
4	8	8	1		

ANSWERS

9.　**1**　1　　　　**5**　$25\frac{1}{6}$　　　**9**　$1\frac{13}{20}$

　　　2　$3\frac{2}{3}$　　　**6**　$\frac{1}{4}$　　　　**10**　7

　　　3　$3\frac{1}{2}$　　　**7**　$\frac{5}{16}$

　　　4　3　　　　**8**　$2\frac{1}{5}$

10.　**1**　$\frac{5}{6}$

　　　2　$\frac{9}{10}$

　　　3　$\frac{2}{3}$

Page 16　　　Exercise 1.4

1.　**1**　100　　　　**4**　£30
　　2　16p　　　　**5**　£3.96
　　3　apples

2.　$3\frac{1}{2}$p

3.　£12

4.　4p

5.　20

6.　£54

7.　£149

8.　£1.60

9.　£49.95

10.　40

11.　**1**　$\frac{2}{3}$　**2**　$\frac{1}{4}$　**3**　$\frac{1}{9}$　**4**　$\frac{2}{15}$　**5**　$\frac{3}{8}$

12.　**1**　£2.70　　　　**4**　36 min
　　2　8 inches　　　**5**　10 oz
　　3　60 cents

13.　150

14.　360

15.　£750

16.　May 1st

17.　$1\frac{1}{2}$ miles

18.　1995

19.　4.05, 14.00, 15.15, 18.05, 23.55,
　　1.10 a.m., 5.18 a.m., 10.30 a.m.,
　　5.05 p.m., 9.50 p.m.

20.　4 hrs 43 min

21.　4.05 p.m.

22.　5 hrs 10 min, 01.20

23.　40 min

24.　5°C, 104°F

25.　£4.55

26.　81 lb

27.　£12

28.　16 days

29.　15 days

30.　£180

Page 18　　　Exercise 1.5

1.　1089 or 198

2.　143

3.　**1**　31　　　**2**　30

4.　**1**　$\frac{3}{5}$　　　**2**　$1\frac{1}{5}$

6.　**1**　even number　　**4**　even number
　　2　even number　　**5**　odd number
　　3　even number

7.　**1**　1st one, by 6
　　2　3^7, by 139
　　3　196, 676

8.　David

9.　24

10.　49 min

11.　£735

12.　$\frac{1}{9}$

13.　£2.65

14.　20 min

15.　£60.50

16.　£146.20, 48 hrs

17.　£63

18.　**1**　4.16 p.m. (1616), 25 minutes
　　2　1608 (4.08 p.m.), 36 minutes

19.　**1**　£3.65
　　2　£29.75 each, total £59.50
　　3　£74.20

20.　£5.64, £67.68, £90, £118.80

21.　9 miles

Page 24   **Exercise 2.1**

1. 1 $5a$ pence

    2 $120b$

    3 $c - d$

    4 $(3e + 2f)$ pence

    5 $(100 - gh)$ pence

    6 £$\dfrac{k^2}{100}$

    7 $\dfrac{m}{3}$ pence

    8 $\dfrac{n}{20}$

    9 $\dfrac{100p}{q}$ pence

    10 $\dfrac{2st}{5}$

2. 1 c
    2 0
    3 $8e$
    4 $3g - 4h$
    5 $6j - 2k$
    6 m
    7 a^2
    8 b^3
    9 1
    10 d^2

    11 e^5
    12 f^4
    13 $45a^2$
    14 $16bc$
    15 $20e^3$
    16 $3f$
    17 $9g^2$
    18 $5h$
    19 $\dfrac{4m}{n}$
    20 $1\frac{1}{2}$

    21 $2ab$
    22 $2c^3$
    23 $8d^2$
    24 $2ef$
    25 $8a + 5b$
    26 $3c^2 + 6$
    27 $42d + 3$
    28 $\dfrac{a}{c}$
    29 $9g^4$
    30 $4j$

3. 1 32   5 2   8 0
    2 25   6 18   9 $2\frac{1}{2}$
    3 5   7 27   10 4
    4 24

4. 1 23   5 0   9 1
    2 34   6 5   10 15
    3 50   7 3
    4 0   8 100

5. 1 $a = 21$ 5 $e = 7$ 8 $h = 22\frac{1}{2}$
    2 $b = 19$ 6 $f = 7$ 9 $j = 5$
    3 $c = 8$ 7 $g = 6$ 10 $k = 3$
    4 $d = 140$

6. 1 $a = 3$ 8 $h = 32$ 15 $r = 8$
    2 $b = 4$ 9 $j = 70$ 16 $s = 7$
    3 $c = 5$ 10 $k = 8$ 17 $t = 2$
    4 $d = 4$ 11 $m = 6$ 18 $u = 16$
    5 $e = 10$ 12 $n = \frac{1}{2}$ 19 $v = 0$
    6 $f = 4$ 13 $p = 5$ 20 $w = \frac{3}{4}$
    7 $g = 26$ 14 $q = 8$

Page 27   **Exercise 2.2**

1. 1 -2 5 0 9 $-\frac{1}{2}$
    2 -8 6 -20 10 $-1\frac{1}{2}$
    3 2 7 -5
    4 2 8 -8

2. 1 1 5 -2 9 -1
    2 -7 6 -5 10 6
    3 9 7 -7
    4 0 8 -3

3. 1 $3a$ 5 $9e$ 9 $3j$
    2 $-b$ 6 $-2f$ 10 $-k$
    3 $5c$ 7 0
    4 $-3d$ 8 $7h$

4. 1 -14 5 -1 9 $-3x$
    2 3 6 $-3x$ 10 $-4x$
    3 0 7 $5x$
    4 -4 8 0

5. 1 88 5 0 9 4
    2 -18 6 -3 10 -1
    3 -8 7 -5
    4 63 8 1

6. 1 $16xy$ 5 -1 9 $4x^2$
    2 $-28xy$ 6 $-6xy$ 10 0
    3 $-\frac{2}{3}$ 7 $-24x^2$
    4 $27x^2$ 8 $\dfrac{1}{x}$

7. 1 1 5 $-4\frac{1}{2}$ 9 5
    2 5 6 12 10 25
    3 0 7 2
    4 -24 8 -8

8. 1 -2 5 -10 9 5
    2 0 6 -1 10 3
    3 0 7 8
    4 2 8 2

9. 1 $x = 3$ 6 $x = -1$
    2 $x = -7$ 7 $x = 0$
    3 $x = -8$ 8 $x = -10$
    4 $x = -\frac{2}{3}$ 9 $x = 7\frac{1}{2}$
    5 $x = -1\frac{1}{2}$ 10 $x = \frac{1}{4}$

Page 29   **Exercise 2.3**

1. 1 125 5 $\frac{1}{49}$ 8 1000
    2 36 6 $\frac{1}{4}$ 9 $\frac{1}{9}$
    3 $\frac{1}{8}$ 7 8 10 $\frac{1}{10}$
    4 1

2. **1** 10^5 **4** 10^4
   2 10^8 **5** 10^2
   3 10^2

3. **1** 3   **4** 0
   2 4   **5** -1
   3 -2

Page 30   Exercise 2.4

1. **1** $2a$ **4** 1
   2 0   **5** a
   3 a^2

2. **1** $7a^3$ **2** $12a^6$ **3** $\frac{3}{4}$

3. $4x^2$

4. **1** $\frac{1}{6}$ **2** $\frac{5}{6}$ **3** $\frac{1}{15}$

5. $10x - y$

6. £$\dfrac{k(y-x)}{100}$

7. **1** 210   **4** 150
   2 $2\frac{1}{2}$ **5** 14
   3 880

8. **1** $-7°$ **4** $-8°$
   2 13   **5** $-5°$
   3 15

9. **1** 6   **5** $3\frac{1}{2}$ **8** 11
   2 0   **6** 12   **9** 6
   3 1   **7** $\frac{1}{6}$ **10** 120
   4 26

10. **1** $x = 2$ **4** $x = 10$
   2 $x = 1\frac{1}{5}$ **5** $x = 2$
   3 $x = -2$

11. 11

12. 2, 20, -7; $x = 3$, $-\frac{2}{3}$

13. $\dfrac{3x}{2}$

14. **1** $-\frac{2}{3}$ **2** 23   **3** 4

15. 0

16. $4\frac{1}{2}$

17. 650

18. 35

19. £$(60 + 25n)$, £360

20. **1** $(20 + 20c)$ min   **2** $\dfrac{1+c}{3}$ hrs

21. **1** 27   **4** 3
   2 $\frac{1}{9}$ **5** 81
   3 1

22. $\frac{1}{3}$, 4

23. 8 years

24. 7

25. 18

Page 34   Exercise 3.1

7. **1** 3   **2** 6   **3** 7

8. **1** an infinite number
   2 1   **3** 2   **4** 3

Page 38   Exercise 3.2

1. **1** acute   **2** reflex   **3** obtuse
   4 reflex

2. **1** $25°$ **2** $118°$ **3** $73°$

3. **1** $a = 136°$, $b = 78°$, $c = 50°$,
   $d = 96°$
   2 $e = 154°$, $f = 26°$
   3 $g = 112°$, $h = 68°$, $j = 112°$
   $k = 68°$

4. **1** $a = 126°$, $b = 126°$
   2 $c = 30°$, $d = 30°$
   3 $e = 62°$, $f = 118°$

5. **1** $160°$ **2** $40°$
   3 $c = 35°$, $d = 145°$, $e = 145°$
   4 $67°$ **5** $54°$ **6** $70°$

6. **1** $80°$
   2 $67°$
   3 $c = 125°$, $d = 55°$, $e = 40°$
   4 $f = 63°$, $g = 117°$, $h = 63°$

7. **1** $j = 60°$, $k = 50°$, $m = 70°$
   2 $n = 125°$, $p = 145°$, $q = 35°$

Page 41   Exercise 3.3

1. **1** $\angle A = 81°$, $\angle B = 54°$, $\angle C = 45°$
   2 $\angle A = 116°$, $\angle B = 37°$,
   $\angle C = 27°$

2. **1** $\angle A = 28°$, $\angle B = 76°$, $\angle C = 76°$
    2 $\angle A = 18°$, $\angle B = 144°$,
          $\angle C = 18°$

3. **1** $72°$ **2** $48°$ **3** $24°$
    4 $30°$ **5** $26°$

4. **1** $30°$ **2** $38°$ **3** $60°$
    4 $35°$

5. $\angle B = \angle ACB$, $\angle ACD = 32°$,
    $\angle CDB = 90°$, $\angle DBC = 61°$,
    $\angle BCD = 29°$

6. $\angle ACD = 32°$, $\angle CDB = 64°$,
    $\angle DBC = 64°$, $\angle BCD = 52°$

7. **1** $a = 50°$, $b = 50°$, $c = 40°$, $d = 40°$
    2 $e = 20°$, $f = 20°$, $g = 20°$
    3 $h = 75°$, $j = 75°$, $k = 30°$
    4 $m = 40°$, $n = 100°$, $p = 40°$, $q = 70°$,
          $r = 70°$

Page 44   Exercise 3.4

6. $BC = 7.6\,\text{cm}$, $\angle B = 34°$, $\angle C = 88°$

7. $\angle A = 58°$, $\angle B = 47°$, $\angle C = 75°$

8. $AC = 7.5\,\text{cm}$, $\angle B = 43°$, $\angle C = 47°$

9. $AE = 4.5\,\text{cm}$, $EC = 4.5\,\text{cm}$

10. $AD = 4.7\,\text{cm}$, $CD = 4.3\,\text{cm}$

Page 49   Exercise 3.5

1. A and F, B and D, C and E

2. **1** C **2** $\triangle ABC \equiv \triangle DEC$
    3 DE **4** $\angle EDC$
    5 They are parallel

3. **1** AC
    2 $\triangle ABC \equiv \triangle ADC$, $\triangle ABX \equiv \triangle ADX$,
          $\triangle BCX \equiv \triangle DCX$
    3 $\angle ADC$ **4** DX

4. $80\,\text{m}$

5. $\triangle ABC \equiv \triangle DEF$, $\angle DFE$

6. **1** DC, ED **2** $\angle CDE$

7. **1** $\triangle AEN$, $\triangle ACN$, $\triangle ACD$
    2 CD, AE **3** $\angle ACN$

Page 51   Exercise 3.6

1. **1** E   **2** H   **3** S

2. **1** reflection in EF
    2 rotation about E through $180°$
    3 translation direction and distance
          CE
    4 reflection in BE

3. $\frac{1}{600}\,\text{s}$

4. $135°$

5. **1** $30°$ **2** $105°$ **3** $105°$

6. **1** $72°$ **2** $35°$ **3** $20°$

7. $\angle A = 34°$, $x = 52$

8. **1** $71°$ **2** $35\frac{1}{2}°$ **3** $109°$

9. **1** 30, $65°$ **2** 50, equilateral
    3 9

10. **1** $74°$ **2** $106°$ **3** $37°$

11. **1** 36

12. **1** 12 **2** 24 **3** 12

13. $108\,\text{m}$

15. $\angle ADE = 29°$, $\angle EAD = 27°$

16. $7.1\,\text{cm}$

17. A and H, B and D, C and G,
    E and F

18. $\angle ACB = 48°$, $\angle DCB = 70°$,
    AAS or rotation about mid-point
    of BC, DC

Page 57   Example 2

    $\frac{4}{9}$, $\frac{37}{90}$

Page 60   Example 6

    1 week 9   **2** weeks 1 and 2

Page 63   Exercise 4.1

5. $13\,\text{p}$

10. Food, £15; transport, £9.50;
    camp fee, £7; extras £4.50

11. £10

12. $\frac{1}{4}$

13. A 14, B 4, C 22, D 10

14. a 14, e 11, i 7, o 8, u 5

Page 76   Exercise 5.1

1. **1** 7.612
    2 7
    3 0.241
    4 10.02
    5 25.831

2. **1** 21.013
    2 6.95
    3 0.0094
    4 9.082
    5 4.886

3. **1** 15.48
    2 0.06
    3 1.456
    4 9.42
    5 9.64

4. **1** 0.97
    2 0.0008
    3 0.0416
    4 2.143
    5 6.0001

5. **1** 0.75
    2 0.4
    3 0.7
    4 0.37
    5 0.125

6. **1** 13.2
    2 250
    3 0.3792
    4 1030
    5 0.0015
    6 0.021 32
    7 2.72
    8 3100
    9 0.0031
    10 0.004

7. **1** 594.2
    2 1020
    3 0.3
    4 32
    5 246.8

8. **1** 0.072
    2 0.003
    3 0.001 32
    4 0.63
    5 0.002

9. **1** 8.792
    2 0.066 417
    3 198.38
    4 0.24
    5 0.001 271

10. **1** 39
     2 79.7
     3 19.9
     4 300
     5 0.79

11. **1** 2.86
     2 51.67
     3 0.09
     4 7.28
     5 1.14

12. **1** 0.667
     2 0.714
     3 0.444
     4 0.167
     5 0.727

13. **1** 29.712
     2 1.628
     3 202.916
     4 4.680
     5 0.004

14. **1** 29.7
     2 1.63
     3 203
     4 4.68
     5 0.003 53

15. **1** 56 800
     2 83.0
     3 253
     4 207
     5 1000

16. **1** 20
     2 3
     3 0.0009
     4 0.05
     5 50

17. **1** 20.0
     2 3.06
     3 0.000 784
     4 0.0510
     5 47.4

18. **1** 107
     2 0.000 028 4
     3 1.33
     4 0.356
     5 4720

19. 2.50, 7.89, 25.0, 78.9

20. **1** 1.5×10^4 **6** 3.124×10^3
     2 3.64×10^2 **7** 2.5×10^{-2}
     3 9.52×10^{-4} **8** 6×10^{-3}
     4 5.276×10^{-1} **9** 2×10^2
     5 2.32×10 **10** 9.62×10^{-1}

21. **1** 1860   **6** 0.23
     2 0.007 65   **7** 400
     3 0.0933   **8** 9876
     4 85 600   **9** 0.101
     5 0.000 076   **10** 0.005

22. **1** rational   **4** integer
     2 irrational   **5** natural
     3 natural

Page 81   Exercise 5.2

1. **1** 50   **8** 6000   **15** 300
    2 3000   **9** 8000   **16** 52
    3 1000   **10** 31   **17** 1000
    4 50   **11** 10 000   **18** 30
    5 365   **12** 135   **19** 1 000 000
    6 4000   **13** 150   **20** 1000
    7 200   **14** 2000

2. **1** 920
    2 4
    3 £15
    4 2.5 kg
    5 50

3. 50

4. 7

5. 54 kg

6. 48 km/hour

7. £9

8. 6 g, 0.14 mm

9. **1** 10.64 kg   **4** 4 ml
    2 101.4°F
    3 1.250 kg

10. **1** 1356   **2** 6239   **3** 7804

11. 1183 units, £63.88, £70.38

Page 83   Exercise 5.3

1. 2150

2. 0.4

3. 0.006

4. 28

5. 0.036

6. 0.054

7. 10.688

8. 1

9. $\frac{3}{40}$

10. **1** 22.149
    2 0.0514
    3 81.6

11. 1

12. **1** 9877
    2 9876.52
    3 9880

13. **1** −3   **2** 3

14. 16

15. 1.08×10^2

16. **1** C   **6** B
    2 D   **7** B (11 days $13\frac{3}{4}$ hours)
    3 B   **8** A (nearly 2740 years ago)
    4 A   **9** C
    5 D   **10** E

17. 800 g

18. 1.5×10^8 km

19. 8.99×10^{-5} g

20. **1** 8429   **2** 79

21. **1** 4.50 p.m.   **2** 16.50

22. 250 units, 258 therms, £95.46, £104.96

Page 87   Exercise A1

1. 96   6. 27 litres   11. 1.4 kg
2. 36 p   7. 600   12. £3.01
3. 2 054 006   8. 5.17 p.m.   13. 2800
4. £1.50   9. £23   14. 0.95
5. 8   10. 30   15. $\frac{3}{5}$

Page 87   Exercise A2

1. E   9. C   17. B   25. B
2. C   10. C   18. D   26. D
3. C   11. A   19. D   27. E
4. E   12. B   20. D   28. B
5. E   13. B   21. B   29. E
6. D   14. D   22. D   30. A
7. A   15. E   23. A
8. B   16. D   24. A

Page 91   Exercise A3

1. £4.77, £5.23

2. **1** $x^2 + 2$ **4** $3x^4$
    2 $8x^8$ **5** $8x^3$
    3 $5x$

3. **1** 100   **5** 1000   **9** 100
    2 1000   **6** 100   **10** 1 000 000
    3 60   **7** 1000
    4 1000   **8** 60

4. **1** $-45°$ **4** $-140°$
    2 $+90°$ **5** $+60°$
    3 $180°$

5. **1** $2^5 \times 3$ **2** 150   **3** 41, 43, 47

6. **1** pf
    2 $\frac{y}{x}$ pence
    3 $12 - x$, $x(12 - x)$
    4 $(x - 2)$ years
    5 $£(12x + 52y)$

7. $AB = FE$, $BC = ED$, $AC = FD$

8. **1** $6\frac{7}{12}$ **4** $1\frac{2}{3}$
    2 $\frac{1}{2}$ **5** $5\frac{1}{2}$
    3 5

9. **1** Jan, 10.7 cm   **2** Feb, 2.7 cm
    3 Apl

10.	**1**	4.73	**5**	0.09	**9**	0.506
	2	490	**6**	0.09	**10**	2.3
	3	0.0063	**7**	0.8		
	4	0.024	**8**	0.18		

11. **1** £60 **2** 3

12. 68°

13. **1** x **4** 1
2 x^6 **5** $\frac{1}{10}$
3 x^3

14. **1** 5.63 **4** 0.10
2 3.23 **5** 0.06
3 37.28

15. **1** 12 **2** 82

Page 94   Exercise A4

1. 2

2. **1** Thursday **2** £76.20

3. **1** 12 **4** 9
2 59 **5** 5
3 0

4. 68°

5. 6, 5.97

6. $\frac{2}{15}$, £300 000

7. **1** translation **4** translation
2 rotation **5** reflection
3 reflection **6** rotation

8. 2.7 cm

9. **1** £130 **2** 50

10. R 16, S 10, T 23, U 11

11. 600, £33.10

12. 99°

13. Your age

14. **1** 116 **4** 6
2 240 **5** 6
3 7

15. **1** Hotel Marti, £444
2 £273, £819
3 £596.40

Page 116   Exercise 6.2

1. **1** $\frac{1}{6}$ **2** $\frac{1}{3}$

2. **1** $\frac{1}{4}$ **2** $\frac{11}{20}$ **3** $\frac{3}{10}$

3. **1** $\frac{1}{2}$ **2** $\frac{1}{6}$

4. $\frac{1}{8}$

5. **1** $\frac{1}{13}$ **2** $\frac{1}{4}$ **3** $\frac{5}{26}$

6. **1** $\frac{2}{11}$ **2** $\frac{4}{11}$ **3** $\frac{3}{11}$

7. Yellow 2, red 1, blue 3

8. **1** $\frac{11}{25}$ **2** $\frac{3}{5}$ **3** $\frac{6}{25}$ **4** $\frac{3}{7}$

9. $\frac{4}{15}$

10. **1** $\frac{6}{25}$ **2** $\frac{1}{25}$ **3** 0

11. **1** $\frac{4}{7}$ **2** $\frac{2}{7}$ **3** $\frac{8}{49}$

12. $\frac{1}{2}$

13. **1** $\frac{1}{25}$ **2** $\frac{1}{5}$

14. $\frac{1}{64}$

15. **1** $\frac{1}{10}$ **2** $\frac{1}{100}$

16. **1** $\frac{1}{16}$ **2** $\frac{1}{4}$

17. $\frac{4}{25}$

18. **1** $\frac{1}{3}$ **2** $\frac{16}{81}$

19. $\frac{1}{12}$

20. **1** $\frac{1}{12}$ **2** $\frac{1}{10}$ **3** $\frac{1}{120}$

21. **1** $\frac{4}{9}$ **2** $\frac{2}{9}$

22. **1** $\frac{1}{12}$ **2** $\frac{1}{6}$ **3** $\frac{1}{6}$ **4** $\frac{1}{9}$

23. **1** $\frac{1}{15}$ **2** $\frac{1}{5}$ **3** $\frac{1}{5}$

24. **1** $\frac{1}{12}$ **2** $\frac{7}{12}$

25. **1** $\frac{1}{4}$ **2** $\frac{4}{17}$

26. **1** $\frac{1}{16}$ **2** $\frac{5}{16}$ **3** $\frac{3}{8}$

27. **1** $\frac{1}{45}$ **2** $\frac{16}{45}$ **3** $\frac{28}{45}$

28. **1** $\frac{1}{50}$ **2** $\frac{17}{50}$

Page 120   Exercise 6.3

1. $\frac{7}{100}$

2. **1** $\frac{1}{4}$ **2** $\frac{7}{24}$

3. **1** $\frac{1}{16}$ **2** $\frac{3}{16}$ **3** $\frac{3}{16}$

4. **1** $\frac{2}{15}$ **2** $\frac{1}{40}$ **3** $\frac{1}{60}$

5. **2** 7 **3** $\frac{1}{216}$

6. **1** $\frac{4}{9}$ **2** $\frac{1}{6}$ **3** $\frac{7}{18}$

7. **1** $\frac{1}{2}$ **2** $\frac{1}{6}$ **5** $\frac{1}{2}$
    6 $P(0) = \frac{1}{4}$, $P(1) = \frac{1}{2}$, $P(2) = \frac{1}{4}$
    7 $P(6) = \frac{1}{7}$ **8** $\frac{1}{7}$

Page 124   Exercise 7.1

2. **1** all **2** rhombus, square
    3 rectangle, square

3. **1** 2 **2** 4

4. $112°$

5. $85°$

6. **1** $a = 115°$, $b = 65°$, $c = 115°$
    2 $d = 45°$, $e = 45°$, $f = 90°$

7. $74°$, $87°$

8. $110°$

9. **1** right-angled
    2 right-angled isosceles
    3 isosceles

10. **1** $\angle XCB$, $\angle XDA$, $\angle XAD$
    2 $\triangle XAD$ is isosceles
    3 $\triangle AXB \equiv \triangle DXC$ or $\triangle ABC \equiv \triangle DCB$
    or $\triangle ADB \equiv \triangle DAC$

11. $\triangle DNB$

12. **1** B, BX, X **2** AY

13. **1** X
    2 $\triangle CDX$, $\triangle DXA$, $\triangle CDA$, $\triangle CDB$
    3 $\angle BCD$
    4 CX, DX

14. **1** (i) rotation about E through $180°$
    (ii) reflection in BD
    2 rotation about E through $180°$

15. **1** parallelogram, rectangle
    2 kite
    3 rhombus, square

16. 5.4 cm, trapezium

17. 6.9 cm, $51°$, BD is axis of symmetry

18. $58°$

19. $141°$, 4.3 cm

20. $AC = BD = 7.1$ cm, angles all $90°$

Page 127   Exercise 7.2

1. $(360 - 6x)°$

2. $x = 20$; $60°$, $80°$, $100°$, $120°$; trapezium

3. **1** $84°$ **2** $48°$ **3** isosceles

4. **1** $85°$ **2** $76°$

5. **1** both equal to DC
    2 isosceles
    3 $g = 90°$, $h = 60°$, $j = 15°$, $k = 45°$

6. $AB = 4.3$ cm, $AD = 8.0$ cm,
    $\angle DAB = 105°$

7. **1** parallelogram **2** trapezium
    3 rectangle **4** rhombus

8. $x = 4$, $y = 3$; $AB = CD = 11$ cm,
    $BC = AD = 15$ cm

9. **1** kite **2** rhombus
    3 square

10. **1** parallelogram **2** rectangle
    3 rhombus **4** square

Page 130   Exercise 8.1

2. **1** (i) $36°$ (ii) $144°$
    2 $162°$

3. **1** 12
    2 (i) $45°$ (ii) 8
    3 36

4. $108°$, $135°$, $117°$

5. **1** isosceles **2** $\angle BAR = 108°$,
    $\angle BAD = 90°$, $\angle RAD = 162°$ **3** $9°$

6. **1** isosceles trapezium
    2 rectangle
    3 obtuse-angled isosceles
    4 right-angled
    5 equilateral

7. **1** $120°$, hexagons,
    2 $90°$, $135°$, $135°$, octagons

8. $a = 30°$, $b = 75°$, $c = 150°$

9. $140°$

10. $\angle B = \angle E = 80°$,
    $\angle C = \angle D = \angle F = 140°$

11. **1** $AD = 9.7$ cm **2** $AB = 5.9$ cm

12. **1** $AD = 12\,\text{cm}$

13. **1** 540°, 85°   **4** 50°
     2 720°, 147°   **5** 30°, 90°, 90°
     3 1080°, 135°

Page 135   Exercise 8.2

1. 25 edges   4. *E, G*

2. (b), (c), (e)   5. **2** 3

3. 7, 12, 7   6. rectangle

Page 137   Exercise 8.3

1. **1** 108°
    2 obtuse-angled isosceles
    3 36°
    4 72°
    5 isosceles trapezium
    6 rhombus

2. **1** 120°   **2** 162°

3. 18°

4. $\left(\dfrac{360}{a}\right)^{\!\circ}, \left(\dfrac{360}{b}\right)^{\!\circ}, \left(\dfrac{360}{c}\right)^{\!\circ}$, $a = 4$, square

5. pentagon, 5 diagonals; *n* sides,
    $\frac{1}{2}n(n-3)$ diagonals; 170

6. **1** 60   **2** 52

7. 12, 6

8. 14, 36, 24

9. 4

10. 6

Page 145   Exercise 9.1

1. **1** mean 9, median 8
    2 mean 44, median 39
    3 mean 8, median 7
    4 mean 40.7, median 35
    5 mean 1.9, median 1.95

2. **1** median 9, mode 12
    2 median 28, mode 27
    3 median 4.5, mode 5

3. **1** 64.4   **4** $2\frac{13}{36}$
    2 £917.40   **5** 2.9 kg
    3 2 hrs 1 min

4. **1** mean 57 kg, median 55 kg
    2 12 yrs 2 mths
    3 164 g
    4 22°C
    5 10 min 25 sec

5. **1** 13   **4** 76
    2 73   **5** 0.7
    3 12

6. **1** 57.4   **4** $2\frac{1}{4}$
    2 £122   **5** 2.1 kg
    3 1 hr 57 min

7. 32 runs

8. 8 yrs 7 mths

9. 4.6 kg

10. 8.8 p

11. 62

12. £8.25

13. **2** mean 2.7, median 2, mode 2

14. **2** mean 1.6, median 1, mode 1

15. **2** mean 3.8, median 4, mode 4

16. **2** mean 30.7, median 30, mode 30

17. 5.3

18. 1.5

19. mean 6.8, median 7, mode 8

20. mode 37, mean 37.6

Page 148   Exercise 9.2

1. **1** mean 4.9, median 5, mode 5
    2 mean 5.6, median 6, mode 6
    3 A, 6; B, 4
    4 B
    5 A

2. 2.8, North-west

3. 4 hours

4. 17 p

5. £110

6. 9 years

7. 14.7, 4

8. mean 3.9, median 4, mode 3,
    probability 0.6

9. 11.6, the mean

10. frequencies 21, 26, 25, 7, 3, 2;
    mean 1.4, median 1, mode 1

11. theoretical frequencies 2 to 12;
    5, 10, 15, 20, 25, 30, 25, 20, 15, 10, 5

12. 1 2 3, 1 2 4, 1 2 5, 1 3 4, 1 3 5, 1 4 5,
    2 3 4, 2 3 5, 2 4 5, 3 4 5;
    probabilities 6 to 12:
    0.1, 0.1, 0.2, 0.2, 0.2, 0.1, 0.1

Page 151   Example 1

parallelogram

Page 155   Exercise 10.1

1. **1** parallelogram, $E(4, 4\frac{1}{2})$
    2 $J(-5, 7)$, 4 axes
    3 rhombus; $x = -4$, $y = -6$;

2. $AB \frac{1}{2}$, $CD -3$, $EF -\frac{1}{4}$, $GH \frac{2}{5}$

3. **5** $x = 3.3(3.25)$, $y = 2.3(2.25)$
    6 $x = -2$, $y = 11$

4. D is $(5, 5)$, BD is $y = 5$

5. $y = -8, -2, 13$; gradient 3; $(0, -2)$

6. $-1, 3$

7. $x = 2$, $y = 1$

8. **1** $y = 2$, $x = 3$; $x = 2.7$, $y = 3.7$

Page 157   Exercise 10.2

1. A and E, B and F, C and D

2. $-1\frac{1}{3}$

3. $x = 2.8$, $y = 10.4$

4. $(8x + 16y)$ pence, $x + y = 25$,
    $8x + 16y = 320$ $(x + 2y = 40)$,
    10 packets of sweets,
    15 bars of chocolate

5. Gradient $\frac{1}{4}$, $(0, 1.75)$

6. $10x + 8y = 600$; $y = 75$, $x = 60$,
    $y = x + 12$,
    28 m in 1st roll and 40 m in 2nd roll

7. $x + y = 30$, $30x + 15y = 600$
    $(2x + y = 40)$; 10 skilled, 20 trainees

8. **1** 0.4   **2** 1.1   **3** -0.2
    4 -1.2 **5** 0.8

Page 160   Exercise B1

1. 15   6. 3   11. 80°
2. 12 p   7. 6   12. £40
3. $\frac{1}{3}$ 8. $10\frac{1}{2}$ km   13. 15.15
4. 50   9. 78 cm   14. $\frac{1}{8}$
5. 2000   10. 6 kg   15. £2

Page 160   Exercise B2

1. E   11. B   21. C
2. B   12. A   22. B
3. A   13. D   23. C
4. A   14. C   24. E
5. C   15. A   25. A
6. D   16. E   26. C
7. C   17. C   27. C
8. A   18. B   28. D
9. E   19. B   29. D
10. B   20. D   30. C

Page 164   Exercise B3

1. **1** 47   **4** 34, 51
    2 15, 51   **5** 27, 15
    3 47, 57

2. **1** sphere   **4** cuboid
    2 cylinder   **5** cube
    3 cone

3. $\frac{4}{5}$

4. 69°

5. mean 8, median 7, mode 2

6. 48°

7. **1** 6.87×10^2
    2 5.28×10^5
    3 2.3×10^{-1}

8. **1** $x = 33$ **4** $x = 6$
    2 $x = 2\frac{1}{3}$ **5** $x = 3$
    3 $x = 5\frac{1}{2}$

9. 36°

10. **1** -17 **4** -60
    2 24   **5** $1\frac{2}{5}$
    3 21

11. **1** $x = \dfrac{y - c}{m}$ **3** $x = \dfrac{b - a}{c}$

 2 $x = (y + 3)^2$ **4** $x = \sqrt{y - 4}$

12. **1** $2\frac{2}{3}$ **2** 4   **3** $2\frac{3}{4}$

13. $\frac{1}{2}$

14. £4.00

15. **1** $y = -x$ **4** $y = 3 - x$
 2 $y = \frac{1}{2}x$ **5** $y = 2x + 1$
 3 $y = x - 1$

Page 167   Exercise B4

1. **1** triangular prism
 2 cuboid
 3 pyramid on square base

2. $39°$

3. $\frac{16}{25}$

5. **1** 165   **2** $120°$ **3** $\frac{5}{12}$

6. $64°$

7. 62 kg, 70 kg

8. $AB = 5.8\,\text{cm}$, $\angle ABC = 118°$, rhombus

9. $\frac{1}{6}, \frac{5}{9}$

10. 90 minutes

11. mean 2.06, median 2, mode 2

12. **1** $45°$ **2** $135°$ **3** square

13. **1** $x + 12y$ **4** $7x^2$
 2 $x^2 - xy - y^2$ **5** $\frac{1}{3}$
 3 $2y - x$

14. **1** trapezium   **4** rectangle
 2 parallelogram   **5** rhombus
 3 parallelogram

Page 177   Exercise 11.1

2. **1** OT
 2 $\triangle OPT \equiv \triangle OQT$
 3 $\angle TOQ$

3. **2** yes   **3** $\angle DOC$ **4** yes

4. $90°$

5. **1** $a = 90°$, $b = 33°$
 2 $c = 90°$, $d = 70°$
 3 $e = 20°$, $f = 140°$
 4 $g = 45°$
 5 $h = 65°$, $j = 25°$, $k = 40°$

Page 179   Exercise 11.2

7. $39°$, 4.1 cm

8. 9.9 cm, square

9. $93°$, 3.8 cm

12. 9.6 cm

Page 184   Exercise 11.3

1. 3.2 cm

2. 3.6 cm

3. 4.6 cm

4. 2.7 cm

5. 5.2 cm

9. 2 circles with same centre as original circle, radii 7 cm and 9 cm

Page 185   Exercise 11.4

1. **1** $45°$ **2** $67\frac{1}{2}°$ **3** $22\frac{1}{2}°$

2. rectangle

3. **1** OT
 2 $\triangle OPT \equiv \triangle OQT$, $\triangle OPX \equiv \triangle OQX$, $\triangle TPX \equiv \triangle TQX$
 3 QX **4** $\angle QXT$ **5** $90°$

5. $2x - 5 + 2x + 15 = 90$, $x = 20$

6. **1** isosceles (obtuse-angled)
 2 $40°$
 3 $50°$
 4 isosceles (acute-angled)
 5 $80°$

7. $\triangle OAB$, isosceles right-angled; $\triangle OBC$ and $\triangle OAC$, isosceles obtuse-angled; $\angle A = 70°$, $\angle B = 65°$, $\angle C = 45°$

9. $BC = 5.8\,\text{cm}$, radius 3.6 cm

11. $AC = 8.6\,\text{cm}$, $BC = 7.5\,\text{cm}$, radius 2.4 cm

Page 192   **Exercise 12.1**

1. **1** $121\,\text{cm}^2$ **3** $77\,\text{cm}^2$
   2 $48\,\text{cm}^2$ **4** $34\,\text{cm}^2$

2. **1** $28\,\text{m}^2$, $22\,\text{m}$ **3** $87\,\text{cm}^2$, $48\,\text{cm}$
   2 $81\,\text{cm}^2$ **4** $40\,\text{m}^2$

3. $84\,\text{cm}^2$, $48\,\text{cm}$

4. **1** $88\,\text{cm}$, $616\,\text{cm}^2$
   2 $37.7\,\text{cm}$, $113\,\text{cm}^2$
   3 $6.28\,\text{m}$, $3.14\,\text{m}^2$

5. $14\,\text{cm}^2$

6. **1** $27\,\text{m}^2$ **2** £108

7. 1000

8. **1** square, $0.52\,\text{cm}$
   2 circle, $0.25\,\text{cm}^2$

9. $59\,\text{cm}^2$

10. **1** $3.14\,\text{cm}$ **2** $9.3\,\text{cm}^2$

11. $144\,\text{cm}^2$, $\triangle ABE$ $30\,\text{cm}^2$, $\triangle ADF$ $36\,\text{cm}^2$,
    $\triangle FCE$ $21\,\text{cm}^2$, $\triangle AEF$ $57\,\text{cm}^2$

12. $7.74\,\text{cm}^2$

13. **1** d
    2 c, a $5.5\,\text{cm}^2$, b $5.76\,\text{cm}^2$, c $5.04\,\text{cm}^2$,
    d $6.15\,\text{cm}^2$

14. **1** $11\,\text{cm}$ **4** $24.5\,\text{cm}^2$
    2 $25\,\text{cm}$ **5** $14.0\,\text{cm}^2$
    3 $38.5\,\text{cm}^2$

15. **1** $6\,\text{cm}^2$ **4** $6.5\,\text{cm}^2$
    2 $6\,\text{cm}^2$ **5** $4\,\text{cm}^2$
    3 $5\,\text{cm}^2$

Page 196   **Exercise 12.2**

1. **1** $11.2\,\text{cm}$ **4** $8.1\,\text{cm}$
   2 $10\,\text{cm}$ **5** $4\,\text{cm}$
   3 $2.2\,\text{cm}$

2. **1** $15\,\text{cm}$ **4** $3.3\,\text{cm}$
   2 $6.7\,\text{cm}$ **5** $2\,\text{cm}$
   3 $7\,\text{cm}$

3. **1** $30\,\text{m}$ **2** $x = 10\,\text{cm}$, $y = 8\,\text{cm}$

4. $5\,\text{cm}$

5. $17\,\text{cm}$, $9\,\text{cm}$

6. **1** $5\,\text{cm}$ **2** $16\,\text{cm}$ **3** $21\,\text{cm}$

Page 199   **Exercise 12.3**

1. **1** $600\,\text{cm}^3$ **4** $45\,\text{cm}^3$
   2 $125\,\text{cm}^3$ **5** $27\,000\,\text{cm}^3$
   3 $50\,\text{m}^3$

2. **1** $198\,\text{cm}^3$ **4** $78.5\,\text{cm}^3$
   2 $126\,\text{cm}^3$ **5** $251\,\text{cm}^3$
   3 $4400\,\text{cm}^3$

3. **1** $21\,\text{cm}^2$ **2** $189\,\text{cm}^3$

4. $35\,\text{m}^2$

5. $385\,\text{cm}^3$, 12

6. **1** $5\,\text{m}$ **4** 15
   2 $54\,\text{cm}^2$ **5** 3
   3 (i) $240\,\text{cm}^3$,   (ii) 30

7. $180\,\text{cm}^3$

8. **1** $7.5\,\text{m}^2$ **2** $30\,\text{m}^3$

9. **1** $62.8\,\text{cm}^2$ **2** $87.9\,\text{cm}^2$

10. $450\,\text{m}^3$

Page 200   **Exercise 12.4**

1. 160, 7

2. $5.2 \times 10^{-3}\,\text{m}^2$

3. **1** $90°$ **3** $21\,\text{cm}^2$
   2 $6\,\text{cm}$ **4** $42\,\text{cm}^2$

4. $42\,\text{cm}^2$

5. **1** 25   **2** 21

6. $1100\,\text{m}$

7. $24\,\text{cm}^2$

8. $\triangle APS$ $3\,\text{cm}^2$, $\triangle BPQ$ $12\,\text{cm}^2$,
   $\triangle CRQ$ $8\,\text{cm}^2$, $\triangle DRS$ $10\,\text{cm}^2$,
   $PQRS$ $31\,\text{cm}^2$

9. **1** $120\,\text{cm}^2$ **2** $15\,\text{cm}$

10. **1** $1020\,\text{m}^2$ **2** $239\,\text{m}^2$

11. **1** $45\,\text{cm}^2$ **2** $7.5\,\text{cm}$

12. $\frac{1}{5}$,   **1** $12.6\,\text{cm}$ **2** $62.8\,\text{cm}^2$

13. **1** $25\,\text{cm}$,   **2** $15\,\text{cm}$,
    3 $66\,\text{cm}$ **4** $234\,\text{cm}^2$

14. $10\,\text{km}$

15. 5

16. 13 feet

17. **1** 11 cm   **2** 4 cm   **3** 5 cm

18. **1** 12 cm
    2 circle, centre O, radius 12 cm

19. **1** 90°   **2** 15 cm
    3 40 cm   **4** 60 cm^2

20. **1** 90°   **2** 8 cm, 16 cm

21. **1** 6π **2** 24π cm^2, cone

22. 1290 cm^3

23. 2250 kg

24. 20 cm

25. **1** 100 000 m^2 **2** 30 000 m^3

26. 32 min

27. 27 600 kg

28. 324 cm^3

Page 206   Exercise 13.1

1. **1** $3a + 3b$ **6** $8p - 13q + r$
   2 $c - 10d$ **7** $44 - 5s$
   3 $8e - f$ **8** $x^2 - x - 6$
   4 $-3g - 9h$ **9** $2x^2 - 9x + 4$
   5 $j + 6k$ **10** $x - x^2$

2. **1** $x = 28$ **6** $x = 15$
   2 $x = -\frac{1}{6}$ **7** $x = 2$
   3 $x = 10$ **8** $x = -1\frac{3}{5}$
   4 $x = \frac{3}{4}$ **9** $x = -1$
   5 $x = -3$ **10** $x = \frac{1}{3}$

3. **1** $4a$ **2** $\dfrac{c}{9}$ **3** $\dfrac{5e^2}{3}$

4. **1** $\dfrac{13a}{24}$ **4** $\dfrac{d}{2}$

   2 $\dfrac{28b}{9}$ **5** $\dfrac{e}{6}$

   3 $\dfrac{11c}{10}$

5. **1** $\dfrac{2a}{3}$ **3** $\dfrac{ce}{15}$ **5** $\dfrac{5q^2}{3}$

   2 $\dfrac{2b}{5}$ **4** $\dfrac{3g}{2}$

6. **1** $x = 30$ **6** $x = -20$
   2 $x = 20$ **7** $x = \frac{4}{5}$
   3 $x = 13$ **8** $x = -6$
   4 $x = 12$ **9** $x = \frac{1}{2}$
   5 $x = 30$ **10** $x = 2\frac{1}{3}$

Page 209   Exercise 13.2

1. **1** $x = \dfrac{c + b}{a}$

   2 $x = \sqrt{\dfrac{E}{3}}$

   3 $x = \dfrac{v - u}{a}$

   4 $t = \sqrt{\dfrac{s}{5}}$

   5 $length = \dfrac{area}{breadth}$

   6 $R = \dfrac{A - P}{P}$

   7 $n = \dfrac{t + 360}{180}$

   8 $distance = speed \times time$

   9 $x = \dfrac{3y + 4}{2}$

   10 $V = \sqrt{PR}$

2. **1** $7(2x - 3y)$ **6** $t(t + 1)$
   2 $3y(x + 3z)$ **7** $a(a + b - 2c)$
   3 $2\pi(a - b)$ **8** $3(3 + x^3)$
   4 $3(2a - b + 3c)$ **9** $2x(x + y)$
   5 $5x(3x - 5)$ **10** $2(2b - 1)$

3. **1** 35   **2** 204   **3** 31
   4 15.3   **5** 37

Page 209   Exercise 13.3

2. minimum (0, 0), $x = -3.2$ and $x = 3.2$

Page 211   Exercise 13.4

1. **1** $x - 1$ **4** $20 - 4x$
   2 $2x - 5y$ **5** $9x - 10$
   3 $9x - 13$

2. **1** $12xy$ **2** $\dfrac{11xy}{12}$ **3** $1\frac{1}{3}$

3. **1** $20a^{13}$ **2** $3b^4$

4. **1** $x = -6$ **4** $x = 4$
    2 $x = -1$ **5** $x = 22$
    3 $x = 1\frac{1}{2}$

5. $\frac{13}{16}$

6. **1** 21   **2** 36

7. £3

8. **1** $n = \dfrac{a - 360}{180}$ **4** $F = \frac{9}{5}C + 32$

    2 $r = \dfrac{s - a}{a}$ **5** $n = \dfrac{2s}{a + l}$

    3 $x = \dfrac{b^2}{4}$

9. **1** $5(x + 3y)$ **4** $6(x^3 + 2)$
    2 $3x(x - 2)$ **5** $x(x^2 + y)$
    3 $4b(a - 3c)$

10. **1** $18\frac{3}{4}$ **2** $\sqrt{\dfrac{6V}{h}}$

11. **1** $c = \dfrac{b^2}{a}$ **2** $b = \sqrt{ac}$

12. 2

13. $n(n + 1)$

14. **1** 24.3   **4** 31.42
    2 169   **5** 6800
    3 9700

15. $y = 3x^2$, 45 m by 135 m (134 m)

16. $y = \dfrac{600}{x}$, $x + y = 60$, 47 m by 13 m

Page 216   Exercise 14.1

5. 180.2 cm

6. 12.9 years, 12 yrs 11 mths

7. 7.3 cm

8. 15.4 min

9. **1** 180 to 182 cm (179.5 to 182.5 cm)
    2 12 yrs (12 to 13 yrs)
    3 7.5 cm (7.25 to 7.75 cm)
    4 15 to 20 min

10. **1** 75
    2 10.5 to 11.5 kg
    3 10.9 kg
    4 $\frac{4}{25}$

Page 217   Exercise 14.2

1. **2** 5.6 cm

2. **1** 170 to 174 cm   **3** 171.4 cm

3. **1** 12 to 14 marks   **3** 11.05

4. **1** 75 to 80 kg
    2 77.5 kg
    4 74.6 kg

5. **1** 4 to 6 yrs   **3** 5.2 yrs

6. **1** 13.8 cm

7. **2** £95

8. 40.0 cm

11. **1** 40   **2** $\frac{3}{10}$ **3** 8 to 9 min
    4 7.7 min

Page 226   Exercise 15.1

1. **1** $\frac{9}{25}$
    2 $\frac{9}{20}$
    3 $\frac{7}{40}$
    4 $\frac{1}{30}$
    5 $\frac{2}{3}$

5. **1** 72%
    2 8%
    3 60%
    4 $37\frac{1}{2}$%
    5 $66\frac{2}{3}$%

2. **1** 0.47
    2 0.95
    3 0.225
    4 0.0625
    5 0.999

6. **1** £6.24
    2 £2.99
    3 £108
    4 £60
    5 £336

3. **1** 75%
    2 62.5%
    3 15%
    4 $33\frac{1}{3}$%
    5 87.5%

7. **1** 20%
    2 $16\frac{2}{3}$%
    3 $22\frac{1}{2}$%
    4 20%
    5 12%

4. **1** 1.44 m
    2 600 g
    3 5 min
    4 1.5 cm
    5 £4.60

8. **1** £700
    2 £4.00
    3 300 ml
    4 £150
    5 £9000

9. **1** £60   **4** £72
    2 £264   **5** £300
    3 £168

10. **1** £64.93
    2 £310.84
    3 £176.40

11. £27.60

12. £160, £24

13. £2040, £170

14. £1715

Page 228   Exercise 15.2

1. 50%, 25%, 20%, 10%, 5%, 1%

2. $\frac{3}{10}, \frac{1}{3}, \frac{2}{5}, \frac{2}{3}, \frac{3}{4}$

3. $53\frac{1}{3}\%$

4. 12%

5. £75

6. 60%

7. £117, £78

8. £8

9. £141.50

10. £3630

11. £1800, £0, £354, £6.81

12. **1** 125.44 cm²   **2** yes

13. 4.5%

14. 121 units, £6.05, £23.40, £3.51, £26.91

15. £32 100 (£32 076)

16. **1** 22.4% variable   **2** 10 years
     3 £7779.20   **4** £5.44, £5304

17. Wages £22 500, Food £18 000,
 Fuel £6000, Extras £7500; £56 730

Page 231   Exercise C1

1.	15 p	6.	20%	11.	34 m
2.	£115	7.	£4.95	12.	55°
3.	41 cm²	8.	15	13.	2.5 kg
4.	11	9.	23, 29	14.	7 years
5.	45	10.	16%	15.	24

Page 231   Exercise C2

1.	A	7.	C	13.	D
2.	D	8.	C	14.	D
3.	E	9.	E	15.	E
4.	D	10.	B	16.	B
5.	C	11.	D	17.	C
6.	C	12.	E	18.	B

19.	D	23.	A	27.	B
20.	D	24.	A	28.	D
21.	D	25.	A	29.	D
22.	A	26.	B	30.	E

Page 236   Exercise C3

1. **1** 640   **4** 5300
     2 260   **5** 0.52
     3 0.085

3. 63 p

4. 80

5. 8 amps

6. **1** 532   **4** 500
     2 0.035   **5** 9
     3 0.04

7. $a = 70°, b = 55°, c = 35°$

8. **1** 1.9×10^3 **2** 7.6×10^5

9. **1** 6 cm   **2** 24 cm²   **3** 4.8 cm

10. 616 cm², 15 cm

11. 360

12. 4.5 min

13. 76°, 6.1 cm, 31 cm²

14. **1** $x = -2\frac{1}{2}$ **4** $x = 10$
     2 $x = 8$ **5** $x = 2$
     3 $x = -\frac{4}{5}$

15. £2646, £270

Page 238   Exercise C4

1. **1** 3 (feet)   **2** 16 feet

2. **1** $2x(x + 4y)$ **2** $x(x - 12)$
     3 $4(3x^2 + 1)$

3. £46.00

4. **1** 15.9 m   **2** 5.6 m

5. £45

7. 3 cm, 4 cm, 9 cm, 27 cm²

8. **1** square   **4** rhombus
     2 rectangle   **5** trapezium
     3 parallelogram

9.   1, 2, 5

10. $2x^2\,cm^2$, $x = 3$, 41.0 cm

11.   **1** $a = \dfrac{v^2 - u^2}{2s}$ **2** $h = \dfrac{3V}{\pi r^2}$

       3 $r = \sqrt{\dfrac{S}{4\pi}}$

12. $80\,m^2$, $16\,000\,m^3$

13.   **1** $A = 2x^2 + 4xh$ **2**   110

       3 $h = \dfrac{A - 2x^2}{4x}$ **4**   6 cm

15.   frequencies 6, 6, 7, 8, 3;
      modal class 16 to 20 hrs
      (15.5 to 20.5 hrs), mean 12.3 hrs

Page 250   **Exercise 16.1**

1.   **1**   4 : 5   **4**   5 : 24
    2   5 : 12   **5**   3 : 10
    3   5 : 8

2.   **1**   90 p, £1.35   **4**   £1.50, 25 p
    2   56 p, 98 p   **5**   £2.80, £1.20
    3   42 p, 18 p

3.   **1**   £450   **4**   £7.50
    2   £67.50   **5**   £27.50
    3   £160

4.   8 : 27

5.   40°, 60°, 100°, 160°

6.   2.7 cm

7.   £2437.50

8.   £1600, £2800, £3600

9.   4.5 l

10.   2.5 kg, 1 kg

11.   42

12.   3 : 80

13. $1\,m^3$, $2\,m^3$

14.   **1**   2 : 3   **2**   9 : 10   **3**   4 : 9
     4   2 : 5

Page 252   **Exercise 16.2**

1.   2

2. $y = x$, 5

3.   9

4.   12

5. $y = 200x$, 2000

6. $\frac{1}{4}$

7.   50

8.   28

9. $y = \dfrac{12}{x}$, 3

Page 253   **Exercise 16.3**

1.   £40.50   6.   £6.50

2.   7 lb   7.   12.5 km/litre

3.   £30   8. x 80 p, y 84 p, Brand x

4.   3 pints   9.   12 min

5. $2\frac{1}{2}$ gall   10.   £6.84

Page 254   **Exercise 16.4**

1.   £294.40

2.   £613.80

3.   90 p in the £

4.   £350

5.   £31.20

Page 255   **Exercise 16.5**

1.   18 900 drachmae   6.   £2293.58

2.   346.50 francs   7.   £34.13

3.   16.92 dollars   8.   £1423.49

4.   663 000 yen   9.   £4.78

5.   129 600 dinars   10.   £19.34

Page 256   Exercise 16.6

1. 1 hour 48 min

2. 220 miles

3. 36 miles per hour

4. 28 miles per hour

5. **1** $1\frac{1}{2}$ hours   **2** 81 km/hour

6. **1** $67\frac{1}{2}$ km   **2** 13.5 km/hour

7. 95 km/hour

8. **1** 5 : 6   **2** 6 : 5

Page 257   Exercise 16.7

1. £240, £300, £360; 96°, 120°, 144°

2. **1** 21 : 31   **3** 3 : 5
        2 9 : 14   **4** 2 : 3

3. £55.25

4. **1** 2.4   **2** 10

5. 2 : π : 4

6. £4

7. 3.8%

8. £500

9. £456

10. 18 m²/litre

11. Family size

12. **1** 48 miles per hour
         2 36 miles per hour
         3 38 miles per gallon

13. Alan, £1

14. £8, 95.20 francs

15. 6 kg

16. $2\frac{1}{2}$ hours

17. $W = \frac{1}{105}ld^2$, 10 kg

18. 12.5 tonnes

19. yes, average speed 45 miles per hour

20. 42 km/hour

Page 261   Exercise 17.1

2. 4

3. **1** 2 : 5   **2** 2 : 5   **3** yes
        4 2 : 5

4. **1** 5 : 6   **2** 5 : 7   **3** no

5. 4 : 5

6. **1** 2 : 3   **2** 2 : 3   **3** yes

7. 3 : 4

8. **1** 3 : 4   **2** 9 : 16   **3** $\frac{7}{16}$

9. 6 cm

Page 264   Exercise 17.2

1. **2** 2 : 5   **3** ∠F

2. **2** ∠E

3. **2** 3 : 4   **3** 3 : 4   **4** 6 cm

4. **1** 2 : 3   **2** 2 : 3   **3** yes
        4 2 : 3   **5** ∠D   **6** ∠E

Page 266   Exercise 17.3

2. 25 cm

3. **1** length 30 cm, width 24 cm
        2 3200 cm³, 10 800 cm³, 8 : 27

4. **1** ΔAXD, ΔCXB   **2** 3 : 4

5. 80 m

6. **1** ΔSAB
        2 ΔRAB or ΔTAB, ΔDAB

7. **1** ΔABC, ΔADE, ΔAFG
        2 3 : 4 : 6
        3 C

8. **1** 1.5 cm   **2** 66°

9. 2

Page 271   Exercise 18.1

1. **1** 042°   **4** 165°
        2 250°   **5** 090°
        3 307°

3. **1** 222°   **4** 345°
        2 070°   **5** 270°
        3 127°

4. **1** $90°$ **4** $300°$
   2 $80°$ **5** $290°$
   3 $90°$

5. $1:50\,000$, $4.2\,km$

6. $8\,cm$, $5.4\,cm$

7. $2\,km$

8. $90\,m^2$

9. $B–C$ $179\,m$, $C–D$ $182\,m$, $B–D$ $169\,m$

10. $30\,m$

11. $94\,m$

12. $15\,m$

13. $313°$, $2240\,m$

14. **1** $040°$ **2** $10\,km$

Page 274   **Exercise 18.2**

1. **1** N 70°W **4** S 70°E
   2 S 25°W **5** N 42°W
   3 N 53°E

Page 274   **Exercise 18.3**

1. $8\,m$, $12.5\,m$ by $16\,m$, $1600\,m^3$

2. $670\,m$

3. $242°$, $25\,km$, $1\,hr\ 35\,min$

4. $49\,m$

5. $323°$, $1:200\,000$, $13\,km$, $205°$

7. $14\,m$

8. $420\,m$

9. $100\,m$

10. $097°$

11. **1** $5\,m$ by $4\,m$ **2** $3.5\,m$ by $3\,m$
    3 $3\,m$ by $3\,m$ **4** $20\,m^2$, £360

Page 281   **Exercise 19.1**

1. **1** reflection in $y = x$
   2 rotation about origin through 90° clockwise
   3 translation 1 unit in x direction and -8 units in y direction
   4 rotation about origin through 180°

5 reflection in $y = -x$
6 translation -6 units in x direction and -2 units in y direction
7 reflection in $x = -1$
8 reflection in x-axis
9 reflection in y-axis
10 translation -7 units in x direction and 6 units in y direction

2. 4, $(2, 1)$

3. **1** reflection in y-axis
   2 rotation about $(0, 0)$ through $180°$
   3 rotation about $(-\frac{1}{2}, 0)$ through $180°$
   4 reflection in x-axis
   5 translation -1 unit in x direction

4. $A_1(3, 3)$, $B_1(6, 3)$, $C_1(6, 9)$; $3:1$

5. reflection in the line $y = x$

6. **1** $(4, 7)$ **2** $(0, 3)$

7. 3, $(4, 5)$, $3:1$

8. $A_1(-1, 1)$, $B_1(-4, 2)$, $C_1(-3, 7)$,
   $A_2(1, -1)$, $B_2(4, -2)$, $C_2(3, -7)$,
   reflection in x-axis

9. $A_1(-1, 1)$, $B_1(-2, 4)$, $C_1(-7, 3)$,
   $A_2(-1, -1)$, $B_2(-2, -4)$, $C_2(-7, -3)$,
   reflection in the line $y = -x$

10. $A_1(1, 1)$, $B_1(4, 0)$, $C_1(3, -5)$, $A_2(1, 1)$,
    $B_2(0, 4)$, $C_2(-5, 3)$, rotation about A through 90° anticlockwise

11. $A_1(4, -1)$, $B_1(7, 0)$, $C_1(6, 5)$, $A_2(-4, 2)$,
    $B_2(-1, 3)$, $C_2(-2, 8)$, translation -5 units in x direction and 1 unit in y direction

Page 286   **Exercise 19.2**

7. **1** $\begin{pmatrix} 4 \\ 6 \end{pmatrix}$, $\begin{pmatrix} 4 \\ 2 \end{pmatrix}$, $\begin{pmatrix} 0 \\ -4 \end{pmatrix}$, $\begin{pmatrix} -4 \\ 2 \end{pmatrix}$, $\begin{pmatrix} 6 \\ -4 \end{pmatrix}$, $\begin{pmatrix} -4 \\ 2 \end{pmatrix}$, $\begin{pmatrix} 8 \\ 4 \end{pmatrix}$

   2 $\overrightarrow{GH}$, $\overrightarrow{LM}$ **3** $\overrightarrow{JK}$ **4** $\overrightarrow{NP}$

8. $(-2, 0)$, parallelogram

Page 288   Exercise 19.3

1.   1   enlargement centre (0, 0), scale factor 2
     2   rotation about (0, 0) through 90° anticlockwise
     3   reflection in $y = -x$
     4   translation 5 units in x direction
     5   rotation about (0, 0) through 90° anticlockwise
     6   enlargement centre (0, 0), scale factor 3

2.   1 $A(3, -2)$, $B(6, -1)$
     2   $A(2, 2)$, $B(8, 4)$
     3   $A(-1, -1)$, $B(-2, -4)$
     4   $A(-1, 1)$, $B(-2, 4)$

3.   1   translation -6 units in x direction and -7 units in y direction
     4   reflection in $y = x$

4. $x = 2$, $y = -3$

5.   1   reflection in y-axis
     2   rotation about (0, 0) through 90° clockwise
     3   reflection in $y = -x$
     4   translation 4 units in x direction and -4 units in y direction
     5   enlargement centre (0, 0), scale factor 3
     6   reflection in the line $x = 3$

6. $A_1(-2, -1)$, $B_1(-4, -3)$, $C_1(-7, 0)$, $A_2(-2, 1)$, $B_2(-4, 3)$, $C_2(-7, 0)$, reflection in the y-axis

7.   translation $2T$

8.   9 square units

10.   1 $\vec{AE}$ 2 $\vec{CB}$ 3 $\vec{AE}$
     4   $\vec{AC}$ (or $\vec{BE}$)
     5   $\vec{BG}$ (or $\vec{GC}$)

11. $\begin{pmatrix} 3 \\ 2 \end{pmatrix}$, $\begin{pmatrix} 1 \\ -4 \end{pmatrix}$, 2

Page 294   Exercise 20.1

1.   1   2.74 cm   2   4.60 cm
     3   5.47 cm

2.   1   6.34 cm   2   3.71 cm
     3   12.7 cm

3.   1   6.95 cm   2   3.28 cm
     3   2.66 cm

4.   1   19.5°   2   33.7°   3   26.7°

5.   1   45.6°   2   48.2°   3   36.9°

6.   1   50.2°, 39.8°   2   53.1°, 36.9°
     3   28.8°, 61.2°

7.   1 $\frac{8}{17}$, $\frac{15}{17}$, $\frac{8}{15}$, $\frac{15}{17}$, $\frac{8}{17}$, $\frac{15}{8}$
     2   13 cm, $\frac{12}{13}$, $\frac{5}{13}$, $\frac{12}{5}$
     3   12 cm, $\frac{4}{5}$, $\frac{3}{5}$, $\frac{4}{3}$

8.   1   2.55 cm   6   8.67 cm
     2   8.39 cm   7   13.2 cm
     3   2.24 cm   8   14.6 cm
     4   5.07 cm   9   15.6 cm
     5   7.47 cm   10   5.23 cm

9.   7.73 cm

10.   1   37.9°   4   40.5°
     2   53.1°   5   33.6°
     3   58.0°

Page 299   Exercise 20.2

1.   74.9 m   4.   90°, 21.5°

2.   75.0 m   5.   246 m

3.   201°   6.   16.7°

Page 300   Exercise 20.3

1.   78 m

2.   12.2 km, 260°

3.   1   11.8 cm   2   59 cm^2

4.   90°, 2.15 cm

5.   1   63 km   2   102 km

6.   1   5.45 cm   2   8.39 cm
     3   22.8 cm^2 4   45.7 cm^2

7.   1   90°   2   293 m
     3   851 m   4   277 m

8.   1   21.3 m   2   44.5 m
     3   6.6°

9.   1   9.51 cm, 47.6 cm^2
     2   $\frac{1}{5}$, 62.8 cm^2, 15.2 cm^2

10.   6 km, 7.1°

Page 303   Exercise D1

1. £3.20
2. 8 years
3. 12
4. 28
5. 35 cm^2

6. £7.92
7. 32
8. 7 kg
9. 30°
10. 1 002 345

11. 93
12. $\frac{5}{6}$
13. 85
14. 12
15. 40 kg

Page 303   Exercise D2

1. A
2. C
3. C
4. A
5. D
6. D
7. B
8. A
9. B
10. B

11. D
12. D
13. E
14. E
15. D
16. E
17. E
18. A
19. B
20. A

21. D
22. A
23. B
24. B
25. E
26. E
27. E
28. E
29. C
30. B

Page 307   Exercise D3

1. 25 cm

2. **1** 1
   2 3
   3 0
   4 infinite number

   5 6
   6 4
   7 2

   8 3
   9 5
   10 7

3. **1** 5 cm   **2** 132 cm^2 **3** 60 cm^3

4. 190 m   5. £662   6. 65 km

7. 3 km   8. 3 : 4   9. £75.00

10. **1** 3   **2** 3 : 1

11. £960, £1600, £2240

12. **1** equilateral
    2 obtuse-angled isosceles
    3 right-angled

13. $W = 10$, $a = 54$

14. 8 cm, 120 cm^2, 28.1°

15. **1** 255°   **2** 305°   **3** 125°

Page 309   Exercise D4

1. £30.15   2. 3.5 m   3. 6 m

4. **1** $\frac{1}{6}$, 20   **2** $\frac{1}{13}$, 9   **3** 12

---

5. 15 cm   6. £13.70

7. $AB = 110$ cm, 110 m

8. £39

9. $\triangle ABD$, BD

10. 20.4 km, 276°

11. $A_1(5, 4)$, $B_1(4, 5)$, $C_1(6, 8)$,
    $A_2(5, -4)$, $B_2(4, -5)$, $C_2(6, -8)$,
    -7 units in x direction, 6 units in y
    direction; reflection in line $y = 2$

12. **1** $x = 9$ **2** $x = 12$ **3** $x = 36$

13. $DE = 13.5$ cm, $DF = 12$ cm

14. height 27 m, $AB = 75$ m

15. boy

Page 323   Example 4

(0, 0)

Page 324   Example 6

$x = \frac{1}{2}$, $(\frac{1}{2}, -6\frac{1}{4})$

Page 326   Exercise 21.1

1. **1** $y = 3x$
   2 $y = 2x^2$
   3 $y = 10 - x$
   4 $y = \dfrac{60}{x}$
   5 $y = 2x + 3$

2. **1** $y = x^2$
   2 $y = \frac{1}{2}x$
   3 $y = \dfrac{24}{x}$
   4 $y = 10 - 2x$
   5 $y = 3x^2$

3. y values:
   1 $-2, 2, 6, 10, 14$
   2 $1\frac{1}{2}, 2, 2\frac{1}{2}, 3, 3\frac{1}{2}$
   3 $0, 5, 20, 45, 80$
   4 $6, 3, 2, 1\frac{1}{2}$
   5 $9, 6, 3, 0, -3$

4. y values:
   1 $-3, 0, 5, 12, 21$
   2 $0, -1, 0, 3, 8$
   3 $-1, 0, 3, 8, 15$
   4 $4, 1, 0, 1, 4$
   5 $12, 6, 2, 0, 0$

8. -9

9. line $x = 1\frac{1}{2}$, $x = -1.4$ or 4.4

10. line $x = \frac{1}{2}$, $x = -1.8$ or 2.8

11. $(\frac{1}{2}, -2\frac{1}{4})$, $x = \frac{1}{2}$; $x = -2.4$ or 3.4

12. $(4, 2)$

13. **1** $y = \dfrac{x}{3}$ **2** $y = 3x^2$

     3 $y = 3 - x$ **4** $y = \dfrac{3}{x}$

15. $1, -\frac{2}{3}, -\frac{2}{3}, 1$, parallelogram

16. A 0.3, B 3.5, gradient 1.6, gradient -1.6

17. A 3.6, B 0.7, gradient -0.36

Page 331   **Exercise 21.2**

2. **1** $x^2 + 6x + 5$
   2 $x^2 - 8x + 12$
   3 $x^2 - 16$
   4 $x^2 + 6x + 9$
   5 $x^2 + 9x + 14$
   6 $x^2 + x - 12$
   7 $x^2 - 5x + 4$
   8 $x^2 - 1$
   9 $x^2 - 2x - 15$
   10 $x^2 - 2x + 1$
   11 $x^2 + x - 20$
   12 $x^2 + 2x - 3$
   13 $x^2 + 7x + 6$
   14 $x^2 - 11x + 28$
   15 $x^2 - 4x - 5$

Page 331   **Exercise 21.3**

1. 24, 60

2. 7, 4, 7, 16; 4

3. **1** $y = 2 - 2x$ **4** $y = 2$
   2 $y = x + 2$ **5** $y = 2x$
   3 $y = 2 - x$ **6** $y = 2x + 2$

4. C

5. gradients -0.2, -0.6, -1.5

6. $x = 0.7$, $y = -2.3$ or $x = 4.3$, $y = 1.3$

7. $x = -1.2$, $y = 1.2$ or $x = 3.2$, $y = -3.2$

8. $x = 2$ or 5

9. x between 1 and 5, y between 2 and 7

10. x not more than 7, y at least 4, x greater than y; (chocolate, cream): (5, 4), (6, 4), (7, 4), (6, 5), (7, 5), (7, 6)

11. **1** $x^2 + 6x + 8$ **4** $x^2 - 100$
   2 $x^2 + 14x + 49$ **5** $x^2 + 2x - 48$
   3 $x^2 - 5x + 6$

12. $(x + 4)^2\,\text{cm}^2$, $8x\,\text{cm}^2$, $(x^2 + 16)\,\text{cm}^2$

13. $x = 16$, $96\,\text{cm}^2$

Page 336   **Exercise 22.1**

1. examples:
   1 cube, cuboid, cone, sphere
   2 (0, 5), (1, 4), (2, 3), (3, 2)
   3 mm, cm, m, km
   4 Jan, Mar, May, Jly
   5 BBC1, BBC2, ITV, Channel 4

2. **1** rectangle, square
   2 mg, g, kg
   3 centre, chord, circumference
   4 (0, 0), (1, 1)
   5 2

3. **1** does not belong to
   2 belongs to
   3 does not belong to
   4 does not belong to
   5 belongs to

4. **1** 12
   2 infinite set
   3 infinite set
   4 10

5. **1** 1, 2, 3, 4, 5, 6, 7, 8, 9, 10
   2 1, 3, 4, 6, 9
   3 1, 2, 3, 4, 5, 6, 7, 10

6. **1** squares
   2 1, 2, 5, 10
   3 equilateral triangles
   4 53, 59

7. **1** 6, 10   **2** 3, 6, 9, 10

8. **1** a, e   **2** b, s   **3** 8   **4** 21

9. **1** multiples of 10
   2 all prime numbers except 2
   3 all multiples of 5 except 5

10. **1** {isosceles right-angled triangles}
    2 {equilateral triangles}
    3 { }
    4 { }

13. 32, $\frac{8}{15}$

15. **1** 21   **2** 25   **3** $\frac{3}{4}$

17. 4

18. 4

19. 840, $\frac{1}{10}$, $\frac{2}{5}$

Page 339   Exercise 22.2

1. **1** Jan, Jly   **2** Jan, Jly
   3 Mar, Aug, Oct, Dec
   4 Feb, May

2. **1** 7   **2** 23

3. **1** $\frac{4}{33}$ **2** $\frac{2}{11}$ **3** $\frac{2}{5}$

4. $\frac{2}{5}$

5. A: 9, 18, 27, 36, 45. B: 1, 4, 9, 16,
   25, 36, 49. A and B: 9, 36.
   1 $\frac{1}{10}$ **2** $\frac{7}{50}$ **3** $\frac{1}{5}$ **4** $\frac{1}{25}$
   5 $\frac{4}{5}$

7. **1** Bob, Mary   **4** Ann, Derek, Jill
   2 Chris, Mary   **5** B and C
   3 Mary

8. **1** 30   **4** 15
   2 4   **5** 1
   3 6   **6** 18

10. **1** $\frac{19}{36}$ **2** $\frac{1}{36}$ **3** $\frac{5}{36}$ **4** $\frac{3}{8}$

Page 344   Exercise 23.1

1. **1** 34, 40   **6** 18, 24
   2 18, 21   **7** $\frac{1}{81}$, $\frac{1}{243}$
   3 160, 320   **8** 127, 255
   4 729, 2187   **9** 158, 318
   5 -12, -15 **10** 720, 5040

2. **1** 7, 9, 11, 13, 15
   2 2, 5, 10, 17, 26
   3 $\frac{1}{2}$, $\frac{2}{3}$, $\frac{3}{4}$, $\frac{4}{5}$, $\frac{5}{6}$
   4 2, 4, 8, 16, 32
   5 2, 6, 12, 20, 30

3. **1** $2n - 1$ **4** $6n - 4$
   2 n^3 **5** $105 - 5n$
   3 $\dfrac{1}{n}$

4. 8 should be 9, 400

6. **1** (4, 11)   **2** (5, 25)
   3 729 should be -729

Page 347   Exercise 23.2

1. **1** x is greater than 7
   2 x is less than or equal to 8
   3 x is not equal to 1
   4 x is greater than 1 and less than 4
   5 x is greater than or equal to -5

2. **1** $x < 6$ **4** $-3 < x < 10$
   2 $x \geqslant -2$ **5** $x \leqslant 5$
   3 $x \neq 0$

4. **1** $a < c < b$ **4** $a < b < c$
   2 $c < b < a$ **5** $b < c < a$
   3 $c < a < b$

5. **1** 4, 5, 6
   2 4, 5
   3 -2, -1, 0, 1, 2
   4 -7, -6, -5
   5 0, 1, 2, 3, 4, 5

Page 349   Exercise 23.3

7. **2** 1 hexagon, 1 triangle, 2 squares

Page 352   Exercise 23.4

1. **1** 26, 37   **6** $\frac{1}{15}$, $\frac{1}{18}$
   2 18, 9   **7** 9, 0
   3 32, 64   **8** -11, -14
   4 1, $\frac{1}{3}$ **9** 10 000, 100 000
   5 19, 23   **10** 64, 55

2. 820   3. 10

4. **1** 2^n **4** $4n + 17$
   2 $107 - 7n$ **5** $3n^2$
   3 $\dfrac{n}{n + 1}$

5. 28

8. $x + y \leqslant 10$, $y \geqslant 6$, $x \geqslant 2$,
   dogs, elephants: 2, 6; 2, 7; 2, 8; 3, 6;
   3, 7; 4, 6; 4 dogs, 6 elephants, £24

10. $AB = 3.1\,\text{cm}$

Page 355   Example 1

1 14 miles   2 81 km

Page 355   Example 2

Walk 6 km/hour
cycle $1\frac{1}{4}$ hours, 27 km, 21.6 km/hour
rests 30 km
bus 2.15 p.m., $\frac{1}{2}$ hour, 60 km/hour

Page 356   Example 3

18 m/s, 26 m/s

Page 357   Exercise 24.1

1. 1 £52   2 32 dollars
2. 29.6 litres, 2.2 gallons
3. 1 47 km/hour   2 28 m/s
4. 1 (1) and (4), 67 km/hour
    2 (2), 33 km/hour
    3 30
5. 1 33 km   2 11.8 km, 2.01 p.m.
6. 2.55 p.m., 115 km
7. 31.25 m; 0.45 s, 4.55 s; 10 m/s
8. 2.75 s
9. 1 120 m   2 5 m/s^2
10. 1 20 km
    2 25 km/hour, 17.75 min after leaving
       A
11. 1 22 m/s
    2 20 s, 105 s from the start
    3 0.6 m/s^2

Page 361   Exercise 24.2

1. 1 B   2 A   3 D   4 C

Page 363   Exercise 24.3

1. 57
2. 167 cm
3. 72 kg
5. X £49, Y £41

Page 365   Exercise 24.4

1. 21°C, 176°F, 37°C
2. 1 1700 (1740) dinars
    2 £7.80 (£7.76)
3. 1 $\frac{1}{2}$ hour   4 16 km/hour
    2 15 km/hour   5 10 km
    3 1.40 p.m., 9 km
4. 1 2.14 p.m.   2 11.7 miles
5. 1 27 km   2 17 minutes
    3 80 km/hour
6. 4.0
7. 39 m/s
8. 14.5 s
9. 7.7° per minute, 14° per minute
11. B
12. 157
13. 3.1, $c = 3.1\ d\ (c = \pi d)$
14. 41
15. £64 000

Page 375   Exercise 25.1

1. £4
2. £5.94
3. 3 kg
4. 140, 310, 480, 85, 445
5. 600, 800, 1150, 2025, 975
6. 45, 78, 24, 13, 82
7. £4.16, £2.67, 39 p, £3.89, £1.70
8. $\frac{1}{10}, \frac{3}{4}, \frac{1}{3}, \frac{3}{5}, \frac{1}{8}$
9. 12 p, 46 p
10. 49, 81, 144, 169, 36
11. 27, 125, 1, 1000, 8
12. 9, 33, 8, 11, 4
13. £16
14. £13.80
15. 17°, 59°, 125°, 83°, 79°

16. 1 32.7   4 3.58
     2 324   5 − 15.1
     3 3.83

17. 1 1.70   4 46.7°
     2 4.29   5 43.7°
     3 0.255

18. 1 5.387×10^4 4 1.57×10^{-1}
     2 4.79×10^{-3} 5 8.118×10^3
     3 1.23×10^4

19. 1 1.8   4 £30
     2 $3\frac{1}{2}$ kg, 35 kg   5 20
     3 108°

20. 1 72.2 m   2 65.9 m
     3 415 m²   4 346 m²

Page 377   Exercise 25.2

1.   £22

2.   £19.95

3.   1.1 kg

4.   286, 671, 913, 495, 319

5.   84, 240, 720

6. $42\frac{1}{4}$, $20\frac{1}{4}$

7.   249, 155, 408

8.   13 p, 38 p, 44 p, 87 p, 53 p

9. $\frac{2}{5}$, $2\frac{3}{10}$, $2\frac{5}{6}$, $1\frac{5}{8}$, $4\frac{7}{12}$

10. 96 p, £1.30, £1, £2

11. 0.12, 7.1, 0.003, 0.56, 0.14, 0.04, 0.3, 3, 0.36, 0.042

12. £3.60

13. 8, 11, 7, 1, 10

14. 6, 2, 10, 5, 4

15. 180°, 36°, 30°, 45°, 72°

16. 1 4   5 10   8   26
     2 15   6 25   9   30
     3 7   7 17   10 20
     4 5

17. 1 10 hr 7 min   4 5 yr 9 mth
     2 6 hr 36 min   5 39 hr 58 min
     3 63 yr 9 mth

18. 1 0.0183   4 3273
     2 6010   5 0.87
     3 0.55

19. 1 11   4 5
     2 22   5 40
     3 10

20. 1 3.248   4 39.69
     2 88.8   5 8.9
     3 2.3

21. 1 60 g   2 4 minutes
     3 30 m

22. 1 22 cm   2 18 cm
     3 29.25 cm²   4 19.25 cm²

23. 1 7.61   4 32.718
     2 9.082   5 38 562.5
     3 37.2

Page 380   Exercise E1

1.   20 cm   6. $\frac{1}{20}$ 11. 110
2.   55   7. July 1st   12. 20 days
3.   £48   8. 40 p   13. 4
4.   20 p   9. 24 cm²   14. £18
5.   16 p   10. 53   15. 20

Page 380   Exercise E2

1.   A   11. E   21. E
2.   E   12. A   22. B
3.   D   13. B   23. C
4.   D   14. C   24. A
5.   A   15. E   25. D
6.   B   16. B   26. C
7.   B   17. E   27. B
8.   C   18. D   28. E
9.   B   19. B   29. E
10. A   20. B   30. C

Page 385   Exercise E3

1.   1 54 min   2 8%

2.   1 9 should be 10, triangular numbers, 36, 45, 55
     2 22 should be 21; 55, 89, 144
     3 6 should be 8, yes
     4 66 should be 65; 44, 37, 30

3.   1 0.12   2 0.0035   3 1.4

4.   585 m

5. £6.60, £8.25

6. 12 cm, $\frac{5}{13}$, $\frac{12}{13}$, $\frac{5}{12}$

7. 3200

8. 11

9. **1** 35 800 **2** 3.08 **3** 0.002 16

10. **1** $4\frac{1}{6}$ **4** $1\frac{5}{6}$
    2 4 **5** $12\frac{1}{4}$
    3 $\frac{2}{3}$

11. £3.78

12. **1** 64° **2** 38°

13. **1** −2 **2** 3
    3 8.52×10^{-1}, 1.97×10

14. 18 m²

15. 6.14 p.m., 2.5 km from A

Page 387 Exercise E4

1. $\frac{3}{10}$, $\frac{1}{3}$, $\frac{3}{8}$, 38%, 0.4

2. 20

3. cheaper one

4. 129°

5. **1** 6 **4** 12
   2 $7\frac{1}{2}$
   3 8.5

6. 8, 1, $\frac{1}{25}$, $\frac{1}{1000}$, $\frac{1}{8}$

7. £99

8. **1** 60% **2** $37\frac{1}{2}$%

9. **1** 150° **2** 15° **3** 45°

10. 44 p

11. **1** 4, $\sqrt{25}$ $(= 5)$,
    2 4, $\sqrt{25}$, −5
    3 0.3, $\frac{3}{4}$, $3\frac{1}{7}$, 3.142
    4 $\sqrt[3]{6}$, π

12. 122°

13. 48

14. **1** $\frac{1}{6}$ **2** $\frac{1}{3}$ **3** $\frac{1}{6}$ **4** $\frac{7}{12}$ **5** $\frac{6}{11}$

15. **1** 3600 **3** C
    2 B and D **4** 14 000

Page 389 Exercise E5

1. 15 p

2. 44

3. **1** B **2** D **3** A **4** C

5. Q: $(-3, -2)$, $(4, -1)$, $(2, 4)$
   R: $(-3, 2)$, $(4, 1)$, $(2, -4)$
   S: $(2, 4)$, $(-8, -2)$, $(-4, 8)$
   T: $(3, 2)$, $(5, -2)$, $(0, 4)$
   U: $(2, 1)$, $(-2, 3)$, $(-1, -4)$

6. $x = 1.2$, $y = 0.8$

7. **1** $\frac{4}{7}$ **2** $\frac{2}{7}$

8. **1** £5.75 **3** £3.60
   2 $12\frac{1}{2}$% **4** £60

10. **1** 20 **2** £12.54 **3** £1.70

11. 10.6 km

12. **1** 4 : 7 **2** 4 : 7

13. **1** 31.4 cm **2** 60°
    3 equilateral **4** 5 cm

14. **1** $x = \dfrac{a - b}{c}$ **2** $x = (a - b)^2$
    3 $x = \dfrac{a}{b}$ **4** $x = \dfrac{a + c}{b}$

15. 100; 105°, 75°, 105°, 75°;
    parallelogram

Page 392 Exercise E6

1. **1** $7(1 - 2x)$
   2 $x = 9$, LHS $= 33$

2. 480 francs, £40

3. modal class 2 to 4 cm, mean 5.2 cm

5. **1** 16.55 **2** 7 hr 13 min
   3 $12\frac{1}{2}$ p **4** 70 km/hr

6. 270 m

7. **1** −3.25 **2** $x = -2.3$ or 1.3

8. **1** £25 **2** 59%

9. **1** 90° **2** 4.7 cm

10. 141 000 cm³, 39 cm

11. E: reflect in the line $x = 3$, F: rotate
    about $(2, 2)$ through 180°

12. **1** Pythagoras
     2 11 in (5, 11, 13) should be 12
     3 (13, 84, 85)

13. 25%, $12\frac{1}{2}\%$

14. £14.84, £10.98, £3.86

15. **1** 8 km/hr **2** 30 km/hr
     3 5.05 p.m., 33 km from A